CORRESPONDENCE BETWEEN
SPENCER FULLERTON BAIRD
AND LOUIS AGASSIZ —

TWO PIONEER AMERICAN
NATURALISTS

CORRESPONDENCE BETWEEN SPENCER FULLERTON BAIRD AND LOUIS AGASSIZ—

TWO PIONEER AMERICAN NATURALISTS

Collected and Edited by

ELMER CHARLES HERBER

Chairman, Department of Biology
Dickinson College, Carlisle, Pa.

(Publication 4515)

CITY OF WASHINGTON
PUBLISHED BY THE SMITHSONIAN INSTITUTION
1963

CONNECTICUT PRINTERS, INCORPORATED

HARTFORD, CONNECTICUT

Dedicated to the memory of

SPENCER FULLERTON BAIRD

whose sincerity of purpose and unblemished character have been
an inspiration to many

ILLUSTRATIONS

INTRODUCTION*

A study of some 50,000 letters among the Spencer Fullerton Baird Papers in the Smithsonian Institution Archives has revealed Louis Agassiz as one of Baird's constant correspondents. These two high-ranking 19th-century naturalists saved much of their correspondence. Parts of some of their letters and a few complete letters exchanged between them have been published in their biographies. My collection of 297 letters, mostly from the Smithsonian Archives, brings together all their known correspondence.

Spencer F. Baird and Louis Agassiz were pioneers in the development of the field of natural history and in their wake left a healthy respect for American science all over the world. Their activities in that field in this country began essentially at the same time. Their impact on the world of science and their significant contributions in an age of rapid development are vividly revealed in these letters.

In the first 75 years after the signing of the Declaration of Independence little international recognition had been given to the work of American zoologists. In fact, many foreigners actually despised Americans in general for their materialistic concerns and their lack of interest in culture and pure research. Many of the early American zoologists were interested mainly in explorations and making inventories of animals and plants. Descriptions of many species were made quickly, often from incomplete data. Scientists were often not particularly concerned with how the public at large was to be made familiar with new findings. However, the people in the United States were yearning for knowledge, were eager for mass education, and were ready to put an end to the European method of tutelage, by which many young persons were denied opportunities for enlightenment.

There was a need for real leadership in America to inspire budding scientists in true methods of research, point out unexplored areas, and challenge them to find the answers to some of the problems in natural history. Agassiz and Baird emerged as two of these leaders, the first by reason of his charm on the platform and the second by the force of his letters. They put into motion the methods of developing the science of natural history. They had deep human understanding, shrewd powers of observation, solid scientific training, and above all a

* Support for this research from the Penrose Fund of the American Philosophical Society is here gratefully acknowledged.

capacity for communicating effectively a desire for knowledge. Some of the basic facets of their lives will be mentioned first.

SPENCER FULLERTON BAIRD

Born on February 3, 1823, in Reading, Pa., Baird lived there for 10 years until his father died. Our eyes now turn to Carlisle, Pa., where this fatherless child prepared himself for his life's work in natural history. Young Baird was sent to West Nottingham Academy for a little over a year and to the grammar school of Dickinson College for one more year before he became, at the age of 13, a student in Dickinson. He first showed his interest in natural history while at the Academy, where he was known as one of the "possum hunters" who made the students' tramps into the countryside interesting. In his junior year in college he began to list the trips he made around Carlisle and what he saw, how many birds he shot and stuffed, what books he read, and what letters he wrote and received. We find here, in evidence of broader interests, that he read volumes of Shakespeare, Emerson, Coleridge, Longfellow, Carlyle, Tennyson, and others. By the time he was graduated from Dickinson he was a probing naturalist who had ripened into a sharp observer and a good collector.

After graduation from college he tried the study of medicine, but this was not to his liking. He was still impelled by an insatiable curiosity to learn more about fossils, birds, frogs, snakes, turtles, and other forms of nature. His jaunts around the countryside attracted many followers, as well as some jeers, for there was at that time no general interest in research. For help and encouragement in his quest he would walk as much as 20 miles to get books, or he would travel by rail to Philadelphia, New York, Washington, or Boston to discuss vexing questions. He wrote many letters, directing them to important scientists here and abroad, offering to exchange labeled specimens. Soon he found that often his specimens did not fall within a listed description. By making accurate observations with calipers he found true identification characters, often relegating existing names to synonymy. Before long he had the confidence of such well-known men as Audubon, who gave him some of his collection of birds. At this time, when Audubon was doubtful about an identification, he asked Baird to clarify species.

In 1845, after five years of inquiry into nature around Carlisle, he was elected honorary professor of natural history at his Alma Mater, and a year later, full professor. Within a few years he became one of Dickinson's best-loved professors, and the catalog listed his department as "abundantly supplied with numerous specimens illustrative of various productions of the globe." By this time he had published some of his early observations, and also continued the study of languages. His accuracy and clarity of descriptions impressed most scientists.

During the summer of 1847, on his collecting trip to Vermont, he talked with Congressman George Perkins Marsh, who was impressed with Baird's knowledge of natural history and suggested that he make application for a position with the newly organized Smithsonian Institution. Marsh, who became a member of the Board of Regents of the Smithsonian on December 22, 1847, also suggested Baird as a qualified editor to translate and make ready for American consumption the four volumes of the Iconographic Encyclopedia, published originally in German. He began this translation while teaching at Dickinson and finished it after entering upon his duties as Assistant Secretary of the Smithsonian.

In 1850 Baird was appointed to the staff of the Smithsonian Institution. Marsh's recommendation of Baird had doubtless carried weight, and the support of Louis Agassiz and Asa Gray was probably just as important. With this appointment, at the age of 27, went all the specimens he had collected for the cabinets of Dickinson. He thus began an association with the Smithsonian which lasted for 37 years, the last 10 years as its permanent Secretary.

After one more collecting expedition into northern New York the summer he joined the staff of the Smithsonian, he entered into his coveted position with unmatched zeal. He helped to equip and instruct exploring expeditions to bring in all types of material. His letters to collectors and his personal appeals brought results. Material had to be analyzed, new species described, and reports edited. Many an administrator would have been content with a normal amount of publication in connection with these expeditions, but not Baird, for he was no ordinary man. He saw that there was need for monographs, new criteria in description, and more diffusion of knowledge. His volumes relating to mammals and birds were the first exhaustive treatises in those fields in the United States. His total output was some 1,065 published articles and books, of which "The Birds of North America," consisting of a thousand pages, issued jointly with Cassin and Lawrence, and his volume "Mammals of North America," consisting of 764 pages and 84 plates, were his best pure-research efforts. He was long considered the national authority on birds, mammals, reptiles, and fishes. His publications were standard reference works in their respective fields.

As Assistant Secretary of the Smithsonian, Baird participated in the activities of many committees and in the Congressional committee hearings concerning the purchase of Alaska. He impressed the first Secretary, Joseph Henry, with the importance of museum collections as research tools, even though Henry was averse to the odor of alcoholic specimens. With his interest in people and his voluminous letter writing, he developed the system of international exchanges, which later developed into the official exchange of scientific and governmental documents between the United States and other nations. During the summers away from Washington he began a series of researches on seashore life at various localities along the New Jersey and New England coasts. The depletion of fishes interested him very much; from that interest and subsequent discussions evolved the Fish Commission in 1871, with Baird as the first Commissioner. In this role he performed a very important service to the fishing industry of the northeastern States and incidentally established an international reputation as a fish conservationist.

After he became Secretary, following Henry's death in 1878, he was instrumental in bringing about the erection of a building to be used solely for museum purposes. The museum and its collections were reorganized, and accessions increased rapidly, especially in the realm of ethnology. To carry on his fisheries research, permanent buildings were constructed at Woods Hole, Mass. It was here that he died on August 17, 1887.

Baird was a self-taught naturalist, a great leader of men, and one of the pioneers in the study of natural history in America. His impact on American science was ably stated by G. Brown Goode: "No name occupies a more honorable place in the annals of American science than that of Professor Baird. His personal contributions to systematic biology were of great extent. His influence in inspiring and training men to enter the field of natural history was very potent. As an organizer, working at a most fortunate time, he knew how to utilize his extraordinary opportunities, and he has left his impress forever fixed upon the scientific and educational institutions of the United States, more especially those under Government control."

LOUIS AGASSIZ

Louis Agassiz was born on May 28, 1807, in a village parsonage at the foot of the Alps, in Motier, Switzerland. Before he was 10 years old he had collected insects, fishes, and plants from a nearby lake and the countryside. Early in life he interested other village children in his dissections and showed evidences of becoming the great teacher he was destined to be. His first sustained interest was in fishes, which were often kept in a spring-fed pool in the parsonage garden. His mother imagined her son would study medicine as her father had, but the boy was sent to a school to prepare for a career in commerce. Subsequently, he was allowed to pursue a course of medical studies at the University of Zurich.

Despite his promise to complete the study of medicine, he pursued, just as Baird had done, the study of natural history and was awarded a doctor's degree in zoology one year prior to his medical degree. While studying in these two disciplines, he was anxious to be with the top scholars in each. The universities he attended included Zurich, Heidelberg, Erlanger, and Munich, where he was instrumental in forming discussion groups which probed into the theoretical and philosophical. He showed an early brilliance in zoology and paleontology, and with a mastery of these subjects and especially good linguistic ability, he published the following works before he was 37 years old: In German, "Die süsswasser Fische Mittel-europas"; in Latin, "Selecta Genera et Species Piscium"(of Brazilian fishes); and in French (his supreme effort), "Poissons Fossiles." These publications together with his "Ice Age" theory made him an international scientist of first rank. After his formal studies ended, he traveled widely, studied under Cuvier, and taught in the College de Neuchâtel. There he soon attracted a large following and organized a printing establishment which plunged him into debt. This was later sold at auction, but he remained in debt. His financial burden, together with the fact that his wife had gone back to her family, made him anxious to try to redeem his fortunes in the United States. Through the influence of Humboldt, Agassiz received a grant of $3,000 from Frederick William IV of Prussia to study natural history in the New World. He was warmly received in the United States and soon derived enough money from lecture fees to pay off most of his European debts.

His success in lecturing stemmed from his tremendous breadth of knowledge in zoology and paleontology and his ability to project his warm, earnest, enthusiastic nature into the hearts of his listeners. He was also determined to interest scientists and laymen in the more philosophical aspects of the study of animals, their geographical distribution, natural relationships, embryonic growth, and their relationship to fossil remains. While he did research after he came to America, much of his effort radiated around popularizing natural history and training young men to do a thorough investigation on a particular subject. This kind of training demanded many specimens, and the realization that there was no good collection at Harvard challenged him to an all-out effort to gather there one of the best collections in America. Through this effort arose the Museum of Comparative Zoology at Harvard College, which, by the 1860's, housed one of the best zoological collections in the world.

To gather the specimens, to construct a building to store these huge collections, and to pay for his assistants demanded much money and effort. He succeeded in persuading several wealthy Bostonians to cooperate in these projects, but his most amazing feat was to convince hardheaded Massachusetts legislators to appropriate public money to Harvard, a private institution. Hence, to Agassiz is given the credit for awakening public responsibility for advancement in science. To fulfill his ambitions in this connection he always used his personal income to pay for the collection of specimens. When this was not enough, he again began lecture tours and occasionally took on extra responsibilities such as interim professor at the Charleston (S.C.) Medical College or visiting professor at Cornell University.

He was much interested in the Smithsonian, lecturing there on several occasions and serving on the Board of Regents for 10 years (1863-1873). He discussed its function and future with both Joseph Henry and Baird. Although he had several offers to return to Europe to accept important appointments, he refused them all because he loved the greater freedom in America and enjoyed his fame as its greatest popularizer of natural history. He died on December 14, 1873, at Cambridge, Mass.

THEIR MUTUALITY

How these naturalists first heard about each other is not definitely known, but it is probable that Baird, who was offering duplicates of his specimens to European naturalists in his attempts to clarify species, made the same offer to Agassiz while he was still in Europe. He made this offer personally when he was first introduced to Agassiz by Samuel Haldeman in Philadelphia. Agassiz was then on his tour of American scientific institutions following his arrival from Europe on October 3, 1846, and was anxious to meet the young naturalist from Pennsylvania.

In their first recorded correspondence, April 10, 1847, Agassiz suggested that Baird could make good his offer of assistance by collecting animal and plant specimens. Baird did collect many specimens for Agassiz, and after several personal meetings it was agreed that they would cooperate in a monograph on American fishes. Baird immediately began to fulfill his part of the agreement by making plates and describing six species in 1849. This work was edited and published by David Starr Jordan in 1889, two years after Baird's death. Baird completed most of his projects, while Agassiz would often leave one unfinished in order to begin another more grandiose one.

They had much respect for each other, Baird expressing it first when he wrote to Joseph Henry on February 25, 1847, about the possibility of a position at the Smithsonian: "I have had the honor of being called on to assist in perfecting the great 'Bibliographia Zoologica' of Professor Agassiz." They kept in close touch with each other concerning the position, and on July 11, 1850, Baird thanked Agassiz. "At last," he wrote, "I am Assistant Secretary to the Smithsonian, having just received the patents. The salary is $1,500, to be increased, I hope, thereafter. To you more than any other are due my acknowledgments for the result, and I trust I may not disappoint your expectation in recommending me to Prof. Henry." At the end of Baird's September 7 letter he signed himself "Your attached disciple." Agassiz was pleased with such worshipful expressions and appreciated Baird's assistance. On October 9, 1849, he said: "I have received your box in perfect good state and return my best thanks for all the fine things sent to me, which are equally instructive and acceptable." Some time later, after the receipt of specimens from Baird, Agassiz wrote: "The turtles have

been of essential service to me and I truly thank you, for your promptness in forwarding them." Soon after that: "The most instructive set
of turtles I ever saw." Later — "I am amazed at the amount of work
you have accomplished and congratulate you heartily upon your accom-
plishments."

In 1873 while Agassiz was planning his final project, the summer
school of biology on Penikese Island in Buzzards Bay, opposite New
Bedford, Mass., he asked Baird to give some lectures upon his experiences "concerning fisheries & Economic ichthyology." Baird tentatively
consented, but he never lectured there because his fisheries research
station was in Maine that summer. However, he did help in facilitating
the collection of specimens for use at Penikese.

While Baird never wavered in his regard for Agassiz, the same cannot be said of Agassiz for Baird. First came the Charles Girard affair.
Girard was employed by Agassiz in Switzerland for some time and in
Cambridge until 1850, when he decided to work for Baird and the
Smithsonian. This shift in loyalty infuriated Agassiz to the degree that
it was impossible for him to have anything to do with Girard. Perhaps
this was the prime reason for Agassiz's lashing out at Baird on June
27, 1853, over his Catalog of Serpents, which Agassiz called "very
crude." Agassiz wrote Baird: "To tell the truth of my impression I do
not believe that you have had much to do with it and I hope sincerely
for the sake of your scientific reputation that it will turn out so. But
why did you not at least look it over? If you had been willing to listen
to my advice before, you should have known that Girard though capable of sustained work and endowed with considerable ability in distinguishing the peculiarities of animals has no judgment, and is utterly
unable to trace original researches without supervision."

But Baird was ready and able to answer effectively in a firm letter
dated June 30, in which he explained why certain names were chosen.
Baird showed that he had read the literature, had examined the specimens carefully, and had given priority credit where it belonged. Baird
vindicated himself, but Agassiz never conceded it. About 10 years
later Agassiz tried, in a haughty manner, to block the election of Baird
to the National Academy of Sciences. Agassiz contended that Baird
was interested mainly in the descriptive phase of zoology and not
enough in the theoretical and philosophical phases. Baird was nevertheless elected.

This defeat for Agassiz and his clique, called the Lazzaroni, was probably maneuvered by Asa Gray, a professor at Harvard and the foremost botanist of his day. Gray had been a friend of Baird's before Baird was associated with the Smithsonian, when he collected for Gray important stages in the life cycle of the rare box huckleberry *Gaylussacia brachycera* near Carlisle, Pa. Agassiz's loss of power so concerned him that he questioned Henry about it. A long letter was sent by Henry to Agassiz explaining to him that had Baird not been elected, many of the other members of the Academy would have resigned. Henry also advised him not to try to dominate the whole world of American science. This loss of prestige was a blow to Agassiz; nevertheless his popular appeal remained universally high.

TWO GREAT MUSEUM BUILDERS

At an early age Baird had begun to make collections, especially of bird skins. His diary, begun at the age of 15, at first listed field trips around the countryside. He would shoot, collect, and skin as many as 45 birds in one day. Soon he found himself accompanied by a group of students eager to hear his enthusiastic discussions of the differences in snakes, of a strange fossil, or perhaps of the characteristic markings of a new bird.

Agassiz, as a youth in Switzerland, had kept fishes in the family pool and had collected and probed into almost everything he saw. He also had had enthusiastic followers on his collecting excursions. Thus Agassiz and Baird independently fostered the field-trip method of studying nature at first hand, one in Europe and the other in America.

Besides his extensive bird collections, which afforded him opportunities for numerous exchanges, Baird started collecting fishes, reptiles, amphibians, and mammals. He then began to formulate ideas on how to organize collections in a museum. Before Baird was selected as Assistant Secretary, he outlined to Joseph Henry, the Secretary, his aims for the Smithsonian should he be appointed to the office: "My object is to make the Smithsonian Museum eminent above all others American for the value of its vertebrate fossil remains, a department in which everything remains to be done, although of the very highest zoological and geological interest. The collections I have made already under this head far outweigh all others of a similar character in all the American collections combined." Two freight-car loads of specimens collected while at Dickinson went to the Smithsonian Institution at the time of his first appointment. On January 23, 1861, 11 years after he began his career at the Smithsonian, he expressed his philosophy about the Museum to Agassiz: "I am anxious to see collected here [as] complete a series of the Vertebrata and alcoholic invertebrates of North America as possible, and such others from the rest of the world as are necessary properly to elucidate their study and such other closely allied species where we have collections from Government Naval Expeditions. When these are all determined, labelled and reported on, I am willing to let them stand as types only caring to prevent their destruction. All duplicates of elaborated and identified collections I wish to see distributed throughout the best museums and have fresh materials come in."

The excellent reputation of the Smithsonian stems partly from the ability of the early administrators to look ahead in their fields. Henry, through his ability as an able administrator, steered a course which did not deviate from the original purpose of the Smithsonian, "the increase and diffusion of knowledge among men." He was also well known for his organization of a meteorological service which later developed into the Weather Bureau. Baird can be singled out as the one who nurtured the idea of an outstanding museum. Henry was not against a museum if such collections served the Smithsonian's purpose and did not unbalance the budget. Today, our National Museum, as a bureau of the Smithsonian Institution, with over 55,000,000 specimens and worldwide preeminence in many departments, attests to Baird's wisdom.

Agassiz early recognized the need for several specimens of all available species in order to make comparative studies, especially in the field of embryology. At heavy personal expense he built up museums, first at Neuchâtel and later at Harvard. In both cases his insatiable desire for specimens left him in such bad financial straits that he was forced to sell his collections to the institutions with which he was connected at the time. Some years after he arrived in the United States he determined to stay here, for he believed he might "be able to do more for the advancement of science here than in Europe." The intense earnestness of his appeal for funds and specimens is apparent in this statement: "My object is to have a museum founded here which will equal the great museums of the Old World. We have a continent before us for exploration which has as yet been only skimmed on the surface . . . My earnest desire . . . is . . . to put our universities on a footing with those

of Europe, or even ahead of them; so that there would be the same disposition among European students to come to America . . . that there
has always been among our students to avail themselves of the advantages of European universities." People from all walks of life hastened
to give him much desired material. He persuaded the Smithsonian to
part with many of its specimens by agreeing to identify some of the
materials and store them until there was sufficient space and money to
care for them in Washington.

Both men were so ardent in collecting for their museums that they
often paid collectors out of their own pockets. In the case of Robert
Kennicott, who helped to explore northern Canada and Russian America (later Alaska), they personally contributed several hundred dollars
and divided the collections. Baird saw to it that the personnel of U.S.
exploring expeditions included physicians, officers, or meteorologists
who were interested in collecting specimens. Among the men who collected for Baird were George B. McClellan, John Strong Newberry,
Robert Kennicott, Ferdinand V. Hayden, and Henry Elliott. His
friendly letters often exhilarated them and relieved them of their home-
sickness. Elliott wrote from Cheyenne, Wyo., October 28, 1870: "I
tell you truly, Professor, you may think us a quiet set in the way of
letting you hear from us by letter but I am sure that not one day has
passed since we have been out in the field but what your name has
been brought up in some way or other . . . With noble true friends like
you I feel as brave as a lion and shall never fail to succeed and the light
of your precepts and example shines in upon my mind brighter as the
days go by." Is it any wonder that the Museum of Comparative Zoology in Cambridge and the National Museum in Washington grew so
rapidly when their directors engendered so much loyalty and enthusiasm? Both Agassiz and Baird realized that a great challenge was
upon them, and they exerted themselves to the utmost to build museums of superlative excellence.

THEIR RESEARCH

While their respective museums were in formation, both Agassiz and
Baird had a tremendous urge to probe into the classification and natural history of their accessions. The search for new knowledge continued daily and often into the night. They knew very little else and
cared nothing about accumulating wealth or for idle pleasures. After

Agassiz had his first museum building about completed, he confided to Baird: "It is our own fault if hereafter Zoology is not making progress in this part of the country."

One of the first things Baird realized when he tried to identify the birds taken on his shooting trips was that available descriptions were not accurate and that quite a few species were synonymous. He began to organize his descriptions so that they were based on actual measurements. Literature was checked for priority. In many cases he found specific characters that were never previously noted. Thus developed the "Bairdian School" based on exactness of measurements, precise descriptions, data on age and sex, the name of the collector, and where the specimens were described. This superseded the European system of species description, which was often based on a single specimen.

In Carlisle Baird frequently worked alone on characterizing birds, but his outstanding work entitled "North American Birds" was published in part in 1860 with the assistance of Cassin and Lawrence, and in part in 1875 with Brewer and Ridgway. Another study begun by Baird before he came to the Smithsonian was on tailed batrachians. This paper on a group of amphibians so impressed Agassiz that he recommended Baird for the first staff position with the Smithsonian. In addition, Baird also did some studies on fishes before he assumed his post in Washington. After he arrived there he began to study and report on collections from governmental exploring expeditions which he helped to supervise. This resulted in his publications on reptiles and mammals. His volume on "Mammals of North America" was for 30 years the standard treatise. "In completeness, correct assignment of species, craniological characters, keen observation and good detail this volume was better than any before on the subject," according to Dall.

However, Baird's most aggressive research on a large scale was done when he served as Commissioner of Fish and Fisheries from 1870 until his death in 1887. This was the first Federal agency dealing with conservation. Within 10 years this group was recognized at the International Fisheries Exhibition in Berlin as top-flight and was given first prize for having made the most progress in fish culture. First, the commission studied reasons for the depletion of fishes on the east coast; next, it suggested appropriate regulations for fishing; and finally, it devised means for repopulating present species or for the introduction of new species of fishes in the lakes and rivers and along the seacoasts.

Baird's research output, published over his name alone or in joint authorship, included 80 papers relating to birds, 73 to mammals, 43 to reptiles, 431 to fishes, 61 to invertebrates (chiefly in the form of reviews), 16 to plants, 88 to geographical distribution, 46 to geology, 45 to anthropology, 31 to industry and art, and 109 to explorations and travel. He described 186 new species of reptiles, 56 of fishes, 48 of mammals, and 70 of birds.

Though Agassiz published only about 415 titles as compared with over 1,000 for Baird, his work was better known largely because of his charming public lectures. His first publication, already mentioned, was on the fishes of Europe, and soon afterward came his remarkable work on fossil fishes. He was one of the first to integrate the classification of fossil and living fishes. He did most of the fossil studies in Paris under the supervision of Cuvier. That work, describing about 1,700 fossil species, was Agassiz's most significant piece of pure research. His reputation was made. Within a few years there appeared his startling "Ice Age" theory. He lectured on this topic in England and continued research on it after he came to the United States. His Bibliographia Zoologiae was a prodigious work and served taxonomists well for some time. One of his first publications after he came to America was his account of the explorations of Lake Superior, which Baird praised highly. He did a great service for Alexander Dallas Bache and the U.S. Coast Survey with his participation in the coastal survey of Florida. His theory of coral reef formation was an outstanding example of reasoning based on research.

Perhaps Agassiz's most grandiose publication project was his proposed 10 volumes called "Contributions to the Natural History of the United States," for which he had collected by advance subscription pledges the amazing sum of $360,000. This was more than any scientist had ever been responsible for. He published only four of these volumes. The part on the embryology of the turtles possibly received the most acclaim and was quoted for some time. Thereafter, his greatest acclaim came from his teaching and his public lectures.

THEIR SERVICE

Both Baird and Agassiz were deeply conscious of their duties as directors of museums. Several times in letters to Agassiz, Baird showed his concern in not being able to gather more materials from unexplored localities. Such collections would help to complete accessions in certain fields; the rest would be distributed to other institutions of learning. In the first 30 years of Baird's tenure with the Smithsonian he had distributed over 200,000 specimens to educational institutions. Also many students came to study and compare specimens with him.

Agassiz encouraged the founding of local museums, but for the Museum of Comparative Zoology he sought to obtain national prominence by having research done there which was not carried on with zeal elsewhere. In his laboratory he taught students to observe. When he came to Harvard he was very critical of its advanced work, but before he left he had raised the level of the college's graduate work and enhanced the reputation of the zoology department. By many it was accounted the outstanding scientific institution in the Western Hemisphere. He was instrumental in getting Congress to relieve scientific institutions from the payment of duty for alcohol used in the preservation of specimens.

As personalities, both Baird and Agassiz were well liked. They attracted people readily. Baird invited many collectors and students to his home, especially at Christmas time. Personal problems never interrupted the steady progress of his work. He was sought by budding scientists and important congressional committees for advice. Perhaps the best known example of such service was his expert testimony which aided materially in obtaining a favorable vote in Congress for the purchase of Alaska. Baird was able to see in others their potential as great explorers, great naturalists, and great collectors. To this challenge many responded and remained loyal to him ever after. This had its effect in high interest and enthusiasm among scientific workers including those in far-off army posts.

Of Agassiz, James Russell Lowell once said: "His magic was not far to seek, — He was so human!" Even though English was not his native tongue, he won his American audiences from the start by his boyish enthusiasm. His first audience cheered him by their deep attention. He was quick to grasp the fine possibilities for education in America. Soon after his arrival he developed a deep feeling for this land whose strength "lies in the prodigious number of individuals who think and work at the same time." Agassiz also inspired by example; once he examined the developing stages of a turtle for 60 days and nights consecutively at regular intervals until all the stages of its development were established. He was willing to talk to sailors on ships, to workmen splitting rocks, to stagecoach drivers, and to children as though he were discussing some interesting finding with fellow scientists. In his own inimitable way he was the greatest popularizer of science in America.

Agassiz liked his adopted country so much that he often felt the desire to do something in return for his happiness here. One way by which he satisfied this desire was to serve well in many advisory capacities. He had a great impact on the future of Cornell University in his capacity as one of its first visiting lecturers. He had an interest in most scientific meetings and was often the featured speaker. His lectures to teachers were most helpful in elevating science instruction in schools. He was able to convince legislators that public money should be appropriated to educational institutions. In his last letter to Baird, Agassiz wrote: "Everything I have done concerning the study of N. American animals since I have lived in the U. St. was done with a view of advancing science in my adopted country."

Baird served well as a pioneer in the conservation of natural resources, especially insofar as fishes were concerned. As Commissioner of Fish and Fisheries he helped settle vexing fisheries problems with Canada at Halifax. He had great visions of a National Seaside Laboratory at Woods Hole, Mass. Even though that did not materialize as he had planned it, the substitute Fish Commission Laboratory attracted many future biologists, and finally the world-famous Marine Biological Laboratory was established there. At the Berlin Fisheries Exhibition in 1880 he was recognized as the outstanding fish conservationist in the world.

Both Agassiz and Baird received honorary degrees from leading universities and were outstanding in attracting respect for zoological science in America. They were not mere collectors, but men of vision inspired to diffuse knowledge among men.

NATURE OF THE LETTERS

This collection of Baird-Agassiz letters is intended to be complete and falls short of its goal only because neither man kept all his letters or had copies made of those he sent. For four years (1846–50) Baird listed all the letters he wrote and received. Some of those he wrote to Agassiz have not been found. All the letters found were written in longhand and are often hardly legible. After 1850, when Baird became associated with the Smithsonian, most of the letters he wrote were partially reproduced on thin paper, the copies being bound into books. Because of fading, some of those copies have become almost illegible. Others have been removed, presumably by his daughter, Lucy.

The letters are arranged chronologically. When no date appears on a letter itself, the stamped "received" date is used. When a letter is neither dated nor stamped with date received, it is placed in the most logical sequence. The place and date line are uniformly set at the beginning of a letter regardless of where they appeared originally. Punctuation and capitalization in date lines, salutations, and signatures vary in the extreme in the original letters, but for the printed version these have been made to conform more nearly to normal usage such as the writers would have followed had they known the material was to be printed. Obvious misspellings that are likely to occur in hastily hand-written letters have been corrected, and doubtful spellings of generic scientific names have been made intelligible by checking with Scudder's "Nomenclator Zoologicus," Bulletin 19 of the U.S. National Museum, the standard for that era. In a few instances where wording cannot be deciphered, a question mark or the word *illegible* is inserted in brackets.

The contents of the letters here presented cover a wide range of subjects, such as a discussion of Baird's original offer to collect specimens for Agassiz, the prospective joint publication of a monograph of American fishes, Baird's appreciation of the strong support given by Agassiz to Baird when he was anxious to become associated with the Smithsonian, establishing the proper respect and direction for further research in natural history, substantiating genera and species in several fields, helping explorers individually and jointly with their limited finances, the present and future direction of their respective museums, and finally the joint cooperation in Agassiz's great experiment of a summer school for teachers of natural history on Penikese Island.

The tone of these letters varies all the way from that of the friendly, businesslike Baird and the appreciative Agassiz when things were going well, to the biting, authoritative mood of an Agassiz when things were not going his way. There is a general note of optimism for the future of their respective museums and an undertone of willingness to do an enormous amount of effective work in natural history.

Their correspondence had a mutual effect on their respective museums. The collections became more varied than ever before by the addition of accessions from Central America, Mexico, Cuba, Canada, and

Alaska, both from cooperative ventures and from expeditions separately conducted. Since the two men corresponded frequently, their respective museums would be more likely to get the first duplicates when they did not cooperate in a venture. If one was not able to get his institution to pay for collecting expenses, the other one would be asked to help in defraying these. If neither institution could help, these men would then cooperate personally in meeting some of the expenses. There was considerable discussion as to the areas in which a particular museum should specialize and as to what portion of collections might be sent to Europe. Since the space in the first Smithsonian building was limited and the future of collections not certain, some aspects of the development of the Smithsonian museum were considered.

Because Baird had charge of International Exchanges of publications for the Smithsonian, both organizations benefited from their correspondence. Agassiz could get a large amount of free distribution of the published results of his researches, and the Smithsonian could reap heavily from his prestige as an author. The Smithsonian backed Agassiz's prospectus for his "Contributions to the Natural History of the United States." The sending of many free copies of his prospectus aided considerably in obtaining for him that amazing sum of pledges to have the Contributions put into print.

Some of the letters discussed articles prepared for publication, or the scientific integrity of an author. Baird was the editor of the Smithsonian publications and for 10 years the scientific editor for Harper's Magazine. He often inquired of Agassiz about material for both of these publications. Such an interchange of ideas tended to improve the character of these publications and incidentally the reputation of American science abroad.

Other letters touched upon the use of certain characters in classification and the validity of genera and species. In the case of turtles, the usefulness of characters such as serrations on the shell, sheaths, and head movements were discussed. The effects of altitude and latitude on the geographical distribution of certain species were also examined. Species of fishes and of turtles were classified through their correspondence.

Continued correspondence of this sort between these scientists encouraged devotion to the study of natural history because each showed appreciation for the other's labors. Deep desires were expressed in the letters and projects often put into motion as a result. Here one sees a mutual leadership, mutual responsibilities, and mutual zeal in promoting American researches, which, combined, are of great historical significance and which are reflected in the character of American scholarship today.

The primary sources used in the preparation of this introduction were William Healey Dall's "Spencer Fullerton Baird" (Philadelphia, 1915); Elizabeth Cary Agassiz's "Louis Agassiz, His Life and Correspondence" (2 vols., Boston, 1885); and Edward Lurie's "Louis Agassiz, A Life in Science" (Chicago, 1960). Other important sources include Lane Cooper's "Louis Agassiz as a Teacher" (Ithaca, N.Y., 1917; rev. ed., 1945); Thomas Coulson's "Joseph Henry, His Life and Work" (Princeton, N.J., 1950); and the Spencer Fullerton Baird Papers, Smithsonian Institution Archives, which were the most important manuscript sources.

ACKNOWLEDGMENTS

I wish to express my appreciation for the kind cooperation of the staffs of the following archives and institutions for permission to consult and copy certain manuscripts used in this project: American Philosophical Society, Academy of Natural Sciences of Philadelphia, Harvard University Houghton Library and the University Archives, Historical Society of Pennsylvania, University of Rochester Library, Smithsonian Institution Archives, and Yale University Library. Also I wish to express thanks for the help and encouragement given by Leonard Carmichael, Secretary of the Smithsonian Institution, Charles Coleman Sellers, Paul H. Oehser, Edward Lurie, by my wife, and by numerous others; to the Harvard University Film Service and Miss Jessie B. MacKenzie, librarian of the Museum of Comparative Zoology of the same institution, for photographs used.

PLATE I

Louis Agassiz, January 10, 1873, age 63

PLATE 2

Louis Agassiz lecturing (Photograph from files of the Museum of Comparative Zoology, courtesy of Miss MacKenzie)

PLATE 3

THE NATURAL HISTORY

OF THE

UNITED STATES OF AMERICA.

BY

LOUIS AGASSIZ.

/24887

FIRST MONOGRAPH.

IN THREE PARTS.—I. ESSAY ON CLASSIFICATION.—II. NORTH AMERICAN TESTUDINATA.—
III. EMBRYOLOGY OF THE TURTLE; WITH THIRTY-FOUR PLATES.

VOL. II.

BOSTON:

LITTLE, BROWN AND COMPANY.

LONDON: TRÜBNER & CO.

1857.

Title page of volume 2 of Agassiz's *The Natural History of the United States of America*

PLATE 4

Museum of Comparative Zoology on Divinity Avenue, Cambridge, in 1859

University Museum, Harvard University, 1961

THE LETTERS

AGASSIZ to BAIRD

1 Bumstead Ave., Boston
Apr. 10, 1847

My dear Sir,

Months have passed away since I received your very kind letter, and I should fear to have lost your sympathy did I not feel certain you will pardon me for not having answered it earlier when I mention the circumstances which prevented me from doing it as I ought to have done. But conceive of the position of a naturalist entirely devoted to his studies without any other object before him, arriving in a world quite new to him, as so full of interesting objects as this is, and you will easily imagine how I have been carried away by the objects immediately around me. Besides, I had engaged to deliver a course of lectures in Boston,[1] and in the attempt to go in the same time through that work and the examination, anatomical as well as zoological, of every species of animal I could obtain from the market and from some excursions on the beaches in the vicinity, I was brought into such a state of excitement that I at last was taken sick so severely that I have not moved from my bed for these last three weeks. I am now recovering gradually, and hope soon to be up again, and able to go into the country; when I shall have the pleasure of seeing you in the course of the summer at the time which will be most convenient to you.

As you have been kind enough to offer me your assistance in making collections, I take now the liberty to suggest some points in which you could greatly aid me. In the Zoological departments my researches bear always upon the anatomical and embryological side of all questions, and so I prefer to have a great number of specimens of *the most common species in all their ages,* than to have few specimens of many rare species. I will mention as an example, that I should collect as many as twenty and more specimens of all your salamanders, frogs, toads, and have besides the tadpoles in all their different states, the whole preserved in spirit. So with other reptiles; among fishes I should prefer those neglected small species of Cyprinidae and other river fishes; and to preserve them for future anatomical investigation, I use

---

[1] Louis Agassiz had contracted to deliver lectures at the Lowell Institute, Boston, Mass., before coming to America. For about four years he had been wondering whether there might be a position open in the United States where he might earn more money than he did in Neuchâtel so that he could finance a larger part of his publications. The money he received from these lectures and the grant of 15,000 francs he received from the King of Prussia paid for most of his expenses until 1848, when he accepted the chair of Natural History at the Lawrence Scientific School of Harvard University.

23

to inject spirit through the anus and mouth into the intestines, and in larger specimens also into the abdominal cavity through a cut in the wall of that cavity. Even birds and mammalia, especially the smaller species, I preserve in the same manner in spirit, as often as I can secure specimens which are not badly shot. It is time to ascertain through anatomical examination what is the value of all those genera which have been established among birds, and this cannot be done except with such a collection. Even in a Zoological point of view, it is impossible to preserve bats better than in spirits, which must be strong, but not so much so as to occasion a shrinking of the soft parts. Of course, worms, mollusks, and all parasites cannot be preserved otherwise. Now, if you have time to secure for me in this way some of the animals of your country, I should be most obliged, and of course, not only repay you all expenses it will be necessary to make for this, but let you have of our European animals what will be in my power to procure and I hope you will mention your desiderata as freely as I mention mine. I should greatly value all your bats, mice, rats, moles, shrews, weasels, squirrels, etc.

Though I am not much of a botanist, there is nevertheless one branch of that science in which I take the deepest interest and for which I would also ask your assistance. The study of trees has become so important to paleontologists, that no one who has paid some attention to fossils can any longer make progress in this department without studying the fossil trees and comparing them with the actual flora. Now, I know you have paid much attention to this subject, and to me it has acquired a new degree of interest since I have ascertained that the arborescent flora of the European Miocene Tertiary deposits has the greatest affinity with the actual flora of the temperate regions of the United States, a result entirely unexpected, and quite contrary to most of the prevailing notions about the temperature of the continent of Europe during the Tertiary epoch. I am now very desirous to make the most extensive collection of all the trees and shrubs of the United States in order to trace as far as possible this analogy. But such a collection cannot be found in any herbarium, it must be made anew with that peculiar view, and if you feel the least inclined to help me in this inquiry, you would not only help me, but really help advancing one of the most interesting geological questions. If you find it too troublesome, forgive me for having asked for it. As fossil plants are mostly found in parts, it would be necessary to have 1st, young branches with the buds as they are now before opening; cut such specimens as can be dried between paper; 2nd, branches with young bark, one or two inches in diameter; cut cylinders of about six inches length; 3rd, similar cylinders of the stems; old wood with old bark; then mark the tree to collect at a later period, flowers, fruits, and leaves, and of the last, a great number of all the varieties of form from different branches and recent shoots. It is almost late to begin, but I could not write earlier, and in fact, it is rather imprudent for me to go to-day through the exertion of writing; but perhaps in the thickest of the woods, you will still find specimens of all your species in a leafless state, with the buds in the winter state.

Will you present my kindest regards to Dr. Emory[2] and beg from him to excuse me also for not having answered his letter.

With the hope you will not have given me up, for my improper deportment towards you, I remain, my dear sir,

Very sincerely yours,
L. AGASSIZ

AGASSIZ to BAIRD

CAMBRIDGE
April 26, 1848

Mr dear Sir,

There is only one way for me to show you that I deserve no reproach for my long silence and that is to send to you as soon as possible the objects I have been putting aside for you, while arranging a part of my collections during the two last months. It will at least prove to you that I am not forgetful of my promise, although I am the worst of correspondents. Let me know how to send you a barrel and you will immediately receive several fishes from Europe & this vicinity, which I hope will interest you.

Now for your questions. All my difficulties arise from having too much on hand. During the whole winter I have had successively before me between 60 and 100 species of invertebrate animals spawning or developing themselves. Desor[3] and myself we have seen more eggs and embryos during this short period than all embryologists together before. There was and there is work for ten heads and 50 hands here. Could you only spend some days with me, I am satisfied you would be pleased, but you should come soon as the spawning season is rapidly passing away. I have ample room for you and Mrs. Baird here, if you will accept my modest fare. It is entirely out of the question for me to leave now.

---

[2] Robert Emory (1814–48) was president of Dickinson College, Carlisle, Pa., where Spencer F. Baird was the professor of natural history when this letter was written.

[3] Pierre Jean Édouard Desor (1811–82), a young German law student, was employed by Agassiz in 1837 as an assistant to handle artists, engravers, and others associated with his printing establishment. These activities were expensive, used up much of Agassiz's income, and invaded the privacy of his home life. Cecile, Agassiz's first wife, resented this invasion into their family life and after some time left Neuchâtel with two of their children to live with her brother in Karlsruhe. Desor later came to Cambridge to assist Agassiz and again became involved in personal problems, this time with Agassiz himself. Several tribunals were called to settle their problems, which ultimately ended by Desor returning to Europe. He subsequently became professor of geology in the Académie de Neuchâtel.

I congratulate you for your ichthyological discoveries. Do not delay to publish them, provided you have made out the synonymy. I could probably add a good many to your stock if you will take them. I would name the [illegible] *Eurhinus*. Be very cautious about the species of suckers. Male and female differ widely and are all described as two species, so many *Hydrargyras*. Their number has to be reduced to about one half.

I have seen last summer in Mr. Thompson's collection the characinoid fish of Lake Champlain you mention in your letter; but could make nothing with it, not having seen a copy of Müller & Troschel's Nor. Ichth. here. You should not publish your new genus before consulting that work, or at least the abstract of Erichson's Archiv für Naturgeschichte.

I feel much obliged for all the details you give me about your investigation of your Reptiles; I wish I could hear and see more of it.

I also answer the letter you wrote to Prof. A. Gray[4]; it will prove to you that my not writing is certainly not owing to my desire of discovering further botheration. It will on the contrary give me always much pleasure to give any information I can, provided I have time to do it. I can only repeat I wish you were here. Nothing is more important in our science now than embryological researches; nothing easier, nothing more difficult in the same time. To trace the morphological changes, any microscope, magnifying from 10–50 diameters is sufficient to trace the formation of the tissues, their intimate structure, the formation and contents of the eggs. The highest powers we possess are scarcely sufficient. The use of the compressor must be very familiar to the observer; it is only by pressure that you can make opaque yolks transparent.

For 5 or 6 days past my books have been boxed up in E. Boston to be transported to Cambridge; as soon as I have received and unpacked them I will lend you Vogt's *Alytes obstetricans* and our Salmonidae. I have no other copy but my own here; but have written for some. How shall I send them?

Try first unfecundated eggs from the ovary, the smallest you can see with the naked eye, to become familiar with the materials out of which new individuals, the embryos, are forming. Do this for animals of all classes. Cut

---

[4] Asa Gray (1810–88), professor of botany, Harvard University, was a researcher in depth, a most competent worker, who increased enormously the respect for botanical research in America. He published many volumes in his field, but his most enduring work was his "Manual of Botany of the Northern United States." His herbarium became the largest and most valuable in America. He was instrumental in having Harvard confer the degree of Doctor of Laws upon Baird.

Even though Agassiz and Gray were both members of the Harvard faculty, they were often on opposite sides of an argument. Gray soon became an enthusiast of Darwinism, a thesis which Agassiz never supported completely. At one time Gray broke off personal relationships with Agassiz because of the latter's insults. Perhaps one of the several breaks in Agassiz's health resulted from such strained relations. Nevertheless their combined influence on American scholarship and Harvard prestige was tremendous.

the egg out of the ovary itself or place parts of the ovary under the microscope.

I doubt you can have anywhere a good microscope at short notice. I waited 9 months for one and 18 months for another of these which I possess; in the *lower power & extent of field*, Oberhäuser is superior to all & these are precisely the most important parts of a Microscope. Spencer is superior in the highest power. I have satisfied myself of that recently, & I expect much from him, but his instruments are not yet adapted to the wants of observers. He makes excellent optical instruments, but not easily managed for our uses. I wish I could see that man and give him some good advice, because I think he will do better than all the other makers before him. I hope Bayley, who knows him, will give him good advice.

Sincerely yours,
L. AGASSIZ

My respects to Mrs. Baird.

AGASSIZ to BAIRD

CAMBRIDGE, Dec. 26, 1848

My dear Sir,

I feel oppressed by my silence, and it is only to relieve you from a similar painful impression with reference to me, that I write a few lines. You have crowded me with wonderful things, and have never in my life before had a chance to see so many new objects in so short a time. And your delightful letters ought to have been answered, but I have some 6 or 7 public lectures a week to deliver besides my college duties, lecturing and recitations & hardly a moment to myself. I have, however set Mr. Sonrel[5] at work to let you have a specimen of your plates; and I send one of mine of the Cetacea under cover that you may judge of his exquisite style in drawing on stone. Many thousand thanks for the freshwater fishes in alcohol and for the Lepidostei, this last Genus with the 3 new ones which you have just sent, counts now 9 species, 4 flats noted once, and 5 *longirostris*. What work to decipher all that! Charles[6] is constantly unpacking one barrel after another and puts specimens of all for you, as he goes on; so that your turn will at

---

[5] A. Sonrel, who had been employed by Agassiz in Neuchâtel, was one of the outstanding lithographic artists of that era.

[6] Charles Girard (1822–95), a zoologist, was at first a pupil and later an assistant of Louis Agassiz in Switzerland. When Agassiz came to America he brought Girard with him to Harvard, where he worked until 1850. Soon after Desor left for Europe, Girard left Agassiz to become associated with Baird, after which Agassiz became very critical of anything Girard wanted to publish. Baird often had to defend him and his own publications because of that incident. Perhaps Girard's best remembered work was his contribution in the joint publication with Baird in vol. X of the "Reports of the Explorations and Surveys for a Railroad from the Mississippi River to the Pacific Ocean"

last come also, and I hope you will like what I have for you. Could you only be here for a few days.

Sincerely your friend,

L. AGASSIZ

My respects to Mrs. Baird.

AGASSIZ to BAIRD

Apr. 24, 1849

My dear Sir,

The very day of the receipt of your note I went to see about the microscope. All on hand are of the small model for 40 dollars a piece, very good instruments in their way, and satisfactory for investigations not requiring over 300 power. Instead of waiting longer it strikes me I had better take one, which I would select for you. When you want a larger one, it will not be difficult to pass this to one of your students.

I forgot to request you to collect for me embryos of all birds you can find, as soon as the germ is formed up to young birds in the nest before entirely covered with down. It would be important if you were also to collect all animals which do not reach their full size in the first year, as frogs, salamanders, with date, to compare their progress in different latitudes. I shall do the same here. Can you let me have original specimens of Haldeman's[7] Percinas and Gobio.

Sincerely your friend,

L. AGASSIZ

My respects to Mrs. Baird.

AGASSIZ to BAIRD

CAMBRIDGE, *May 18, 1849*

My dear Sir,

I have just received the bank note $40 you sent me for the microscope. I think it is square; I shall however call at Middlefield for a receipt as soon as I go to town. I simply write today to tell you that the money reached me safely.

(1859) describing the "Herpetology" and "Fishes." Several years prior to this publication he was awarded a degree in medicine. While visiting Europe he became involved in supplying the Confederacy with drugs and surgical instruments. After the war he felt that he was no longer wanted and decided to settle in Paris where he practiced medicine for 20 years.

[7] Samuel S. Haldeman (1812–80), scientist, philologist, was born at Locust Grove, Lancaster County, Pa. He studied at Dickinson College and in 1842 began the publication of his "Monograph on the Freshwater Mollusca of the United States." In 1848 he announced the discovery of a new organ of sound possessed by certain of the Lepidoptera. Later he studied American Indian dialects, becoming a recognized authority on that subject. He was also on the lecturing staffs of the Franklin Institute, the Pennsylvania Agricultural College, Delaware College, and the University of Pennsylvania.

The only thing wanting in most microscopes and so in yours, is a magnifying power of 10 diameters, to draw small animals or observe the connections of parts. I am writing to Oberhäuser for a special microscope of low power and shall ask him whether he could furnish you with such addition for your microscope. There were no doublets in town. If there is anything I can *do* for you, let me know; you shall see that I will attend to it, even if I do not *write* much.

My respects to Mrs. Baird.

Sincerely your friend,
L. AGASSIZ

AGASSIZ to BAIRD

CAMBRIDGE, *June 11, 1849*

My dear Sir,

Excuse me for neglecting to send to you the receipt of Wm. Middlefield as early as I might have done. Having nothing particular to mention I delayed it from day to day. There are now several plates of your fishes drawn on stone; I shall have proofs taken next week to send them to you as specimens, to ascertain how you like that style.

I am entirely absorbed by the embryology of some Ascidian Molluscs which interest me in the utmost degree, as they illustrate the growth of cells most wonderfully. Have you had any opportunity of collecting some bird embryos for me? I hope you shall be here at the next meeting. If you will accept a corner of my crowded house you will be very welcome.

My respects to Mrs. Baird.

Sincerely yours,
L. AGASSIZ

AGASSIZ to BAIRD

CAMBRIDGE, *July 25, 1849*

Dear Sir,

I ought to have thanked you for the eggs of *Tebennophorus* & for your offer of *Julus* eggs, but I was of late so completely absorbed by the observations I have been tracing upon a living *Astrea* (Stone Coral!) which I dredged in the Vineyard Sound about Naushon & in Buzzards Bay, that I have had neither ears nor eyes for anything else. The time for our meeting[8] is fast approaching and I trust you will be here and bring a cartload of

---

[8] The annual meeting of the American Association for the Advancement of Science was held at Cambridge that year. Baird attended and stayed at the home of Agassiz. Later he walked with Agassiz to Boston to see Sonrel's drawings of some of Baird's fishes.

interesting materials for the Zoölogical Section. We intend having a good time and doing good work and I hope you will join the little circle at my house. Bring all you have upon your Batrachians in particular.

Remember me kindly to Mrs. Baird.

Sincerely yours,
L. Agassiz

AGASSIZ to BAIRD

Cambridge, *Oct. 9, 1849*

My dear Sir,

I have received your box in perfect good state, and return my best thanks for all the fine things sent to me, which are equally instructive and acceptable. The Lepidostei are particularly welcome. I trust I shall be able to prepare a good paper upon them now.

I have written to-day to Prof. Henry about the Conservatorship of the Museum in such terms as to let him feel how important your connections with that Institution might be for its advance in the Nat. Hist. Department.

Girard says the Southern *Cottus* is again a new one. I have not yet compared it myself.

I send two new plates for your revision and the names. Please return them soon as Mr. Sonrel is anxious to have them printed while the press man is not too busy and can take good care of them. What is the number to be struck off? I think Prof. Henry said 1,000 for the volume and 250 for us. You need not return the proofs, but only send your remarks. Mr. Garrigue[9] will have already written to you that it will give me great pleasure to revise any part of your translation of the Cyclopedia you may wish to send to me, and I will do it always in as short a time as it can possibly be done.

Could you secure a number of *Aphredoderus* for me, that I might dissect some? It has given me much pleasure to peruse your Batrachians. I shall not fail to send a copy to Tschudi and though I do not know where he is at present, I shall include it to a friend who must know his whereabouts. I would gladly accept your antelope had I anything to send you in return but I am very poor in Mammalia.

Your friend,
L. Agassiz

My kindest remembrance to Mrs. Baird.

---

[9] Charles R. Garrigue, a publisher, had agreed to publish with Baird an English translation of the "Bilder Atlas zum Conversations Lexicon." Baird was to be the editor and chief translator. The American edition, called "The Iconographic Encyclopedia," was published in 1852.

BAIRD to AGASSIZ

CARLISLE, *Nov. 18, 1849*

My dear Mr. Agassiz,

I have just obtained an embryo of about three inches long: it has been preserved for several years in spirit, but appears to be in good condition. Shall I send it on now, or wait till I have occasion to forward something else? Have you yet received the jars etc. I sent, some weeks ago?

The meeting of the Smithsonian Regents takes place in a few weeks. What do you think of my chances this fall? I have not the most remote idea.

Very truly yours,
S. F. BAIRD

BAIRD to AGASSIZ

CARLISLE, *Nov. 25, 1849*

My dear Mr. Agassiz,

I received the proofs and your letter a day or two ago but have not had time to reply to them until now. The plates are beautifully executed, equal to the rest. I feel some doubt as to the names, not having kept the run of the specimens. The *Hypsolepis,* I presume, is the one from Cumberland County.[10] You know better than I do whether it is the *cornutus* of Mitchell. If not, give it any name you please. The same with regard to the atromaculatoid species. What is its locality, west or east? If western, it is probably the *Semotilus cephalus* of Raf. I would be much gratified and obliged if you would attach any name you please or think proper to this plate; and the same with regard to any others. You also can say better than I what number should be struck off. I would like to leave all this to you.

I wrote sometime ago announcing at your service a foetus of a cow! Since then I have received a number of reptiles and fish from the Sturms[11] at Nürnberg. The fish consist principally of Cyprinidae, but among them are small specimens of *Cottus.* Would Girard like a specimen or two?

Am now making a desperate effort to get you a suite of Manatee skeletons. I have heard of one in Florida which I can possibly procure, and I send off tomorrow a dozen letters to different persons in Florida, officers, who are stationed in various points where those animals occur. I ask for skeletons and sculls of every age, and implore them for a foetus. I have recently obtained some fine fossil bones from the alluvium of the Upper Susquehanna

---

[10] Cumberland County is situated west of the Susquehanna River in Pennsylvania; the county seat is at Carlisle.

[11] Jacob Sturm and his relatives were zoologists from Nürnberg, Germany. Baird also exchanged birds with Jacob Sturm.

(a second lot) and among these some deer, bear, fox remains of great interest. I have also the prospect of some more from the same locality as also from some caves in the same region. I have a few more *Aphredoderus* here at your service and can certainly get plenty more next summer, as one of my own party of snake hunters brought these to me and can procure any quantity within a short distance of his house.

I am much obliged to you for writing to Professor Henry in my behalf. I think he is well disposed to nominate me when the proper time, in his opinion, has arrived, but I would like that time to be the present winter. I have not lately had any expression of opinion from him as to his views of "this time." Sometime ago, however, it was after the lapse of at least a year. Now I am impatient to be free from the trammels of college life in order that I may go very soon to Florida while the troops are there, and where from my relationship to some of the most important officers, (Gen. Churchill) I can have facilities for procuring specimens which may never occur again: especially as the troops will in all probability not be there in a few months. What hosts of Manatee in all stages and conditions, what quantities of new and rare fishes, reptiles and mammalia I would procure! Such an opportunity may never occur again at any rate in regards to the Manatee. The meeting of the board takes place in less than two weeks, if I am not mistaken.

Sincerely yours,
S. F. BAIRD

BAIRD to AGASSIZ

CARLISLE, *Feb. 15, 1850*

My dear Mr. Agassiz,

I have this day sent to Dr. Gray a parcel containing among other matter the manuscript with the original German text of the Geology of the Iconographic Encyclopedia, which you so kindly offered to revise. I do not know how far I ought to hold you to your promise under present circumstances, as your invaluable time must be fully occupied at present. If, however, you can complete the task of this revision in the course of a month, I will be very much indebted to you for so doing. If you cannot do this, please send back the parcel to Garrigue and I will try and get Hall[12] to attend to it. I would not be in such a hurry but that the printer will want the MSS for copy in about six weeks. I have asked Dr. Gray to lend you his plates Iconographic of Geology, in case you have not got them: or else I will send by mail. I do not ask you to supply deficiencies; only to correct errors, briefly as you please.

I cannot help expressing my gratification at learning that you are soon to

---

[12] James Hall (1811–98), the State Geologist of New York, was also a distinguished paleontologist.

be connected with us by so strong a bond of union as that of marriage to an American lady.[13] All who know her say that she is in every way worthy of you, and to those so happy as to be your friends, [and that] expresses a very great deal in a few words. I hope some day to make her acquaintance and judge for myself as to the correctness of such extravagant encomium.

It is I suppose of no use to beg for a visit on your way either to or from Washington. Nothing would gratify me more, however, than your doing this. I am afraid I shall never see you in Carlisle. I have been anxiously waiting for some action of Prof. Henry and the Regents of the Smithsonian in regard to myself; the session has not yet concluded, so that there is still a chance. I am very desirous of having the appointment made now to date from either July 1, 1850 or January, 1851. This would give me time and opportunity to wind up affairs here, and I am anxious to get to work as Curator. Since my last letter, I have made various acquisitions. Several new bone caves have furnished important remains: as also the alluvium of certain portions of bank along the Upper Susquehanna river. I have also received some fine skins, skulls, and horns of *Cervus canadensis, C. macrourus, C. leucotis, Antelope americana* from the Yellowstone river. Next fall, I hope to get skeletons of all the Mammalia of that region, as also many fossil vertebrata from the Black Hills. I have myself been hard at work making skeletons of various animals, including the domestic species. You never sent me word whether or not you wished that small foetus of the cow, which I obtained some months ago.

I am on the track of a large deposit of fossil bones of deer, oxen, etc. in a meadow near Carlisle, and am only waiting for the advent of spring to have the locality plowed up.

Very truly yours,
S.F.BAIRD

P.S. Should the Meeting of Regents not be over when you get to Washington, might I ask you to use your influence, under direction of Prof. Henry, to accelerate my appointment.

BAIRD to AGASSIZ

CARLISLE, *Mar. 23, 1850*

My dear Mr. Agassiz,

The March number of the Iconographic has completely exhausted the manuscript in the hands of the printer. May I beg you to forward immediately by Adams Express that which you have revised or not, in order that Garrigue may be relieved from the fear of not getting it in time for April.

---

[13] Elizabeth Cabot Cary (1822–1907), Boston, Mass., with her mother had heard Agassiz give one of his first lectures at the Lowell Institute in 1846. Five years after their marriage, Mrs. Agassiz helped to found the Agassiz School for Girls, the predecessor of Radcliffe College.

Send it direct to New York. I regret exceedingly having to worry you with this matter, and ought to have sent the MSS months before I did. The delay was unavoidable on my part, however.

I write two copies of this note, sending one to Charleston,[14] and the other to Washington, hoping that one may reach you very shortly. Wish I could see you this spring.

Very truly yours,
S. F. Baird

AGASSIZ to BAIRD

Charleston, *Mar. 31, 1850*

My dear Sir,

When at Washington I did not forget to speak to Prof. Henry about the Curatorship of the Smithsonian Museum and he told me positively that he looked upon you as the proper man, as his candidate whose election he would urge as soon as he would be sure to carry it. Excuse me for not letting you know; but in the hurry of a business journey, for I am now making my living, as I can not make it full in Cambridge, I have very little time. Your parcel of MSC. was received in Cambridge the morning I left; I took it with me, expecting to have some hours to read it through and I would certainly have done so but for your imperative direction to send it on to New York, which I did yesterday on receipt of your note, just in time for the steamer. On my return to Cambridge I hope to have the happiness of being married to a charming lady of Boston & it is my current desire to pay you a visit with her, as soon as we can leave home. My kindest regards to Mrs. Baird. Since I am here, I have seen that they have at last passed my Lake Superior book through the press; but I have not yet been able to look it through. My Monograph of the Medusa is also printing so that on my return I shall have something to send you.

Sincerely your friend,

L. Agassiz

Prof. Sp. Baird,

I leave tomorrow for Georgia; but I shall be back in Cambridge by the third week of April.

---

[14] Agassiz was at this time spending much of his income from lectures and from the salary at Harvard University either to buy more specimens or to preserve them. In order to add to his income he undertook the position as professor at the University of South Carolina, Charleston, S.C., as a sort of vacation appointment. At the end of the second year he relinquished the position because the extra work proved too much for him; he had contracted a high fever while he was in South Carolina.

BAIRD to AGASSIZ

CARLISLE, *May 5, 1850*

My dear Mr. Agassiz,

On my return from a short trip to Washington only a few days ago, I saw the announcement of your marriage. This took me entirely by surprise as I had supposed the event further off by several weeks at least. Permit me most sincerely to congratulate Mrs. A., from what I know of you, and to congratulate you, from what I hear of her. I think that now we have you safe among us forever; since when you die your memory will still be our proud possession, and while you live, I hope, Mrs. Agassiz will be too true a friend to American Science ever to hear of your returning permanently to Europe. Have you given up your intended trip to the old world, write if so. What do you propose for the summer? I hope to go to Westport on Lake Champlain about the middle of July where I mean to catch all the fish that swim in the Lake and neighboring streams. Can you not visit that region yourself about the same time? Prof. Guyot[15] spoke of a visit to the Lake next July. Does he still maintain this intention?

Should you come South before the middle of July, we hope most earnestly that you will pay us your long promised visit. We shall have a comfortable room for you and will do all in our power to make the visit agreeable. We cannot promise Mrs. Agassiz much in the way of Society, gay or grave, but we can show her some beautiful scenery and a hearty welcome. If you could come about the beginning of June, you would see the country to the best advantage; any time however, either before or after, will be acceptable to us, provided only that you come at all. You have disappointed us so often, however, that it is with some misgivings we look for you, as promised in your letter from Charleston. I owe an apology for not answering this letter before, but I was entirely unaware of your return until I saw the notice, above referred to, in the Boston paper.

My trip to Washington was for the purpose of conferring with Prof. Henry about my appointment this year. He will endeavor shortly to obtain permission from the Regents to call me to Washington in the ensuing Fall. The result I will immediately communicate to you, who have had so great a share in putting me upon the proper track. I have much more to say. Hope to see you and talk matters over, as more satisfactory than writing.

S. F. BAIRD

---

[15] Arnold Guyot (1807–84), geographer and geologist, was born in Switzerland and on the advice and urgent invitation of Agassiz came to America in 1848. For some time he lectured in and near Cambridge, Mass. In 1854 he accepted the chair of Physical Geography and Geology at Princeton and here he remained until his death. The Museum and Departments of Natural Science were housed for a long time in Guyot Hall, named in his honor.

AGASSIZ to BAIRD

CAMBRIDGE, *May 15, 1850*

My dear Sir,

Much obliged for your kind letter to me. I thank also very heartily Mrs. Baird for her kind wishes. I hope it will be in my power to go to Carlisle this summer with my wife, who sends her kindest regards to Mrs. Baird & like myself is very desirous we should meet as soon as possible your amiable invitation.

I do not think that it will be possible for us to go to Lake Champlain this summer; but after receiving your letter have thought the best time for us to go to see you might be after the meeting at New Haven, where I hope you will be present. Guyot is now in Washington & I do not know what will be his movements this summer, as they will greatly depend upon his arrangements with Prof. Henry. I have written to him this very day & urged again your early appointment. By the way he wants to know how soon you can have the Msc. of the fishes ready. Would it not be well we should spend some weeks together upon this matter? Let me know what I should answer to him or better write directly to him.

Sincerely yours,

L. AGASSIZ

I have an idea of editing a "Zoological Journal." Will you cooperate as an ostensible contributor? You will not need assume any responsibility respecting business part; which of course will be a loss.

BAIRD to AGASSIZ

CARLISLE, *May 26, 1850*

My dear Mr. Agassiz,

I want you to suit your own convenience in coming to Carlisle. The sooner it takes place, the better it would correspond to my most ardent wishes. Early summer is our most pleasant season, and the best time to go about and see living reptiles, fish, etc. In the fall of the year, too, or at least before frosts, it is apt to be unhealthy along our watercourses. This would not make any difference in Carlisle, as we have no large stream near us, and experience an immunity from such diseases as fever and ague: at Haldeman's however, who lives right on the Susquehanna in a sickly autumnal neighborhood, the case might be different. On the other hand, I shall probably have more to see next fall. I expect large collections of fishes and Cretaceous vertebrate fossils, (*Poebrotherium* etc.) from the Upper Missouri, next July or August, with skins, sculls, and skeletons of the larger Mammalia. I hope too to give Lake Champlain and her tributaries such a going over as she has not yet had. I shall agree to any agreement you may make, provided you come, actually and in proper person accompanied by Mrs. Agassiz whose acquaintance we are very desirous of forming.

I have been expecting to hear something every day from Washington in respect to the Smithsonian matter. I visited W. in the beginning of May, at Prof. Henry's request, for the purpose of talking over the affair with him. It was his intention to ask permission of the Regents to call me in next winter, whenever the proper opportunity might arrive. I still look for something definite on the subject within the next few weeks. It is quite possible however, that the regents may deny Prof. Henry's request. As to the missing fishes, I have none ready. I did not expect to get at, and work up my species, before getting more of them, as also those which you have collected. I also wanted to have you here before hand, and give me the benefit of your experience. Can't the plates remain in status quo, until we are ready for them. None of your plates have yet been executed, and it was the arrangement to have our joint productions in one paper, was it not? Is Sonrel to do any more of my fish? It would be a grand thing for us to have all our present species and those to be procured this fall together, and then examine and confer respecting each. Cannot this be accomplished?

I have just finished reading "Lake Superior" and can safely say that nothing ever instructed me more. Your Botanical article is a model of emulation, and the Ichthyological not a whit behind it. I wonder if the day will ever come when I shall be able to write such papers: I fear not. I do not see how the men of diluvial currents can stand after the push you give them with your glaciers. I have been finding some scratches on the sandstones of our North Mountain, running North and South, while the mountain chains go nearly East and West.

Any little help which I can render to your "Zoological Journal" will be most cheerfully rendered. Such a periodical ought to be supportable both in respect to articles and subscribers. Will it be on the plan of "Annales des Sc. Nat.," "Wiegmann" Archiv or what.

Very truly yours,
SFBAIRD

AGASSIZ to BAIRD

CAMBRIDGE, *June 1, 1850*

My dear Sir,

I only write a few lines to thank you for your friendly letter. It will give us both great pleasure to go to Carlisle & spend sometime with you when we can work over the fishes very steadily while the ladies are otherwise engaged. I think this is the best plan to finish up that matter. The time most convenient to me would be immediately after the meeting of New Haven. As soon as I write to Prof. Henry again I will mention it to him, or you do it, when you write also. He may be pleased to know that we will work our both parts in conformity by thus comparing notes. I am delighted to hear of all the good things you are getting & shall be very happy to look at them. For my own part I have also something good to report. Today I have been informed that $400 annually had been at length appropriated for the arrangement of my collections, so that I shall presently be able to divide them off & fulfill my promise to send you some good things. Of course Sonrel shall do all your plates & I hope the species will be all figured. We should however ascertain how much matter Prof. Henry will admit of this kind in one volume at one time.

I was happy to hear that you like the Lake Sup. book. Within a few weeks I shall be able to send you my *Medusa;* the first part of which has just gone through the press, while the plates are finishing. I mean to make the Journal something intermediate between the Annals Sc. Nat. & Wiegmann's Archiv. No regular annual reports, but abstracts of foreign papers and much original. My kindest regards to Mrs. Baird, also from Mrs. Agassiz.

Your friend,
L. Agassiz

BAIRD to AGASSIZ

Carlisle, July 11, 1850

My dear Mr. Agassiz,

At last, I am Assistant Secretary to the Smithsonian, having just received the patent. The salary is 1500, to be increased I hope, hereafter. To you more than any other are due my acknowledgments for this result, and I trust I may not disappoint your expectation in recommending me to Prof. Henry. I am to go to Washington about the beginning of October. I start tomorrow for Lake Champlain, and expect to reach Westport, by the end of next week. I go fully prepared with nets and assistants to sweep the Lake and its tributaries of all their treasures. I shall write to you from Westport. Cannot you and Mrs. A. meet us there for a little while at least. If I am not mistaken, Mrs. A. is acquainted with our friends there, Mr. Frank Lee's family.

Yours in the midst of commencement day and in corresponding haste.

Very truly yours,
S.F.Baird

BAIRD to AGASSIZ

CARLISLE, PA., *Sept. 7, 1850*

Dear Professor,

I send off today, a box containing your set of Cuvier & Valenciennes, as also Hamilton's Garigehi Fishes, text and plates. I hope you will excuse the unavoidable delay in fulfilling my promise, as I have been so overwhelmed with occupation as to render it impossible to attend to putting the books sooner. I am still in the midst of packing up preparatory to moving to Washington whither I expect to go about Oct. 1st. A good part of the hurry has been to prepare the specimens from the Upper Missouri for permanent preservation. I think you would be as much delighted to see these as I was. Among them were skins of Grizzly bear, Wolves, Lynxes, Foxes, Hares, Beavers, etc., Skeletons and (or) skulls of Beaver, Buffalo, *Spermophilus bidonicianus*, Little hare, *Hystrix, Cervus canadensis*, Elk, *Cervus macrourus, Ovis americana*, Antelope, *Canis latrans,* Indian Dog, *Mephitis* etc., etc. The essence of the whole however consists in the fossils. Among these are nearly perfect heads or good sets of teeth of various Tapiroids, Anoplotheroids, Lophiodontoids, *Poebrotherium* & amounting I should think, to 13 or 20 species, and numerous genera. I have also almost perfect shells of fossil turtles, from three to eight inches in length. Don't you want to see them?

I leave about Oct. 1st as already mentioned. And hope to get to Washington and unpack. I will be ready to send Charles those *Cottus* I spoke of. I find it impossible to get at them now, as they should be forwarded with the books. Please give my best respects to Mrs. A. and believe me

Your attached disciple,

S.F.BAIRD

BAIRD to AGASSIZ

WASHINGTON CITY, *Oct. 19, 1850*

My dear Professor,

Please send a list of the papers furnished by you to the American Association that is presented verbally. You will also find some memoranda by Secretaries of the Nat. History Section, together with a few newspaper slips. I trust that you will let me have all the above communications, as it is too provoking to see "not received" after anything of yours. Please send on your notes as soon as possible, as you are the only one in arrears towards the commencement of the session, and I wish to put the vol. to press immediately.

I am safely moored in Washington with all my collections and other baggage (excluding wife and child). My present business will be to superintend publications etc. By the way, is there not some mistake in the Lithographer's keeping 250 copies of the plate of *Esox claturatus?*

Prof. Henry returned from Princeton this morning. He has been away for some days. I shall return to Carlisle early in November for my family. We do not go to housekeeping this winter, but take lodgings in a boarding house. I hope to have my fishes and other matters unpacked by the time you get here. You promised us a visit in February, if you recollect.

Very truly yours,
S.F.BAIRD

BAIRD to AGASSIZ

Oct. 25, 1850

Dear Professor,

I enclose some specimens of a luminous insect caught last night in our grounds, where it appeared to be abundant. The light comes from two spots, one on each side of the posterior extremity. I have never seen it before, perhaps you have. I sent Haldeman and Leidy specimens by the same mail. Can you tell me anything about it?

I have not yet unpacked my specimens, but hope to do so shortly. A few days ago I obtained in market a *Leuciscus* entirely new to me. It came from the brackish water of the river below.

Can Thiomey (?) and Holmes do the Tertiary fossils of the U. States? I mean, as they ought to be done. Tell me candidly.

Truly yours,
S.F.BAIRD

BAIRD to AGASSIZ

SMITHSONIAN INSTITUTION,
WASHINGTON CITY, *Dec. 12, 1850*

Dear Professor,

Girard has been here for a week or two, engaged in completing his Monograph of *Cottus,* to which he found many unexpected additions among the species recently collected by myself. Thus he found a new one from Lake Huron, and one or two from other localities. He has also been working up the new Cottid genus from Lake Ontario, of which I spoke, last summer. I find on looking over the specimens in the exploring exped. collections, that several specimens from the Pacific c. survey were the *Cottus asper* of Rich. It is very desirable that the monograph should contain these species, and

Capt. Wilkes[16] is willing to let him examine them, provided that your permission be obtained. Should there be any new species, he consents (if approved by you) that they be published in this monograph, with your names and authority attached. Whenever Girard might make the investigation and then when the specimens are sent to Sonrel to figure, you could attach what names you think proper. Will you not write a line in immediate reply to state whether these ideas meet your views. Prof. Henry has accepted the Monograph for the Smithsonian Contributions, and it is desirable to have it out in time for the 2nd vol. which is nearly ready.

When may we look for you in Washington? Do not, if possible, disappoint us of this long anticipated pleasure. Remember that if you come, you have promised a course of lectures on some branch or other. You will, of course, bring Mrs. A. with you.

We have had quite a siege of it in Washington, since my arrival with my family. My daughter has been ill with scarlet fever, for five weeks, and her nurse also. Mrs. B. is almost worn out nursing the two invalids. They are now better. With kindest regards to Mrs. A. I remain,

Truly and sincerely yours,
S.F.BAIRD

AGASSIZ to BAIRD

CAMBRIDGE, Dec. 20, 1850

(*Confidential*)

My dear Mr. Baird,

I trust you know me sufficiently not to require any particular explanation of the motives which guide me, even if I should do something which would not meet your expectation and that you would in such a case be willing to wait until proper opportunity is afforded to appreciate the case before you form an unfavorable opinion of me. This being admitted let me say in reference to your note of today, which I have but a moment to answer by returning mail, that I have good reasons for declining any cooperation with Mr. Girard in whatever he may undertake hereafter. It is even a matter of surprise to me that such a request is made by him. He should have known that it is impossible for me to have anything to do with him even through the agency of a third person and have not placed you in the awkward position of making such a request for him. Let me however not be misunderstood, I do not wish to appear as an obstacle to his doings; but as he has lost all claims upon me, I do not even care to know what he is doing.

---

[16] Charles Wilkes (1798–1877), a naval officer, was the leader of the first United States Exploring Expedition, the results of which filled 19 volumes. Besides his ability as a leader of scientific expeditions, he was also recognized as having been instrumental in seizing the Confederate commissioners Mason and Slidell from a British vessel during the Civil War.

I shall write more soon on things which interest us both. I was very sorry to hear of the sickness in your family. I hope all are now well.

My kindest regards to Mrs. Baird; from Mrs. Ag. also.

Sincerely your friend,

L.Agassiz

BAIRD to AGASSIZ

Smithsonian Institution,
Dec. 28, 1850

My dear Professor,

Prof. Guyot in a letter, states that you leave for the South about Jan. 10. Will you not be good enough to write immediately and say whether you are coming to Washington on your way, (to lecture or not to lecture), and if not, how long you will be in New York or Phila. and when. I have business in New York and Phila., which will require my presence the first or second week in January, and I wish to so time my movements, as to meet you — I may indeed have to go on to Boston.

Very truly & sincerely yours,

SFBaird

Mrs. AGASSIZ to BAIRD

Cambridge, *Jan. 9, 1851*

My dear Mr. Baird,

At Mr. Agassiz' request, I return to you the enclosed papers, for the examination of which he has tried in vain to find time. He has had much more work on hand this winter than he could accomplish, and begs me to say that it is with great regret he sends these to you unaccompanied with any report from him, but he is utterly hopeless of finding the time necessary for it.

He leaves tomorrow morning early, full of enthusiasm for the interesting investigations which he hopes to make at the Coral Reefs in Florida.

He would have written himself, had he not been so busy with the thousand things, which remain to be done before he can leave, but he sends the kindest regards, and hopes to see you on his return.

Very truly yours,

L. C. Agassiz

The Professor begs me to add that, upon the Crinoids of Prof. Troost, he will send a report to Professor Henry as early as possible.

BAIRD to Mrs. AGASSIZ

Jan. 13, 1851

My dear Mrs. Agassiz,

The roll of MSS came safe to hand this evening, for which please accept my thanks. I have been much amused at reading Dr. Rainey's letter. Did he really suppose that the Prof. had time to answer such stuff? By the way, I learn that the Prof. passed through Washington last Saturday. Perfidious man! Had I known he was going to do so, I would have accompanied him some 60 or 70 miles down the bay.

Very truly and sincerely yours,

S. F. BAIRD

BAIRD to AGASSIZ

Apr. 11, 1851

My dear Professor,

Before receiving your letter, I had prepared a notice for insertion in the papers, calling attention of the public to the Cincinnati meeting and correcting Rainey's mistake. This I hope will be extensively circulated.

Rainey was elected Local Secretary for the Cincinnati meeting but as to his being a member of the Standing Committee, that is a question. He certainly is not by the constitution, except by implication.

I do not know why Anthony was not placed on the Local Committee. It will however be easy to put him there after the meeting commences.

Prof. Henry and Bache[17] with myself will probably leave about the 28th. I earnestly hope that we may meet you in Cincinnati.

You cannot think what pleasure it afforded me to see your well known handwriting after so long an interval, not meaning however to say that Mrs. A's communications were not gratefully received. Present my kindest regards to her and believe me.

Sincerely yours,

S.F.BAIRD

---

[17] Alexander Dallas Bache (1806–67), Superintendent of the Coast Survey, asked Agassiz on Oct. 30, 1850, if it was possible for him to devote 6 or 8 weeks to the examination of the Florida reefs and keys. He was very sympathetic with the study of natural history and was a regular correspondent of both Baird and Agassiz. He also assisted in preparing the Report on Plan of Organization of the Smithsonian Institution. Later he became one of its Regents.

AGASSIZ to BAIRD

CAMBRIDGE, *June 12, 1851*

When a growing reef has thus attained its maximum height, or reached the level of low water, a new process begins consisting chiefly in the accumulation of loose materials upon its summit. Large coral boulders are thrown up and gradually ground into fragments, coral gravel and sand and finally deposited in more or less regular beds, presenting all the complications of a torrential stratification, which are finally cemented by the infiltration of amorphous limestone into compact coral rock. When the materials are combined in a coarse state of decomposition they form a kind of coral breccia, but when cemented after they have been reduced to small globular fragments they constitute a sort of oolite, and even compact limestone where the deposit is formed by precipitation. Thin layers of such compact limestone occur frequently as dividing seams in the larger masses of oolite and there is everywhere such a layer of compact limestone upon the surface of all coral rocks rising above the level of the sea, a circumstance which seems to indicate that such layers are not formed under a permanent sheet of water, but must be the result of action of gales and the spray. This is the more probable since this superficial crust is nowhere horizontal, but follows all the irregularities of the soil.

If it were asked how corals which during their growth have withstood so effectually the violence of the sea, become such an easy prey of the waves after the reef has reached the surface of the water, it would require only to point at the innumerable boring shells and worms which establish themselves in the dying parts of their stems, and at the brittleness arising from these perforations, to satisfy every careful observer that the peculiar mode of life of these boring animals is a provision of nature subservient to the secondary purpose of the corals to furnish materials for the increase of the solid parts of our globe.

Along the outer reef of Florida and in the main range of Keys many islands might be selected and described in such an order as to form a natural series from a living reef without a dead fragment upon its edge to an extensive island apparently formed entirely of coral rock, or of oolite, or even of compact limestone, but in reality presenting only a cap of such hard materials overlying a true reef once living, and now buried under its own fragments.

The circumstance that the main Keys, and the shore bluffs, which have been formed successively to the same height above the level of the ocean, is an unquestionable evidence that the ground over which the general reef of Florida extends has undergone no change of level, that it has neither been raised, nor subsided. This evidence may be carried further by comparing also the everglades, with their intervening ridges and hammocks, which are in reality inland keys and islands, similar to the main keys and the mangrove islands, formed in the same manner as those now surrounded by the sea and which by the uniformity of their level furnish additional evidence that the whole region has been stationary ever since corals began to grow in those latitudes.

My dear Baird,

As the editor of a Journal ought to be very punctual in his correspondence, I mean to make an effort in future to change my habits and begin by answering immediately your note. I have completed the missing part above. Pray send me a slip when it is set in type. I want very much you should be here to select the fishes and other specimens from Florida which may be acceptable to you, and other things in my collection. Shall you not pay me a visit this summer for that purpose? I wish the more you should have all those things as I have many (questions) to ask and I am ashamed of doing so before I have repaid you for your former communications. I am now finishing my Monographs of Cyprinodonts and Gasterostei for the Journal, and would be most obliged for additions from you; next the Cyprinidae to compare with the Oregon ones from the Exp. Exp. and those of the Ohio which you promised in Cincinnati.

Would it be possible for you to let me have the new works on Zoology, Paleontology and Embryology which you receive at the Smithsonian, for a short time after their arrival to enable me to review them for the Journal; and will you occasionally review some for me? My first number will contain a paper on the Nayades, another on the Echinoderms of the U.S. that on homologies of Radiata and one of general matters, forms and types etc., perhaps one on fossil Bryozoa and several reviews, which I mean to make as thorough as possible.

Sincerely yours,

L. AGASSIZ

I have forgotten to mention that W Th. Kite, whom I saw several times after the meeting has at last agreed to allow his bullhead to come east, under the guarantee of the Smithsonian that it shall be returned to him. There remains a slight difficulty, he insists upon it that I should describe it. Of course I should like it, but if Leidy[18] is preparing a general paper upon the fossil

---

[18] Joseph Leidy (1823–91), a professor of zoology at the University of Pennsylvania, was at that time engaged on his Entophyta studies. Baird had collected quite a few millipeds for Leidy's use in researches for that paper. Leidy was also distinguished as an anatomist and parasitologist. His publications ranged from Protozoa to man, his bibliography including over 600 titles.

Ruminants of N. America, I would not interfere with him. You may see what has best be done, since I learned from you of Leidy's project.

Yours, L AG

AGASSIZ to BAIRD

CAMBRIDGE, *June 19, 1851*

My dear Baird,

I do not want the proof of my paper, but only a slip of it, as soon as it is set in type, to quote it in my report to Prof. Bache. So you need [not] be afraid of a delay, I shall make an effort this week to write out my other papers if possible, Prof. Henry has written a very kind note to me on that subject. When you lay out the Cyprinodonts, let me have [specimens] from all the possible localities since my Monograph is now complete, I should like to have the means of alluding to their geographical distribution. I shall have that paper in the first Vol. of the Journal.

My kindest regards to Mrs. Baird.

Your friend,
L. AGASSIZ

Will you once a month let me know what new books you have got?

BAIRD to AGASSIZ

July 14, 1851

Dear Professor,

I have been so busy for some weeks past getting ready our foreign packages, as to have had it quite out of my power to finish the promised keg of fishes. Now, however, it is packed, and will start to move bearing the species whose names are herewith annexed. Since my last sending I have not collected many species of *Hydrargira*, merely extended their localities. I have no *Gasterosteus*. I have *G. inconstans* from Lake Champlain, and Lake Ontario or rather in small streams emptying directly into these lakes. Do you want these?

I find after the keg was all packed that I had forgotten *Leuciscus pygmaeus* of DeKay, which you know is *Hydrargira*, distinct from the others. Can this specific name stand? It is only the largest species.

I send the Ohio fish, others from other localities, not especially called for I send hereafter.

I have not decided what to do this summer before going to Albany. Do you return to Cambridge after this? I may be able to go there for a short time after the meeting.

What is this story in the paper about your having accepted a Professorship at Albany?

Perhaps I may go fishing in the interior of New York, among the small Lakes, before Albany comes on.

We are still at work with packages. You know we have Memoirs of various Societies to send with ours, as well as various scientific publications of Congress. By way of sampling the extent of our operations—we have just put the parcels to be distributed by Flügel[19] into 18 boxes, amounting to about 105 cubic feet, and weighing about 3600 lbs. There is much more for France, Italy, Spain and England together.

When shall we have your Memoirs on Cetaceans? It would be a great addition to the 3rd vol. When will the Polyp be ready to print? We shall have Harvey's Algae, Torrey's Plantae Tremontianae, Leidy's Entophyta and some others. We hope to get it out by next spring.

Sincerely yours,
S.F.BAIRD

BAIRD to AGASSIZ

July 15, 1851

List of Fishes sent Prof. Agassiz.

Cincinnati

No. of Specimens

3	Pimelodus coeruleus
1	" catus
1	" lunesus
2	Grystes fasciatus
1	Lucioperca gusea
1	Centrarchus hexacanthus
1	Corvina ascula
1	Hyodon tergiatis
1	Chatoessus ellipticus
1	Pomolobus chrysochloris
1	Sclerognathus elongatus
2	" cyprinius
1	Catostomus nigricans
1	" anisurus
1	" Duquesnii
1	" " oides n.s.

Number with former lots   Other localities

---

[19] Felix Flügel, Leipsic, Germany, was an agent for Baird.

73	Gasterosteus	nebulosus. H. greteot [?] (L. Huron)	
			2 sp.
74	"	inconstans Racine, Wis., L. Mich.	2 sp.
75	Hydrargira	James River	3 sp.
76	"	Lake Champlain	several
77	"	4 mile creek, Oswego, N.Y.	2 sp.
78	"	Racine, Wis.	
79	"	Sacketts Harbor	4 sp.

S. F. BAIRD

BAIRD to AGASSIZ

July 19, 1851

Dear Professor,

I enclose a letter from James Hall to you which I presume you wish to keep. It came with some papers forwarded by you to us last spring.

Do you want Dr. Troost's paper back again? We heard a short time ago that the specimens were on their way to you.

Sincerely yours,

S.F.BAIRD

AGASSIZ TO BAIRD

CAMBRIDGE, *Aug.* 4, 1851

My dear friend,

How very difficult it is to do right, or at least what you think to be right even with the firm determination to do it. I am struggling with the desire of being punctual in my correspondence with my friends and all I can do is from time to time to send them a few lines. What you have written to me respecting your activity in the Smithsonian Institution has greatly interested me, and I have no doubt you will do a great deal of good in that way. I thank you very much for your specimens, which arrived safely last week. Pray do not forget to bring on the *Leuciscus pygmaeus* of DeKay, for it is one of the very things I have been longing for and which I have failed hithertofore to obtain. I shall not leave Cambridge before the meeting and intend returning home immediately after; will you not come back with me and take a good share of the long-promised specimens from Florida and other places with you. My sister-in-law who has just returned from a long visit at the Lee's on Lake Champlain and often seen your friends there, wants me to insist on your coming at that time, as she intends making us then a visit and would be glad to have one who knows all those people to recall pleasant recollections.

I am working very hard at the Expl. Exped. fishes, and allow my papers to suffer under it, as I must make my living first; but I am progressing to my satisfaction notwithstanding. I hope to have the corals at least ready for the press by the beginning of Sept. I have just revised my report upon the coral reefs. I trust it will be an acceptable contribution to our knowledge of that subject. — I have received some time ago the slip of my paper read in Cincinnati, it was all right. I have a long letter to write to Prof. Henry before Albany, and can find no time for it. My kindest regards to Mrs. Baird.

Your sincere friend,

L. AGASSIZ

MRS. AGASSIZ to BAIRD

CAMBRIDGE, *Nov. 23, 1851*

Dear Sir,

I write by Mr. Agassiz' request, to tell you that he has been prevented from preparing his notes for you, by the preparations necessary for this troublesome suit[19a] at Albany, which is to be tried this next week, and which, with all the preparations of his ordinary work, has occupied his whole time. He would have written himself to explain this delay, but was called to New York yesterday, by the announcement of the arrival of his little girls. He is to bring them to me on Monday, and then proceed immediately to Albany, where he may be detained some days, but will make up notes for you, as soon as possible after his return.

He sends his kindest regards to you and Mrs. Baird, in which I beg leave to join, and am

Very truly yours,

L. C. AGASSIZ

MRS. AGASSIZ to BAIRD

CAMBRIDGE, *Dec. 31, 1851*

My dear Baird,

Mr. Agassiz, who is quite unwell himself, begs me to write you a line in answer to your note of today, and to express to you his sincere regret, that he has been unable to this moment to save time from the crowd of engagements

---

[19a] In 1849 after James T. Foster, a public school teacher in Albany, N.Y., had published *Foster's Complete Geological Chart,* James Hall, one of the leading geologists of that time, became concerned. Soon afterward Agassiz and Hall published unfavorable opinions about the text. Foster's publishers sued Agassiz and Hall for libel. Many scientists rallied to support Agassiz at the trial at Albany if necessary. However, Agassiz's defense in the courtroom of the trial judge was so convincing that the defense attorneys were able to secure a quick dismissal of the case.

which press upon him this winter for a letter to you on the affairs of the Institute & Association, such as he wished to write.

He is now quite ill from fatigue, but has four lectures to give at the Lowell Institute, before he can be off on his Florida excursion, which he longs to commence, as it will give him work in the field, instead of the study.

As he gives his last lecture on the 10th, and must be at Charleston the 15th, on pain of losing two weeks at Florida he is obliged to take the Southern Steamer at N. Y., which will bring him sooner to his destination. He must therefore lose the pleasure of meeting you on the road, and wants me to say how much he regrets this necessity.

I have seen lately your friends Mr. and Mrs. Lee who are spending the winter in Boston, and desired me, if I should have occasion to write, to send *"lots of love"* from them, to you & yours. I give this message, just as I received it.

I hope, should you come this way in January, I shall have the pleasure of seeing you, and with kindest regards from the Professor & myself to you & Mrs. Baird, I am

Most truly yours,

LIZZIE AGASSIZ

P. S. Agassiz begs me to ask if your professorship in Carlisle has been already appropriated; if not, he would be glad to secure it for Professor Blasius of Hannover Germany, who is now here, without employment, and fully competent to occupy such a place. If it is taken, perhaps the position, which your successor had before, may remain to be filled?

AGASSIZ to BAIRD

CAMBRIDGE, *May 19, 1852*

My dear Baird,

I enclose 5 stamps, not knowing how to send it otherwise — 13 cts. I hope you will not forget the *Lepidosteus,* Unios & Astaci for me; for though I am as yet unfit to go to work, it would give me pleasure to look at them.

Yours very truly,

L. AGASSIZ

BAIRD to AGASSIZ

June 22, 1852

My dear Professor,

Gars have been very scarce this spring and it is only within a week or two that the fishermen have commenced bringing them in. I have a few in alcohol and today send off by express four perfectly fresh ones packed in charcoal. I hope they will reach you in good condition. Please let me hear as to their health.

We are now in the midst of our foreign packing. Have just sent off 25 boxes for Flügel. Hope to finish this week. About the first of July I go to Carlisle and then to the north with Mrs. B. *perhaps*.

> Sincerely yours,
> S.F.BAIRD

AGASSIZ to BAIRD

CAMBRIDGE, *June 26, 1852*

My dear Sir,

It is a pity that all the trouble you have taken should be of no use; the gar-pikes came all in the most complete state of decomposition, even broken up and more offensive than anything I have ever smelled. Will it be possible after this to get specimens in alcohol? for I long very much for them, only to have a sight, since I cannot work at them. My health is really broken down. I shall be very happy to see you whenever you can come.

> Yours very sincerely,
> L. AGASSIZ

AGASSIZ to BAIRD

CAMBRIDGE, *July 27, 1852*

My dear Baird,

I lose not a moment to answer your note just received. After consultation with Peirce and Davis we agreed decidedly to postpone the meeting.[19b] If the state of things in Cleveland is known abroad the attendance will be greatly reduced, no ladies will venture to come, the meeting will be reduced to a small business meeting and the talk will be of death and the anxiety of friends at home. Just twenty years ago we had a similar case in Switzerland with our Helvetic association & the next year the meeting was the more interesting for the postponement. I do not see what can be done except simply advertise the postponement at once and consult the members of the standing committee respecting further action. The simplest way would be to take a written vote in the form of consultation and let the President and Secretary direct any further course accordingly.

I am exceedingly sorry of this occurrence. It may however be well to let some people come to their senses about the opposition which was beginning to undermine the association. Are there so many scientific Institutions in this country, that America can afford to see them ruin for the sake of gratifying

---

[19b] Because of a typhoid-fever scare.

mean ambitions? I would make the same remark in reference to the Smithsonian. Who are the vile movers in these new attacks against it? When shall I see you?

Sincerely your friend,
L. AGASSIZ

BAIRD to AGASSIZ

Oct. 15, 1852

Dear Professor,

We are now collecting data in regard to the fifth volume of Contributions, and would be very glad to have your coral paper for it. What is the prospect? It seems a pity not to use up the six beautiful plates in presenting your important facts to the world.

I have not succeeded in finding anything of Remak, excepting some papers in Müllers Archives which do not bear on your discovery. I will however keep a sharp lookout.

Sincerely yours,
S. F. BAIRD

BAIRD to AGASSIZ

Nov. 2, 1852

Dear Prof.,

I send the following memoranda:

Remak. Untersuchungen über die Entwickelung der Wirbelthiere. Berlin 1850–51.

Memoir on same subject in Comptes Rendus (Ins. France) for Sept. 13, 1852 and report in L. Institut. Sept. 22, 1852

Yours truly,
S. F. BAIRD

AGASSIZ to BAIRD

CAMBRIDGE, June 18, 1853

My dear Baird,

Are you the man to listen to the advise of a friend frankly and freely spoken, not from a desire of knowing what he may have to say but from a feeling of confidence and regard? If so let me hear of you soon & I will write more.

Your sincere friend,
L. AGASSIZ

AGASSIZ to BAIRD

CAMBRIDGE, *June 18, 1853*

I enclose your circular with the blanks filled. It is at this time useless for me to answer your questions respecting the meeting in Cleveland; but why do we not receive the invitation, mentioning the date of the meeting?

I have been highly successful during my stay in the southern & western states, especially in collecting fishes, of which I have obtained about 60 new species mostly from the rivers emptying into the Gulf, reptiles, Crustacea, Worms etc. I have also a great many fishes never observed before on the shores of the Un. St. but known as inhabitants of the W. Indies. Since you have completed your examination of the Ophidians let me have my specimens back that I may use them for the Zool. textbook & also those of LeConte,[20] which he had given to me, before he sent them to you for description. I shall let you have the duplicates of those you have not otherwise or not from the same locality. I would also like original specimens of all those species which you can spare. I would send you in exchange others from many localities from which you seem to have none, especially from Alabama & the west. I would also remind you of your promise to let me have original specimens of the Astacida that I may identify some of my species which I can make out from Girard's description, especially those of the northern most states to compare with mine from Lake Superior & those from the South. I have not less than 10 species from Alabama & Louisiana, (altogether about a dozen new species). I cannot be certain without specimens which are there. Again I would remind you of the interesting Washington species. I shall send you all in return. Pray do not forget also the Salamanders & Ichthyoids, I want those for the Textbook. I may have some new ones for you in return or at least from new localities.

Yours very truly,

L. AGASSIZ

BAIRD to AGASSIZ

June 23, 1853

My dear Professor,

I shall at all times be grateful to you for any advice or counsel and will promise to receive it in the same spirit as that in which it is imparted. Please write immediately as I expect to leave very soon for the west. I find it necessary to go to Cleveland sometime before the meeting to make neces-

---

[20] John LeConte (1818–91), scientist and educator, brother of Joseph LeConte, was born in Liberty County, Ga. He was trained by his father to be a naturalist and for that reason visited Baird for several weeks in Carlisle in 1846. After studying medicine and practicing it for some time he served as professor of physics in several universities before becoming President of the University of California.

sary arrangements, and I have besides been ordered off by my physician to arrest the attacks of palpitation of the heart to which I have lately been sub-
jected. I shall accordingly leave if I can get off some time next week.

I will with the greatest pleasure let you have the specimens you desire but
cannot do so very well now. Will it answer if I send them on my return? I
am overwhelmed with work of various kinds and shall be under full pressure
of steam until I leave even if not detained a week or ten days longer in consequence. LeConte's specimens I am directed by him to return to Phila. when
done with, which is not quite yet but as soon as some figures are to be made
of them.

Very sincerely and truly yours,
S F BAIRD

Can you write by return mail?

AGASSIZ to BAIRD

CAMBRIDGE, June 27, 1853

My dear Baird,

I answer your letter without delay, though it will hardly reach you before the close of the week, the Sunday having kept your letter in Boston a
full day at least. It takes in Cambridge three days to get an answer by mail
from Boston.

It is not easy for me to trust to paper what I have to say to you, there being seldom a remedy to misapprehensions from writing. If you will however
remember that nothing but a sincere interest in you could prompt me to
write, my note may not be useless. From beginning I have looked to the
Smithsonian Institution as the greatest foundation for the promotion of science in this country, and I have lost no opportunity of securing the election
of such an assistant in the department of Nat. Hist. as I knew competent to
advance such a noble cause. Your paper on Batrachians had satisfied me that
you have the requisite qualifications. But now what shall I say of your catalogue of Serpents? It is true it discloses great industry by the extensive collections you have brought together from the remotest parts of the country; and
this will always be very creditable to you. But the scientific part of the work
is very crude; I should never have expected that while you are connected
with the Smithsonian Instit. such a volume would be issued with its sanction
and still less that your name should appear on its title page. To tell you the
truth of my impression I do not believe that you have had much to do with
it & I hope sincerely for the sake of your scientific reputation that it will
turn out so. But why did you not at least look it over? If you had been willing to listen to my advise before, you should have known that Girard
though capable of sustained work and endowed with considerable ability in

distinguishing the peculiarities of animals, has no judgment, and is utterly unable to trace original researches without supervision. Moreover he is as obstinate as a mule, if contradicted, which makes it necessary that he should be led with a high hand and kept in an entirely subordinate position. Now this supervision of his work you have not made; you have not tested the value of the characters upon which he has based his generic & specific distinctions. I recognize his hand both in the style of the language used, and in the scientific character of the work. In the hurry of your many engagements you have trusted to him a task to which he is not equal; and there goes forward from the Smithsonian Instit. a production which in quality is far inferior to what is done elsewhere, though by the quantity of the materials you had the means of surpassing every work of that kind. And now I ask you what is there left for the friends of the Smithson. to do? To let that pass unnoticed or to criticise it as it deserves? To let a hasty incorrect performance go abroad as a model or to expose the whole? This language may appear severe. It is so; it is more so towards you personally than I would ever use speaking with others but it is plainly deserved. Let me give you a few examples. First as far as nomenclature is concerned. For *Ancystrodon* there is already the old generic name of *Cenchris,* first introduced by Linnaeus, sanctioned by Daudin & confirmed by Wagler. Why not adopt *Cenchris?* Several similar cases would lead to the suspicion that it is to gratify the writing of *A. contortrix* B & G. And then why spell *Agkistrodon?* Every body who would improve nomenclature ought to know that the Greek JK spells in last letters nc. On the same page you have a similar case, KEJXsis; why don't you correct it also to *legchris* instead of spelling *Cenchris?* Should I further mention the many feminine nouns coupled with masculine adjectives? Why not consult a philologist? For your *Eutopia* there are already two generic names: *Tropidonotus* Kuhl *Natrix* Laur., names may be I have seen applied in a wider or narrower sense, but one of them at least can never be dropped and whatever generic combination *C. natrix* and *C. sirtalis* the European and N. American representatives of that genus shall be called either *Tropidonotus* or *Natrix.* I will not say a word against the multiplication of genera nor against the queer names given to some of your new ones but merely allude to the nomenclature of those adopted. What is the use of your *Scotophis* when we have four names for their European representatives? There never were more perfect counterparts in two continents than *Col. florescens* (Callopeltis) and *C. alleghenensis* or *Col. lineatus* (Elaphis) & *Col. vittatus.* Who will ever think of dropping those names for your *Scotophis?* And so on with *Ophibolus* etc. Have you already noticed that your nomenclature makes it appear as if Europe and America had no two serpents allied even generically? Or is that a new theoretic view inferred by Girard from the Astaci which he believed to differ throughout generically and in structure from those of Europe? Shall next our Foxes in Europe and America be generically distinct? our Squirrels? our Rabbits & Hares? Such might be the inferences a geographer studying the geographical distribution of species in Europe and America would derive from your book compared with the works published in Europe. I tell you it is too bad! Now for the characters.

You divide Colubridae into A. Loral and anteorbital *both present* B. Loral and anteorbital *absent*. The first genus in the table of those with loral and anteorbital both present is *Elaps*. I have examined 8 specimens of *Elaps fulvius* (I see from your catalogue that you have only 3) in no one of which is there a loral. Have your specimens lorals or is this mere neglect? And upon such characters is a division of a family into sections based! Why *Elaps* which has poisonous fangs should at all come under Colubridae, the most harmless of all snakes, is more than I know. Of *Heterodon* it says two nasals, I find in *H. simus* three or four; one or two lorals, I find, 3, 4 and even 5 in the same species. The frequent variation of the anteorbitals and postorbitals is hardly ever noticed. A mere accidental revision of a few species has shown me in *Bascanion* 3 postorb. as well as 2; in *Masticophis* 2 on one side 3 on the other of the same specimen; In *Coronella doliata* a loral on one side, none on the other, sometimes none at all. Your genus *Osceola* is based upon such a specimen of the latter kind of that very species. You see here a *generic distinction* founded upon the variations occurring among individuals of the same species! *Storeria* has 1, 2 or 3 posterior orbitals and so forth. I am not writing a review of your catalogue, but merely pointing out to you some examples may be the worse of the loose manner in which this work is done, to justify severe criticism, and here I stop, hoping to obtain from you some clue to all these imperfections, which in my eye will be the best evidence that you have taken my remarks as they were meant, namely as the sad expression of an anxious friend.

Yours very truly,

L. AGASSIZ

I will not increase your pressure by urging you to send me the specimens at once; but let me have them as soon as you possibly can, for I want them badly while I feel inclined to do something for the textbook, before I am able to do more difficult work.

BAIRD to AGASSIZ

SMITHSONIAN INSTITUTION,

WASHINGTON, *June 30, 1853*

My dear Professor,

I am exceedingly indebted to you for the frankness with which you have criticised the Serpent Catal. and so far from being offended, I am grateful for the interest which prompts you to go into the discussion of the various points

involved. It would ill become me, a beginner, to assume everything near per-
fection, as the result of my work, and it is only by the criticism of friends
(among whom I am proud to rank you) that I may hope to improve. I beg
that you will always tell me freely of whatever you think is susceptible of
improvement in my doings.

So much by way of preamble. And now if you will allow me to explain
some of the inconsistencies and inaccuracies to which you refer, some of
them satisfactorily I hope. I must however state in the outset that I am not
excusable on the ground of having left the work mainly to my collaborator
without proper censor. On the contrary, the rough work was divided about
equally, genus by genus, each making out the full descriptions & investigations of his share subject to the criticism of the other. Every line written by
Mr. G., however, I carefully read and discussed, in many cases going over
the whole subject and comparing and examining all the specimens in connection with the description. The analytical tables I did entirely myself, and you
may not wonder at the inaccuracies when you learn that it was an after-
thought, carried into effect in the space of two or three days. I expressly
refer to its inadequacies in the preface and give it merely an analysis, not a
natural arrangement.

My plan of operations was to tabulate all the characteristics of every specimen of each species, so that I could at a glance determine the limits of variation. I enclose a rough sketch of the form used, although having many more
divisions than the present slip. I commenced work without any definite idea
of the system to be adopted, and without the idea of setting up genera as you
suggest, but was gradually put to my own convictions as to the construction of the new genus groups. In the first place I found a most desirable
constancy in the rows of scales, smoothness or roughness, number of plates
on the head, etc. with occasional variations it is true, but the adherence to
one type indicated the existence of a new genus and my rejection of the old
genera was all based on my doings. I had all the authorities with scarcely
an exception: Daudin, Fitzinger, Merrem, Bonaparte, delli I Ithlica [?],
Sturm, Wagler, Schlegel and what was much better, I had careful labels of
specimens of nearly all the allied species from the collections of Sturm and
Bonaparte. So as to be able to compare directly the serpents themselves I have
made many notes on the subject, and hope at no distant day to review the
whole subject and give "the reason of the faith that you have in me." The
catalogue is simply what it professes to be — a descriptive list of specimens;
not a History of the American Ophidia, which I shall give hereafter. The
catalogue gives a poor idea of the work required to make it even what it is
— the thousands of specimens carefully examined, the queries of unpublished data made etc. I could not introduce all the measurements made, only
those were selected which served to illustrate the subject.

I will now proceed to the discussion of the examples you have given me and endeavor to show that it was not an oversight, but intention in most cases. L. *Agkistrodon.* This genus was established by Palisot de Beauv. in 1799 and based especially on the copperhead. *Cenchris* of Daudin bears the date of 1802 and of course loses priority. *Cenchris* of Linnaeus I find no mention of. The 1748 edition of Systema Naturae I have not got, but in *Boa contortrix* the original description *Cenchris* is not noted. I am not aware of its existence in the section of Trigonocephali out of N. America where there are but four species including *Toxicophis.* As to the etymology and mode of spelling: I merely took the name of Palisot as I found it in the original paper. I know that it had been differently spelled but doubtful how far I was entitled to make a change, or even whether one was necessary, I allowed it to remain.

Tropidonotus Ruhl, applied neither to American nor European snakes. It was founded on a Javanese species essentially different from them. *Natrix* I find different from our sometimes Tropidonoti in many points, which though slight, are sufficient. I have abundant specimens of *N. torquata* and other species. A striking feature of distinction is that of coloration, which as much as anything else accompanies other generic characters. I refer to the pattern, not to the tint that *Eutainia* being three longitudinal light stripes on a darker background. That I have not purposely multiplied genera is shown by my throwing *Leptophis* into *Eutainia;* combining, not separating.

Scotophis. The type of this genus is *Col. allegheniensis* not *C. vittatus.* The latter was thrown in although having some important differences from my aversion to multiplying genera. In coloration it is widely remote. Its similarity to *Natrix lineatus laphis* is given by Bonaparte. I recognized from his figure but unfortunately had no specimens and I observed some distinctive marks in the description.

Callopeltis, of which *C. flavescens* and *leopardonus* may be taken as types. *Scotophis* has no relations of importance. The perfect smoothness is not the least peculiarity of *Callopeltis* as compared with *Scotophis.* The same remarks apply to *Coronella* and *Ophibolus* with the same comparisons. Although closely allied they are yet distinct. And here I may reply to your remark as to my not recognizing any European genera. *I do not believe that any genera of serpents are common to the two continents.* There may be a few exceptions, but I do not believe in them yet. Why not so, as well as the Urodela of Anura. *Rana* & *Bufo* alone are common; of Saurians, there are none generically the same until you get to Japan, where also are our nearest Urodelan analogues.

I plead guilty to *Elaps,* which has no loral. It should have gone into the next division. As to its alliance with Colubridae, I have already said my tables were an analytical index or key, not a classification. Still, J. E. Gray and other authors put *Elaps* with *Coluber;* and I agree with them. The poisonous character is perfectly connected with the Colubrini, this not being necessarily the test of the divisions. The teeth are fixed, not arranged as in most of the other poisonous species. Why have Hydrophidae or rather Hydridae both venomous and non-venomous species? The similarity between *Elaps fulvius,* and *Ophibolus doliatus,* is striking and scarcely allowable of ordinal distinction.

The multiplicity of plates in *Heterodon* which I fully recognize, is scarcely reducable to rule. *H. nasicus* is even more unmanageable than *H. simus.* I prefer to consider the nasals and lorals as nearly constant, and to consider the supplementary plates as multiplication of the prefrontals. The excess of lorals to which you refer I assign to the ant-orbitals. I have had the same perplexity in *Crotalus,* as to the restraining and dif. of the plates.

I do not think your remarks as to the irregularity of plates in *Bascanion* and *Masticophis* are as generally applicable as you suppose. I this morning examined thirty specimens of *B. constrictor* from different localities and found but one exception to the rule I have given as to plates: this having on one side three instead of two post orbitals. Most usually when there is any deviation from the rule it is un-symmetrical, occurring only on one side. I have carefully noted all such facts, and mentioned most of those observed in the description. I have as often observed the lorals of the frontals coalesced into one of the nasal loral. Ant-orbitals united as a deviation from the types & the arrangement and number of the cephalic plates, yet I would not infer a want of constancy in the division into plates, adopted by authors. I have made the same observations in *Storeria* as in *Bascanion* with the same conviction as my general accuracy. There is a typographical error in the diagnosis of *Storeria occipito-maculata.* It should be 4 *orbitals,* two anterior, two posterior. I have found very few exceptions to this & to the number in *S. Dekayi.*

I feel very confident that *Osceola elapsoides* generically and specifically is distinct from *Ophibolus foliatus.* There is a similarity but not much greater than between Ulther [?] and *Elaps.* The fusion of the post frontal and the lorals with the 19 dorsal rows in *Osceola* as distinguished from distinct loral and 21 rows of scales in *Ophibolus foliatus,* into other good characters, are constant, many specimens of each which I have examined.

I have now, my dear Professor, attempted vindication from the charge of carelessness and youthful precipitancy, brought against me as well as I have time at the present writing as I do by return mail, with the nineteen other letters requiring the same dispatch. I need not assure you again however that it is with the utmost feeling of respect and gratitude for the interest you have taken in me which prompts you to a friendly castigation. I admit my faults, and deficiencies, which I hope time will correct, and hope that you will assist by continuing your kind criticism and advice. I trust you will oblige me by marking on a copy of the catalogue any notice of bad grammar or other errors and let me have it soon. It will be necessary to reproduce the work soon and I wish to make all necessary alterations. Whatsoever you do in the matter will be gratefully acknowledged. When we meet which I trust may be in Cleveland, we will talk over the subject more at length, when perhaps I may be able to explain other supposed errors in the catalogue than those you have pointed out.

Very sincerely yours,

S. F. BAIRD

AGASSIZ to BAIRD

CAMBRIDGE, *July 5, 1853*

My dear Baird,

I am exceedingly sorry for your sake, that it is as you say with the Cat. of Serpents. I had hoped to find reasons to relieve you of the charges of doing *hasty* and *careless* work, which were pressing upon my mind. It would be strange if no argument would be made by a sensible man in vindication of even entirely wrong a position; but there [that] is not the question. I wanted to make you feel that your publication, be it a catalogue or any thing you may please to call it, was not what should come forth from the Smithsonian Institution under your name. Your own letter is from beginning to end an evidence of the correctness of my apprehensions. You say the table "was an after thought, carried into effect in the space of two or three days." Is that an excuse or a condemnation? It is just owing to such things that I am made anxious in your behalf; for there are things of which a careful observer can never be guilty with impunity to his reputation. Does Dana, for instance, ever print such loose pages?

I do not know from what quarter you derive your information upon that point, but I know *de visu,* that our european *Callopeltis* are not remarkable for the perfect smoothness of the scales, as you say, but on the contrary have exactly like your *Scotophis,* carinated scales upon the back, certainly as marked as *Sc. guttatus,* passing to smooth scales upon the sides. Where is the generic difference? I repeat the same with *Ophibolus Sayi.* How does it differ generically from *Coluber viridiflavus?* I know our european reptiles too well, to have any more doubt about it, as if the question related to our most common fishes. What might have been rectified by a careful revision of your nomenclature you now proclaim as a principle: *I do not believe that any genera of serpents are common to the two continents.* Is that natural philosophy? When in spite of your negation *"C. natrix* is inseparable generically from *C. sirtalis."* This *Coluber Natrix* is the first snake I have known as a boy and if you had a sufficient number of specimens you would

know that some of its variations have even that peculiar system of coloration which you claim is characteristic of *Eutaenia*. Your revision of *Lauritus*
with *sirtalis* is quite as objectionable as the other points noticed before. But
my remarks did after all not go so much to redeem these minute details as
to call to your attention the spirit pervading the whole performance, which
is too much influenced by the necessities of every day and therefore lacks in
the same proportion in scientific truth. This is a great point I want you to
consider.

I do not yet know whether it will be at all possible for me to go to
Cleveland. I would therefore repeat my request that you let me have the
species mentioned in my last letter, as soon as you can after your return to
Washington.

Sincerely your friend,

L. AGASSIZ

I trust you will take this reiteration of my remarks in the same spirit as
the first. We have a remarkable french proverb saying: Noblesse oblige. I
would apply it to you in a modified form: "Position oblige." Pray never
forget that you are in a position in which your doings should not require
explanations or to be received with certain allowances but ought to be worthy
of general imitation.

Yours, LAG

AGASSIZ to BAIRD

CAMBRIDGE, July 30, 1853

My dear Baird,

I meant not to have written to you before I would hear of you, but I
received this morning a letter which induces me to address you at once. You
may remember the letter left by Major Emory[21] for me with Prof. Henry several years ago asking me to take charge of the specimens he would collect
during his expedition. You may also remember that noticing your wish to
receive those objects for the Smithsonian Inst. I even abstained from answering his note and thus was in fact rude to Maj. Emory when I ought to have
expressed my thanks at least for his offer. Lately, about 6 weeks ago, I enclosed one of my circulars to him, without even an allusion to that occurrence. Nevertheless I received this morning a renewal of his first proposition. I confess I look upon it in a very different light now, and hope you
will do nothing to influence Major Emory either directly or indirectly in
disposing of his specimens either one way or the other, as I shall myself do
also. There is no necessity that either you or anybody should have a mo-
nopoly on those things.

---

[21] Maj. William H. Emory (1811–87), chief of the scientific corps, U.S. Army, and
later commissioner of some of the Boundary Surveys.

I look forward with great longing for the things you have promised me; try to remember them all, as also those for which I had asked you before the meeting.

I have very good prospects to have extensive collections made for me from Kentucky.

Sincerely yours,

L. AGASSIZ

AGASSIZ to BAIRD

CAMBRIDGE, *Aug. 5, 1853*

My dear Baird,

I have just received from Dr. R. W. Gibbs of Columbia two specimens of another *Etheostoma* from the Alabama Riv. near Montgomery; with a colored drawing. Do you want them now? or shall I wait to send them until some other things can be put aside for you?

Sincerely yours,

L. AGASSIZ

AGASSIZ to BAIRD

CAMBRIDGE, *Aug. 9, 1853*

My dear Baird,

I have ntither the *Styla* nor the Cystignathi you wish for, unless they are among my specimens of last winter which have not yet been unpacked. It is possible I shall find them in the mess, having had many specimens presented to me during my last stay at the South by several physicians, but I am so crowded now with half unpacked barrels that I could not open more immediately. I shall however keep a lookout for you.

My *Emys* is decidedly *cumberlandensis,* if Dumeril is to be trusted, but a comparison with specimens from Tennessee is still needed. I have also made out *Emys Troostii* among the Missourian which I had overlooked at first. *Emys Bellii* is quite an acquisition; you will perceive that it is wanting in the Mus. in Paris.

I look forward with great pleasure to the Chinese fishes. But do not forget the things I expect from you and the keg from Col. Wailes. Have you written to him. Also the maps, and one copy marked with the localities from which you have fishes. Have you any Sharks, Skates & Petromyzons? I have lately worked out the Placoids. I find I have *eight genera* of them not mentioned in Storer's Synopsis! not to speak of species. Let me have what is at your command of this family, that I may complete my revision, including jaws & teeth. You see I select the families for which I suppose you have the least fancy to work out first.

Sincerely yours,

L. AGASSIZ

AGASSIZ to BAIRD

CAMBRIDGE, *August 11th, 1853*

My dear Baird,

Your little note gave me great pleasure. Do not think me either meddling or inquisitive for what I wrote you; but we have truly a serious task before us, that of establishing the right spirit and giving the right direction in the studies of Nat. Hist. in this country. It is plain that the fruits to be matured will depend upon the seeds now sown, and we cannot be too careful in striking out every selfish tendency, and in promoting what may do most good. You must judge every step of mine in that light. Far from urging any thing that might be chiefly useful to my aims I make it, for instance, a point with all my correspondents to induce them to establish local collections for themselves wherever there is a chance that they may be preserved & made useful. Your remarks about european collectors in this country led me to write you my last strictures. All we are justified to do against any such efforts which may seem a nuisance to us, is to be more active than they can be, and to render their collections useful in spreading abroad the results of our own studies. For my own part I shall always act in that spirit.

I long to see what you have have for me. I have not yet received my barrels from Missouri and begin to feel somewhat anxious about them. Clark[22] is proceeding with the arrangements of the specimens of last winter. There are truly beautiful things among them. I have not yet felt equal to writing out my criticism of the Serpents.

Sincerely your friend,

L. AGASSIZ

AGASSIZ to BAIRD

CAMBRIDGE, *Aug. 23, 1853*

My dear Baird,

After an absence of a week on Cape Cod I found your note of Nov. 14th and the box with a jar which I take to be the Chinese fish. Let me know if you can ascertain from Mr. Varden where they were collected, for there is a shark among them which is of the highest interest and the precise locality of which I should want to know.

Meanwhile I have received again 4 barrels & cans of specimens, 2 from Alabama with several new freshwater fishes, among others 3 new *Pomotis*, over the 5 new ones I had collected myself. This makes me wish for those you have described in the Proceedings of the Ac.Nat.Sc. There are also duplicates of some of those *Zygonectes* of which I had only isolated specimens, so that your chance for those is now secured. Many reptiles also, but nothing new, only interesting as to locality, except one *Cistudo* which seems to differ

---

[22] Henry James Clark (1826–1873), a private assistant to Agassiz who did most of the basic preparation for four volumes of the "Contributions."

from the *carolina*. By the way I caused Clark to overhaul my southern reptiles for you, but neither the Cystignathi, nor the *Hyla* you desire could be found among them. Another collection from Athens Ga. from Dr. J. LeConte contains also half dozen new species of fishes & 2 new Astaci; which also remind me of the authenticated specimens of Girard, species you were to send me. The last collection is from Hollidaysburg upon the Juniata, which of course contains nothing new for you; but among LeConte's fishes there is an *Etheostoma* which I do not know.

I am sorry I can not keep the Lepidostei longer, and I will have the most made of them at once & return them. You can say to Mr. Bonbreak, that they are in the best condition he can wish them. When shall the directors & curators of Museums in this country understand the proper use of collections? While engaged in the work upon Echinoderms the Museum of Paris allowed me original specimens of Lamarck during 5 years; I had even some fossil fishes during 9 years in my keeping, before they were returned to their respective Museums and nobody ever pressed me for them. Prof. Potter had written to me he would see that I could keep them until I had done but I have not heard of him since & that was the reason why I did not write again to Mr. Everhart.

Yours very truly,
L. AGASSIZ

BAIRD to AGASSIZ

Oct. 8, 1853

My dear Professor,

You will, I trust, excuse the delay in my replies to your notes in consideration of the great mass of work heaped up here, and my desire to examine the various packages on hand so as to give you an account of them. I have, however, thus far scarcely been able to open a box or keg and can only say that I found a number on my arrival of great promise. Among them is a small vessel of Axolotls from Mexico of which I shall be able to send you several specimens. I find nothing from the expeditions but plants, some few snakes, only one or two fishes. Several lots however are on their way. My own gatherings have not come in.

I assure you that I have not the slightest desire to monopolize Major Emory's things nor any other and shall always be willing to share such mutual desiderata. Major Emory's collections however contain thus far very few fish yet I expect a number from Mr. Clark,[23] in the course of the fall, which will be richer affairs. You must note, however, the grounds on which I ob-

---

[23] John H. Clark, a native of Virginia and a student at Dickinson College while Baird was teaching natural history, was a member of various Government surveys.

jected to your superintendence of the Major's things. It was not a desire to have them for the Smithsonian Institution but on account of the fact that they were all made by a protege of my own, brought up and trained by me, between whom and myself there exists the warmest affection: for whom I got the appointment of computer, and who was in no way obliged to make collections, this not being his office, but did make them for the love of me. He has from the beginning done full duty in the mathematical line, and is now not naturalist but assistant astronomer to the expedition.

I am much obliged for the offer of Dr. Gibbs' *Etheostoma*. I would be pleased to have the drawing; for the specimens however you had better keep until you arrange collections and can pick out others. I am in no hurry, as I do not know when I shall be able to make a beginning, as soon as possible, however.

Sincerely & truly yours,
S.F.BAIRD

AGASSIZ to BAIRD

CAMBRIDGE, *Nov. 3, 1853*

My dear Baird,

In accordance with my promise I will give you a short account of my new acquisitions. The specimens I expected from Missouri have at last arrived; there are many new fishes, mostly representative forms of the Ohio types, among others six new *Pomotis,* the reptiles are few, only new localities for known species however *Emys Bellii* of Gray in fine specimens (Its origin was not known before),‡ and one specimen of *Crotaphytus collaris.* I wonder whether it is identical with the southern one described by Holbrook. Have you it from Texas? One barrel from Hampton Roads sent by Mr. John Leib of the Coast Survey has proved particularly instructive. Contains many species not known before north of Charleston, and others not known south of N. York; also a new *Cyprinodon* and a new *Uranoscopus.* Another barrel from Woods Hole interesting for the range of our northern species. Several barrels are again on the way from Alabama.

‡There is also an *Emys* allied to *Cumberlandensis,* but having no specimen of this I can not identify it with certainty. Have you *Cumberlandensis?* for comparison. If so, let me have it for a while. There are also fine specimens of *Naiades* in alcohol.

Sincerely yours,
L. AGASSIZ

I can not lay my hands on the drawing of the Alabama *Etheostoma,* to save my life. It must be buried under a pile of papers and cannot be lost. I mention this only to explain my delay in sending it.

BAIRD to AGASSIZ

Nov. 7, 1853

My dear Professor,

I have just received your letter of the 5th ult announcing your delightful novelties. I am delighted to hear the missionaries have safely arrived. I have grieved with you over their possible loss. I have not much to report on my part although several valuable lots are expected this month. I am somewhat painfully anxious about the fate of a box of collections of Gov. Stevens party from St. Paul and Fort Union. Why it has failed to make its appearance I do not know. It contains all the alcoholic specimens gathered on the route. Still I do not quite despair.

Crotaphytus we have in many localities: Texas, New Mexico, etc. It is not found anywhere east of the Mississippi and Missouri.

I have not *Emys cumberlandensis:* [illegible] Several new turtles have been sent from the Western waters.

Have you *Hyla delitescens?* [Illegible.]

Sincerely yours,
S.F.BAIRD

BAIRD to AGASSIZ

Nov. 14, 1853

My dear Professor,

I hope very soon, perhaps in a few days to send you the Wailes Unios. together with our Petromyzons. The Plagoternas are scarcely represented in our cabinet, only two or three very common species from the coast of New England. There may be one or two from the South which I shall send.

I enclose a letter just received from the pertinacious Franklin and Marshall College.[24] I have done what I can to satisfy them: but cannot you have such drawings made of those gars as will permit you to return them within some specified time?

I had a letter a few days ago from Col. Wailes in which he says: "The explanation as to the very small collection of Unios forwarded for Prof. Agassiz was not at all necessary. In reply to a letter from him regarding a collection of our fishes, I mentioned incidentally having at your instance sent them for him, and did not intend to imply dissatisfaction nor much less offence, that he had not noticed them, which in fact I did not feel."

I have just [illegible] in the Upper Amazon, 4,000 above Para with

---

[24] Franklin and Marshall College, Lancaster, Pa., had recently been formed by combining Marshall College, Mercersburg, and Franklin College in Lancaster. Baird had assisted in supplying objects for the museum at Marshall College while he was at Dickinson College.

[illegible] of a friend who goes there in a few weeks. He will take 100 gallons of alcohol with him: We shall get some nice things there. I think also I am certain of a barrel of *Polypterus palmas* for you from Capt. Palmer to be looked for next spring.

Sincerely yours,
S.F.BAIRD

BAIRD to AGASSIZ

Nov. 28, 1853

My dear Professor,

I regret much as you can the obstinacy and stupidity of those Draynothean boys in the matter of the gars. [Illegible.]

I have been busy with manuscripts and proofs making entries. Our exchanges are also tremendous. Since my return we have had over a thousand, all of which I have had to enter three times. The parcels for others have been overpowering. Yesterday I sent off an express wagon filled with packages you received from Europe in a week, some 60 in number, a large number for Cambridge. Several for you enclosed to Prof. Peirce.[25] Call on him for them. This with over 300 letters and circulars on business connected chiefly with the above has been my occupation since my return. It is killing me! but I must do it and nearly all with my own hands. I mean to keep all my promises, and will do so as long as I can — those to you above all — but sometimes I dont see my fish room for a week at a time!

Ever Yours,
S. F. BAIRD

BAIRD to AGASSIZ

WASHINGTON, *March 9, 1854*

My dear Professor,

At last after long and to me vexatious delays, I have the gratification of fulfilling some of my many promises by sending a lot of specimens as per the enclosed list. You must and will pardon the apparent neglect hitherto

---

[25] Benjamin Peirce (1809–80), professor of mathematics, Harvard University, was a friend and associate of Agassiz for a long time. Peirce, together with Agassiz, Gould, and Felton from Harvard, Dana from Yale, Bache from Washington, D.C., and others formed an informal organization known as the "Scientific Lazzaroni." They exerted a wide influence in American science and were considered by some outsiders as being somewhat ruthless in securing university appointments for men they considered worthy. Elections to such organizations as the National Academy of Sciences were considered by some of their members as a prerogative of the group.

when you realize the immense amount of occupation which has been on my shoulders. Industrious as I flatter myself I always am, I have been obliged to work harder than ever even to keep up with my duties, especially with the amount of time which is daily wasted by the thoughtless visits of strangers and others, occupying an average of at least four hours in the working day.

I have also done a considerable share of zoological investigation, especially among birds and batrachians. I have completed the enumeration and determination of some 350 species of birds from New Mexico and the counties west of the Mississippi, principally collections of Lt. Couch, Mr. Clark, and Doctors Suckley and Evans. I have detected several new species and determined the range of others. I have also nearly finished my examination of the Ranidae and Hyloids, [illegible] I have added a good many new species, and razed some old ones and have established several genera, among them one for the little *Hylodes maculatus* of yours. This cannot go with the genus as established, or rather restricted by Dumeril and Bibron, as it has a web to the foot, vomerine instead of palatine teeth etc. I think I have found new characters for defining the limits both of the families & genera. I have been much embarrassed however by the lack of specimens of *"Aptegnathus ornatus"* as well as more satisfactory ones than I possess of *C. nigrita*. These of course are true *Hyloids*.

The wood frog of Cambridge received from you I make out as new. Will the name *R. Cantabrigensis* do, as honoring the place?

Another cause of delay in sending you specimens has been the expectation of receiving some additional collections, long delayed in their arrival. Some have come but others are still delayed probably between St. Paul, Fort Union & the Yellowstone. [Illegible.] We have received other boxes, principally reptiles and some fishes [illegible]. The fishes are all Cyprinidae, besides the Salmonidae and a small *Etheostoma*. Of all these as well as from the other collections you shall have specimens. In the collections from the Columbia river are several *Leuciscordo* which you may have already determined and described from the collections of the Ex. Ex. For these, if any, I must of course adopt your names & citations as whatever general understanding there may have been respecting the partition of genera between men working up the American fishes. You would be entitled to everything first collected by the Ex. Ex. Will you let me know whether you have anything from the Columbia in this line? One species is somewhat like *Chilonemus culgroetus* [?] and the other like *Leuciscus americanus*.

Very few collections from the interior of the United States have been received since I last wrote you (which letter by the way you have not yet answered) except an additional lot from Dr. Barry of Racine, one from Mr.

Kennicott[26] of Aux Plaines, Ill. and from Mr. Sargeant at Rock River, Ill. and one from Prof. Winchell[27] at Selma, Ala. [illegible.] I have been much disappointed at the non-reception of some collections made by Lt. Trowbridge in California, which he wrote me a good while ago would be immediately forwarded. I sent him out some alcohol, to be sure that he had all the means and appliances.

I think you will find some new Cyprinodonts among these. I send many collected by myself. Are you surprised to see such a range for *Zygonotus?* Of course you will describe the novelties. I wish you could make up a paper on this family for speedy publication.

I would have sent more specimens than I do, did I know how far you have been supplied. Of course you are receiving collections every day in prodigious quantity, and I fear I may after all have contributed nothing not already in hand. I can only send the specialties which you are engaged in studying and these with little hope of any great acceptance. Of course you shall have types of all the new species I may describe, and I hope you will do the same. As soon as possible I will send a series of the reptiles: for this I must wait, however till I can assort the prodigious stock now in hand.

I was much interested in reading your article in Silliman on the fishes of Alabama. The collection of Prof. Winchell includes a good many of those already enumerated as far as I can identify them. Although the descriptions of some are almost too brief to allow this satisfactorily you have demolished quite a number of my new Etheostomas as I have all the Illinois species and some of the others. However "n'importe" there are plenty more left. The number of species I have is perfectly absurd. You know what special search I make for these in my trips — these for my sake, Cyprinodonts for yours.

I send the LeConte collections, according to your wishes: keeping only such specimens as can conveniently be spared, and sending the bulk to you. I retain several unique specimens for the present but will forward them hereafter. I also send some [illegible] Unios from Chile, the Wailes lot: do. from the Rio Grande. By the way I have some

---

[26] Robert Kennicott (1835–66), Aux Plaines, Ill., one of the most enthusiastic collectors for the Smithsonian Institution, was also engaged in a joint project with the Russian Telegraph Company and the Chicago Academy of Science in exploring the region destined to become part of Alaska. Baird was also much interested in the region and regularly exchanged letters with Kennicott. To him and others in his party a great deal of credit is given for furnishing important data concerning the natural resources of Russian America when the question came up during negotiations for its purchase. Baird and Agassiz, personally, and in the name of the institutions they represented, helped finance portions of Kennicott's exploring expenses.

[27] Alexander Winchell (1824–91), Selma, Ala., was one of the most versatile collectors for the Smithsonian Institution. He collected both animals and plants and did research in geology.

Lepidostei for you from these waters or shall have when they arrive! One fine *L. platonomidae* [?] from Alabama, 5 feet long: if you have none from there. I also send *Sciaena mexicanus* and some other miscellanea which you will see on the list as new species from Wisconsin & New York.

Now that I am started I almost feel as if I could write all day but other duties will prevent my continuing this scrawl which you probably cant half make out. Let me hear from you soon and in the meantime believe me

Sincerely and affectionately yours,
S. F. Baird

I had almost forgotten to send my kind regards to Mrs. A. and your family in which Mrs. Baird begs to join.

I will send soon a list of all the localities from which we have received fishes. This however will require time to complete.

BAIRD to AGASSIZ

March 9th 1854

Prof. L. Agassiz:

Sir,

By authority of Major Emory I have the honor herewith to transmit a series of specimens of fishes from the collections of the U.S. Mexican Boundary Survey.

I remain, very respectfully,
Your obedient servant,
S. F. Baird
in charge Zoology of U.S.M.B.

BAIRD to AGASSIZ

March 29, 1854

My dear Professor,

I have just received and read with much interest the pamphlet sent by you and containing the completion of your article on the Tennessee turtles. Like everything emanating from your hand it contains a host of important suggestions and generalizations such as none but you could present. I wish that some of the specific descriptions had been fuller, as I have not been able to identify several species, especially when not in the best condition; as of *Zygonotus* &. However, I trust to receive from you such types as you may be able to spare of these and others described.

I have not heard yet whether you received the series of specimens sent on to you some weeks ago. I trust they arrived safely and proved interesting. We have had no arrival of fishes since that time, but hope for some shortly. I am still awaiting the advent of a collection made in Minnesota last summer by Governor Stevens' party; this was due many months ago, and has not yet come. I sent some new things from the Columbia in my last (not yet answered statement).

I write you that you were mistaken in saying that no Sticklebacks occurred in the Mississippi waters: I have them from several localities; even from the upper Missouri above Fort Benton.

I shall have my paper on the Batrachia ready shortly when I want to send it to you for examination and criticism. As I wish to put it to press as soon as possible, I will not forward it till I learn that you are at home, and can return it speedily. From hearing nothing from you I thought that possibly you may be out on a lecturing tour.

Very truly yours,
SPENCER F. BAIRD

AGASSIZ to BAIRD

CAMBRIDGE, *March 29, 1854*

My dear Baird,

I have been so busy last week examining the Crinoids of Troost with Prof. Hall, that it was impossible for me to examine your barrel of specimens and since I am leaving Cambridge tomorrow to be absent about ten days, I will simply acknowledge its receipt, that you shall not be anxious about it, or about my silence. Happily Mr. Clark unpacked it at once; the specimens might otherwise have suffered from want of alcohol.

Yours very truly,
L. AGASSIZ

You have by this time received my notice of Tenn. fishes, in advance of the publication of the 2nd part in the next No. of Sill. Jour. and you will perceive that I have kept clear of the ground reserved for you, beyond what was absolutely necessary in enumerating the fishes of the Tenn. Riv. Let me mention, since I think of it, that among the specimens you sent me long ago from Poland, as *Etheost. caprodes,* there was mixed with others one specimen of a new species of Physostomi, also that you will find reasons to establish a new genus intermediate between *Poecilichthys* and *Etheostoma,* among your species of which I have specimens. Had you made known to me your new accessions from the N.W. to which you refer in your letter I would have mentioned them as such.

LAG

BAIRD to AGASSIZ

May 8, 1854

My dear Professor,

I at last have the pleasure of fulfilling a promise which had been made for some time, by sending you by express today a box containing about half a bushel of living Unionidae. They are packed in damp grass and I trust will reach you in good condition. They are remarkably fine and many of them in their season of reproduction. They consist of the following species:

Unio complanatus, purpureus, nasutus, fisherianus, radiatus, ochraceus, cariasus

Anodonta aerolata, catareata

Alasmodonta undulata, rugosa.

They have been named by Dr. Kirtland[28] who spent a few days with us after the meeting of the Association. If you have not enough, let me know and I will try to get more.

I was very sorry you did not come to the meeting of the Association. I had much to tell you about. There was much regret felt too by many members who had never met you, and with whom the prospect of your presence was their chief inducement in coming. Natural History made a miserable showing, nothing in Botany, a paper on the Killer Whale by Lt. Mencey and another by Dr. Hanril, covered the Zoology and there were three papers on animal and vegetable physiology.

I sent a couple of vials to you by Prof. Lovering, and a large can by express, both received from Blake in California. I hope they arrived safely. The San Francisco Academy continues its preposterous reclamation of priority of discovery for Dr. Gibbon. I wrote him that newspaper publication is inadmissible in science and that while I regret that as a Californian mars his claim to a California fact, it could not hold gold. [Illegible.]

Have you unpacked the specimens I sent you some weeks ago?

Yours truly,

S.F.BAIRD

---

[28] Jared P. Kirtland (1793–1877) was born at Wallingford, Conn. He was graduated from Yale University as an M.D. but continued his observations and collections in natural history, his early interest. At the age of fifteen he had discovered parthenogenesis in the moth of the silkworm and later that bivalve fresh-water mollusks are bisexual. He accompanied Baird as a member of a natural history exploration to the regions around Lake Superior in 1853. He published papers on insects, birds, and especially on Ohio fishes. In medicine he is important as one of the founders of the Cleveland Medical College, later the medical department of Western Reserve College.

AGASSIZ to BAIRD

CAMBRIDGE, *May 24, 1854*

My dear Baird,

After lingering through the earlier part of the spring, I was at last taken quite sick and kept in my room and bed for several weeks. I am hardly able to go about now; but I take my first chance to acknowledge the receipt of the Unios. Though opened at once by Mr. Clark I am sorry to say the animals were so far decayed as only to make me regret their loss more deeply for they were in the finest state of pregnancy. If you could without too much trouble collect a small number of each kind again and after ascertaining in some specimens that their gills are still filled with eggs, which I think must be the case, put at once some in alcohol, you would oblige me greatly.

I have duly received the cans and jars forwarded lately. Meanwhile you may have received some specimens for me sent by Dr. Henry from New Mexico by Capt. Pope who is expected to reach Washington about this time. When they arrive please forward them at once. As soon as I can venture over alcohol I shall lay out for you a fine lot of specimens including all my new species of which I have duplicates and this is the case with most of them. I have within a year received 92 barrels and cans of fishes from almost every part of the country. The number of new things is no longer great, but the geographical distribution is very interesting. I shall presently make out a catalogue of the species of the states of Missouri, Iowa and Illinois from which I have received about 20 barrels as a means of comparison with Kirtland's Ohio fishes. You ought to do the same for Michigan and Wisconsin when we would have a good beginning to compare the northern with the southern states. By the way can you not help fitting out Mr. Barry for a trip across Wisconsin, my means are so exhausted that I can hardly do much for him. I continue to receive large contributions from Louisiana, Alabama & Georgia, but I can not obtain access to Arkansas & Texas. People seem dead to all appeals there. I still expect representatives of your reptiles, salamanders, frogs etc. and of a number of your fishes, *Pomotis* etc. There besides many things at best which will not go upon paper I must await an interview. Remember what you can of our preliminary arrangements about which I have not heard a word for now one year and a half.

During this winter I have made some investigations of great importance upon that eternal question of species. Would you tell me for instance how many species of *Hypsolepis* you know? How many of the type of *Leuciscus chrysoleucus?* How many *Grystes* we have? need go no further. I give you a month to answer these three questions! Another you may answer at once. Having adopted a number of Rafinesque's genera I must next characterize them, for though he has named and to some degree defined them he has not given the characters we want now a days, do you care to characterize yourself the genera *Hypsolepis, Ceratichthys,* and *Chilonemus* or should I, referring them to you, include them in a revision of generic characters I am preparing? Let me also ask what you are going to do with your additions to your Astaci? I have about a dozen new species, which I would publish at once, but I would prefer to wait if you are not going to give yours to Girard. I have made a thorough revision of the whole family and I should not like to have nothing but criticisms left to publish, I find I have already enough of it thus far.

Hoping soon to hear from you,
I remain
Yours truly,
L. AGASSIZ

BAIRD to AGASSIZ

May 27, 1854

My dear Professor,

I am very much vexed that the Unios did not get to you in safety. I devoted a whole day with the help of a large party to collecting these, some 16 miles down the river, and expecting confidently that they would reach you alive, thereby giving you the best chance to study them. I do not believe I can get any more this spring as these were collected on the shad grounds, brought in by the shad seines. There are none to be found in situ, near enough to shore, and these were only dislodged and brought up by repeated dragging of seines day and night. The fishing is over (since the 15th) and there are no boats running to these grounds. I will, however, make the attempt, and if unsuccessful can only promise better luck next season.

I have not heard anything from Dr. Henry in regard to his collections. Capt. Pope, however, will not be here for some time as he comes home with Belknap and the route is long and tedious. Does he say what they will send to me? The only intimation is the claim made upon Mr. Cassin for the birds: should anything come. I will, of course, immediately forward anything that may come for you. I hope to send you much from here at any rate, by the end of summer and I have strong hopes of getting several lots from Arkansas and other out of the way places. By the way, you dont say anything about the Texas and other things I sent you a couple of months ago. What about the Characine and the Labrordea? What new things do you find among the Cyprinodonts? What among *Zygonotus?*

I shall hold you to your promise of types of all your new species. They will be religiously preserved with your names. Any other species unnamed I will be glad to have, but by all means, remember the types.

I rather suspect that between us we have material for a pretty complete N.Am. Ichthyology. Your additions have been prodigious — 92 lots! It must have taken a small fortune to pay for transportation, alcohol etc. I dont wonder you did not have much left for Barry. I think, however, he will have enough for his necessary purposes as I sent him $50.00 and have promised him $50.00 more which will probably come out of my own pocket. He left on the 1st of May. I have heard nothing from him for many weeks.

If you will send me your Anura I will label them according to my determinations of these animals. I do wish you could find specimens of *Cystignathus ornatus* and *nigritis* among your stock, as I lack good specimens to complete my monograph. In the March and April numbers of the Proceedings of Academy are the characteristics of my new ones. In all we have about 25 new species. I shall now take up the Salamanders and will soon run through them, as there is comparatively little for me to do there.

I would rather not answer that question about the number of species of *Hypsolepis* we have here even in a month! I only know that we have about 100 localities of the type: if there were fewer it were easier to say. As to characterizing the genera *Hypsolepis, Ceratichthys, Cheilonemus.* I will, of course be glad to have you do it in your proposed revision of genera which I long to see. As to the Astaci — you had better publish at once, without waiting too long. Of course I cannot refuse to make the examination of the species here, as he has commenced on the subject, but you shall have your share at the earliest possible moment.

I will carry out your suggestions about the catalogues of fishes of Wisconsin & Michigan of which I have abundant material. I might include Ohio, where I am equally at home in the way of specimens. I wish I had more time for Natural History. This eternal treadmill of miscellaneous correspondence, details of publications and exchanges, is very time consuming: I have already written this year what fills nearly 600 pages full quarto of a letter copy book, mostly written as closely as this.

Ever truly yours,
S. F. BAIRD

BAIRD to AGASSIZ

June 1, 1854

My dear Professor,

I have just learned that Henry Kroyer of Copenhagen has been spending a month or two about New Orleans making immense collections of fishes and other things and is now proceeding up the Mississippi. He has been paying particular attention to the Cyprinodonts and he told my informant (Victor Motschulsky, the Russian Entomologist) that he had collected 6 or 8 new species in a single day: also that he had discovered great differences between ♂ and ♀ and all that! He must be back at Copenhagen in August when he will doubtless publish his collections of new ones. Now why dont you complete your manuscript of Cyprinodonts and publish in the Journal of Science the characters at once, giving diagnosis of genera and species? I should feel very much grieved to see your species and mine taken away thus when we were the first to occupy the field. I have described various series of Cyprinodonts with your names and want them verified.

Sincerely yours,
S. F. BAIRD

AGASSIZ to BAIRD

NAHANT, July 30, 1854

My dear sir,

Your little note gave me the more pleasure as it was not a business letter, so I answer it at once, that you may be satisfied and appreciate it. I have also been for several weeks by the sea side at Nahant, in the hope of restoring my health, which of late has seemed to grow worse and worse. In time I begin anew upon Wilkes fishes, chiefly with the view of giving a special account of those of the western coast, to secure for the Expl. Exp. the credit of what they did before new publications pour in from that quarter, but I have been obliged to slack my efforts and may not be able to finish this job before the issue of Sill. next number. With the additions I have received myself, the ichthyology of California and Oregon assumes quite an interesting appearance. Lately I have also had a few plates of Cyprinodonts prepared to see what may be done and at the same time to ascertain whether the Amer. Ichthyology could not be published on a similar plan. I send you proofs to have your opinion about this. By the way I have neither your *Heterandria affinis* nor *occidentalis*. If you can not give me specimens I would at least like a sight of them. We are likely to disagree upon the value of some of the species of this family. I never knew anything more difficult and as I wrote you last renewed investigations upon all our species of fishes in general are becoming daily more necessary. Pray set to work and look at those types I mentioned to you.

If you know where Richard[29] is, send him word to return my microscope, which he took to draw fish scales. I want it for my pupils. Please inquire also of Girard what has become of my copy of Richardson's N.

---

[29] John H. Richard, an artist, at that time engaged in preparing plates for papers on ichthyology for Baird and Girard.

Am. fishes and of Heckel's Cottoids Wiener Museum, which I have not seen since he had them.

I shall be much obliged for specimens of what you collect in Cape May. Look out for the Annelids living in the sand. I have long had a Monograph of Am. Annelids in preparation. Indeed I believe I have all those of Northern & Southern States and if you could procure those of the middle states, a sketch of that class, so completely neglected in America, might at once be published. Collect also the Campanularians, Sertularians, Bryozoa and whatever Polypi & Echinoderms may occur. I am also ignorant of what occurs in the middle states belonging to those families.

Yours very truly,
L. Agassiz

Remember me to Mrs. Baird

AGASSIZ to BAIRD

Cambridge, Oct. 5, 1854

My dear Baird,

Moving twice this fall and especially a great move into my new house has not added to my leisure, especially since I have attempted arranging my library, and a natural propensity to delay whatever may be improved by so doing has caused my delay in answering your note. I am much obliged for your offer of a share in your spoils of last summer and shall accept thankfully whatever you send. I suppose I have already the new Cyprinodonts of which you speak. One is remarkable for its comparatively large scales and small fins etc. I thank you also for the hints about possible anticipation by Kroyer & also with reference to the fishes from our western shores. The fact is I do not care and though I might just as well have published my Synopsis of Cyprinodonts these two years, and my other revision of the fishes of Oregon and California at least 6 months ago. I will not run a race with those whose sole object is to secure to themselves the priority in describing species. To join in such a race would be setting the worst example and let me tell you that already more harm has been done by this to the character of Amer. Naturalists with reference to the estimation in which they are held abroad, than you can imagine and it will grow worse and worse if those connected with the Smithsonian Institution as naturalists go on publishing and supporting the publication of the most immature productions. Can you, Prof. Baird, of the Smithsonian Institution, not take your stand like a man and frown down upon such a miserable course, in which our best men will I hope never join, and would you by your acts make it true what its enemies charge upon the Institution that its doings are unworthy of commendation & support? Remember what responsibility rests upon you and what account the historian of the scientific progress in America will ask of you within ten or twenty years.

You will find in the next No. of Silliman a revision of our genera of Cyprinoids, part 1st. I have not attempted to describe the species, hoping you may do it, and only alluded to such as occur in the west of Rocky Mountains or as have been mixed up and require critical revision before they can be quoted as types. I have some strictures on you and others. I hope you will find they refer to the things and not to the man. I feel as I was not justified in remaining absolutely silent before what I cannot approve. I join the proof of a few experimental plates of Cypr. I had made; the lettering is partly incorrect.

Sincerely yours,

L. AGASSIZ

BAIRD to AGASSIZ

Oct. 20, 1854

My dear Professor,

I yesterday embraced the first opportunity afforded since my return, to pack up and send the bottles of fishes collected for you by Dr. Henry. They are from the Mimbres, a stream which is said to flow into Lake Guzman, and to have no communication with either the Gila or Rio Grande. The skin I believe is from the Mimbres likewise: probably from the Rio Grande.

I have not yet unpacked my New Jersey things but hope to get time to do so in a few weeks. I have some 75 species, mostly of all sizes from very young up. If you care for them I will send as complete a series as I can make up; as of some others collected on L. Island and the lower Hudson, just say the word.

I do hope it will not be long before you publish your paper or papers on Puget Sound and other Pacific fish. We have a good many from that region sent by Stevens. [Illegible.]

I will send you a series of these critters from N.J. that will make your eyes water. D. V.

I was much disappointed at not getting to Boston this summer. I had fully intended it but Mrs. Baird's health was such as to prevent my leaving her long enough to make it worthwhile. You said something in your last letter about sending proof or sample of a plate of Cyprinodonts. I never received it and would like very much to have another.

With kindest regards to Mrs. A. I remain

Sincerely yours,

S. F. BAIRD

I propose writing out in full many notes and habits etc. of N. Jersey fish for a paper.

BAIRD to AGASSIZ

March 16, 1855

My dear Professor,

I am ashamed to have kept your last kind letter so long on hand un-answered, but I wanted to send you proofs of the plates of Cyprinodonts engraved from Sonrel's drawings for the report of the Mex. Boundary in return for the exquisite plates you sent me. These were to be forwarded in a few weeks then and I requested the engraver to strike off some extra copies which he promised, and I have been waiting expectantly for them. A few weeks ago I learned in my great disappointment that he had re-ceived the most positive orders from the Interior Department not to take any proofs whatever except such as were delivered to the office and that the plates themselves had been securely locked up in the department. I might possibly find some old sheets with numerous corrections scratched on them if that would answer, but I have not a clean set myself.

We have had a hard time this winter with congressional committees and other extraneous matters so much so as almost to drive me frantic in the desire to do something in science. I have not been able to send the specimens from my last summer's collections as promised, simply be-cause, I have not had time to unpack the kegs containing them. I hope however that as the skies are becoming clearer, we shall soon settle down into our old routine, and catch up on our arrears.

By the way, I have been notified that Prof. Poey of Havana has sent us a set of the Cyprinodonts described in his book. If you have not got them, you shall have a series when they arrive. We have also a couple of garfish from the south at your service when you feel garfishy!

I have read your ten articles in Silliman on Western fishes & with great pleasure and profit, nor felt offended at any of the references to myself. No one has the right to object to a candid criticism of a scientific work, and I hope never to do so. I trust that any error of youth and immaturity of investigation may be corrected by time and continued study; and no one has an humbler opinion of my abilities than myself. I however cannot acknowledge having entered into a scramble for priority of discovery; and feel certain that whenever I have had the opportunity, I have discountenanced such action. What I may have done in this way has been strictly officially [sic] and in behalf of other parties, when after com-pleting an elaborate description I have published the specific characters at once to secure priority to the parties, not to myself. Without such encouragement to effort, the expeditions in the field would do little or nothing and science thus lose all their results. Were I to wish a con-nection of my name with species, there are hundreds in our collections which could be characterized and named, but I rigorously refuse to do this myself or allow it in others; I have it is true published characteristics of new species of genera & species of N. Am. Frogs in brief terms, but these were purely the essential characters taken from a Ms. ready that moment to put to press and containing matter for over one hundred pages which had occupied me eight months in preparation, circumstances prevented its publication however at that time.

I am glad to learn that you have got into your new house and are so comfortably fixed. I too have gone into the housekeeping line within a month or two and like it very much although terribly expensive!

I do wish you would give in Silliman a synopsis of genera and species of Cyprinodonts for the benefit of those who cannot make head or tail of the subject. As must be the case with all except yourself, I was much amused with the affair with Bennett Dowler and the molliensias.

Sincerely yours,

S.F. BAIRD

AGASSIZ to BAIRD

CAMBRIDGE, *May 22, 1855*

My dear Baird,

I forward this day a bundle of books to you, by express, containing 11 parcels with special directions, to be inclosed in your next great european distribution, which I see from your circular is to be dispatched on or after the first of June. According to your directions I made out a specification of the contents of each parcel. Could you inform me of the direction of Dr. Bleeker, the Ichthyologist to whom I want to send also some books? The parcel to Mr. Conlon is somewhat large, but I hope it may nevertheless be accepted and as I wish he should receive it free of expense I beg you will do the necessary to that effect and charge me with the expense.

I am hard at work and I hope you may soon see some results from it. Meanwhile I send you a copy of what has already appeared of my western fishes.

Yours very truly,

L. AGASSIZ

BAIRD to AGASSIZ

May 25, 1855

My dear Professor,

The bundles came today, and they shall be duly dispatched to the respective addresses without expense either to you or to them. At any rate we can certainly frank them to Leipsic and will try to arrange from that point.

Bleaseley's address is Batavia. We put parcels for him in the package for the Batavian Acad. of Sciences to which we send regularly.

If you have any spare copies of your fish papers, I wish you would enclose with your name and let me distribute to a few addresses you have overlooked. Have you sent any to Heckel, Kroyer, Reinhardt, Retzius, Fries, etc.?

I have only quite recently finished the assorting of my last summer's collection. Do you care to have the series I promised you, or will it do a later period when I have more leisure. I have inserted in the Smithsonian Report a brief account of the Nat. Hist. of the species observed which I hope will meet your approval. I will send copies as soon as I can get them, the report not being yet through the press.

Very truly and sincerely yours,

S. F. BAIRD

AGASSIZ to BAIRD

May 31, 1855

My dear Baird,

I forward by this days Express 25 copies of the pamphlets I have left, which you may circulate as you think best in Europe. I should be much obliged if you let me then have a memorandum of the names to whom they were sent, that I should not repeat the invoices. Thus far I have done nothing towards circulating any of my papers in Europe, as I thought best for the sake of all our doings here, that they (the scientists there) should some day or other find out that there may be something doing in this part of the world, for which it may be worth their while to be on the lookout and also to check the expectation already raised that every thing which is published here is as a matter of course to be presented to them. That will not do in the long run, otherwise it would perpetuate in another form the tributary position in which Science in America has been with reference to the old world.

I also enclose a parcel for Dr. Bleeker, containing Medusa of Mass. pt I. & II., Classif. of Insects.

Pray do not delay sending the list of correspondence that I may hurry my prospectus[30] to all parts of the country.

Yours in great haste,

L. AGASSIZ

and on back of "Private circular"

My dear Baird,

Here goes the bird! And so I am tied for 10 years, if I get the necessary number of subscribers. When obtained I shall still be able

---

[30] The announcement of the intended publication of 10 volumes called "Contributions to the Natural History of the United States."

to make my selection of the subjects according to the requirements of the time; but I must first have them and with a view of making a proper circulation of my prospectus I have asked J. Henry to send me the most extensive list of your american correspondents. Please send it without delay.

Yours,

L. AGASSIZ

PROSPECTUS
CONTRIBUTIONS TO THE NATURAL HISTORY OF
THE UNITED STATES
IN TEN VOLS. QUARTO

By LOUIS AGASSIZ

To be published by Messrs. Little, Brown and Co. of Boston, Mass.

For more than eight years, I have now been in this country, devoting my attention chiefly to the study of those classes of the Animal Kingdom which American naturalists have, thus far, not fully investigated. The amount of materials I have already brought together is so great, that the time seems to me to have come when I should proceed with the publication of the more important results of these investigations. Desirous of contributing my share to the rapid progress natural sciences are making at present in this part of the world, I wish to present to my fellow-laborers in this field in the form most easily accessible to them. It has therefore appeared to me desirable to bring it out in a series of independent volumes. This plan will, moreover, leave me entirely free to present my contributions to science with such minute details, and to such an extent, as I shall deem necessary to the fullest illustration of my subject.

Without entering into a detailed account of the contents of this work, it may be sufficient here to state, that it will contain the results of my embryological investigations, embracing about sixty monographs, from all classes of animals, especially selected among those best known as characteristic of this continent; also descriptions of a great number of new genera and species, accompanied with accurate figures, and such anatomical details as may contribute to illustrate their natural affinities and their internal structure.

I shall not extend my publications to classes already illustrated by others, but limit myself to offering such additions to the Natural History of the States I have visited as may constitute real contributions to the advancement of our knowledge.

From a careful estimate of the materials I have now on hand, I am satisfied I shall be able to include the most valuable part of my investigations in ten quarto volumes; each volume containing about three hundred pages, with at least twenty plates. I therefore now open a subscription for such a work, in ten volumes, quarto, in cloth binding, at the price of twelve dollars each volume, payable on delivery. Each volume shall be complete in itself, containing one or several independent monographs; so that, if any unforeseen difficulties should interrupt the publication of the whole, the parts already published shall not remain imperfect. As far as possible, I shall always select first such of my papers as contain the largest amount of new matter, or may contribute most directly to the advancement of science. Having devoted the greatest part of my time to the investigation of the embryonic growth of our animals, I shall make a beginning with the embryology of our turtles, several of which I have traced through all their changes. I trust this monograph will afford our medical students a fair opportunity of making themselves familiar with the results of one branch of physiology, which has the most direct bearing upon their science, and for which the different species of the family of turtles found in every part of the United States will afford them a better opportunity even than the artificial breeding of hen's eggs. Moreover, the extent of my embryological researches, covering, as they do, all the classes of the animal kingdom, will furnish, I trust, a new foundation for a better appreciation of the true affinities, and a more natural classification, of animals. I foresee the possibility, upon this basis, of determining, with considerable precision, the relative rank of all the orders of every class of animals, and of furnishing a more reliable standard of comparison between the extinct types of past geological ages and the animals now living upon earth.

I shall have frequent opportunities of acknowledging the many favors I have received from naturalists of all parts of the country, from the Atlantic to the Pacific Coast, and from the shores of our Great Lakes to those of the Gulf of Mexico; and also of mentioning the many specimens which have been furnished to me from every part of the Union, and of which I shall publish descriptions.

It is a matter of course, that a work like this, illustrated by a large number of plates, cannot be published without a liberal and extensive patronage. As it has been prepared solely with the view of throwing additional light upon the wonderful diversity of the animal creation of this continent, its structure, and its general relation to that of the other parts of the world, without the slightest hope of compensation for myself, I trust I may meet with the approbation of those conversant with the importance of the subject, and receive sufficient encouragement from the enlightened part of the community to enable me to bring to a successful close an undertaking upon which I enter now, and in this form, for no other purpose than to contribute my share towards increasing the love of nature among us.

As the printing of this work cannot begin until a sufficient guarantee is secured for the publication of the whole, I take the liberty of making an appeal to the lovers of science to send to the publishers their own subscriptions, and such others as they may procure, as soon as convenient, and if possible, before the first of August next, that I may be able to proceed at once with a work which, relating to animals peculiar to America, I wish to make, in every respect, an American contribution to science, fostered and supported by the patronage of the community at large.

To render this work more generally accessible, it is intended to publish at the rate of about one volume a year. Such an arrangement will bring the whole within reach of every student of Natural History, and of every friend of the progress of science in the country. The periods of publication, however, cannot be more definitely fixed, because the required uniformity of execution of the plates, to which particular attention will be paid, will demand that they be all entrusted to the same artist, who has drawn on stone most of the plates of my former works.

L. AGASSIZ

CAMBRIDGE, *May 28, 1855.*

The undersigned agree to take the number of copies of the above work set against their names.

Names	Residence	No. of copies

BAIRD to AGASSIZ

May 31, 1855

My dear Professor,

I received your letter and circular today and hasten to reply with the assurance that we will do everything possible to assist in your enterprise. Prof. Henry takes a deep interest in the plan and I think will subscribe to some copies for the Smithsonian. You will please put me down individually as a subscriber.

I think that we may be able to distribute a large number of your prospectuses to advantage. You should send us about 2000 for this country. We shall in a few weeks have completed our 9th annual report and can then enclose a copy in each one without the trouble of a special superscription. Our clerical force is too feeble to copy off the main list which besides is not accurate, many changes having been made previous only to the gentleman who distributes reports and blanks to observers.

Again when we distribute batches of books to our overseas institutes and societies, it will be easy to put in a copy or two of the circulars.

You should however by all means get up a special foreign circular; best perhaps in French; at least there should be an edition in this language. Add to what you already say that owing to expense no copies will be presented nor sold to non-subscribers and that subscriptions must be made beforehand; also that when published the Smithsonian will deliver immediately all the copies. Mention that subscriptions may be paid to Bossange, Paris, Westermanns in Germany and N. Trubner in London. We can distribute one or two to each address we supply, numbering at least 800 Institutions and individuals. This we should have written in three weeks at latest. I should not think there ought to be any difficulty in getting the required no. of subscriptions. At any rate we and I will do all possible to help.

Sincerely yours,

S. F. BAIRD

AGASSIZ to BAIRD

June 1, 1855(?)

You did not send me young *Trionyx* so they will be very welcome; even though I have already some myself; but your measure about 2 inches seems to indicate yours are younger than mine. Any other young whether identified or not, if only the origin be certain will be welcome. I trust from my knowledge of these young in general I may be able to make them out.

If Shaw's name, which I have no means of looking up at this moment, is truly meant for *C. Blandingii,* it must of course be preserved.

I would be very sorry not to see you. I wish to speak to you very openly about all the Smithsonian affairs and I trust it may be to your advantage.

Yours very truly,

L. AGASSIZ

Let me say that it is by no means too late to get either eggs or young turtles. I receive weekly some of our species from those of my correspondents I have trained to look for them. They are constantly uncovered by rain showers or thrown up by the plough, and the young just hatching are found in the water.

AGASSIZ to BAIRD

CAMBRIDGE, *June 2, 1855*

My dear Baird,

I again forward today a parcel, but only containing prospectus of my work, which Prof. Henry writes me you suggested to be sent for distribution among your correspondents. As I am doing just the same kind of work myself I beg you will as soon as possible forward to me the list of those to whom you have sent, or shall send, that I need not send again.

I trust you received the spare copies of my several papers I forwarded the day before yesterday and the parcel for Dr. Bleeker.

Yours very truly in
great hurry,
L. AGASSIZ

AGASSIZ to BAIRD

CAMBRIDGE, *June 4, 1855*

My dear Baird,

The note I have just received from you gave me intense pleasure. It is written in the spirit in which you used to write some years ago and I assure you it gave me on that account far more delight, than for its very acceptable contents. I have immediately sent word to Messrs. Little, Brown & Co. to forward the required prospectuses. They had already sent 200, the number mentioned in Prof. Henry's letter, which was probably meant for 2000 as you write. 800 more for Europe shall be prepared as soon as possible, with the proposed alterations and additions. I am delighted at the idea of bringing it out under the auspices of the Smith Inst. I would thank Prof. Henry, if he thinks it proper, to add to such of my prospectus as are circulated in the N.H. another short circular like the enclosed signed by him. There are still many institutions and individuals who will require such a testimony and recommendation to be persuaded that such a work can not be published without the most extensive patronage. Should however the number of subscribers exceed the sum required for the publication, I have made up my mind to spend the whole of my share of the proceeds to increasing the bulk of the volumes and the number of plates, so that every subscriber may justly feel interested in extending the circulation, a fact which I do not feel quite proper to state myself, but which Prof. Henry, knowing the spirit with which I take hold of such matters might well allude to.

Sincerely your friend,
L. AGASSIZ

AGASSIZ to BAIRD

CAMBRIDGE, June 8, 1855

My dear Baird,

For fear of a mistake I would inform you that the two thousand copies of my prospectus which have been forwarded to you yesterday by Messrs. Little and Brown are for home circulation and contain no other alteration than the mention that no copies shall be presented. The 800 copies for Europe with the additions suggested will be forwarded tomorrow, so that they shall be in time for your first batch for the Old World.

Yours very truly,
L. AGASSIZ

My subscription progresses finely in Boston; if I could meet with half the success in N. York and Philadelphia I could be sure of final success.

AGASSIZ to BAIRD

CAMBRIDGE, June 12, 1855

My dear Baird,

By this time you must have received 2000 prospectus for home distribution and 800 with the names you suggested for Europe. 800 more with the name of Balliere as in this sheet went to him, upon his request for distribution in England. Trubner has got others from Little & Brown. I think this will do. My experience with the fossil fishes has taught me that very little can be expected from France where only 16 copies of the work went, though a french work, whilst about 100 were sold in Germany and over 100 in England. It is England which will give again, in this case the largest number of subscribers. I expect, next Germany, where every body who may feel inclined to secure the work at least reads english. I hardly think a french translation needed, moreover I will request T Müller, Troschel S and V. Siebold to notice the publication in their respective Journals, which is all that is needed to call the attention of those who may not see the prospectus. Please however not to forget to enclose it in all your packages and let me know if you need more. Remind also Prof. Henry of the card, if he should approve of the idea.

As the package I expect from Coulon through Flügel contains my original drawings of fresh water fishes of Europe, unpublished fossil fishes etc. see that it is safely forwarded.

Yours very truly,

L. AGASSIZ

BAIRD to AGASSIZ

June 14, 1855

My dear Professor,

The box of your things from Coulon arrived today and I hasten to send it on by Adams Express after rerouting it.

The circulars have all been received, and shall be made to fly about like hot cakes. Prof. Henry will gladly prepare a little Smithsonian circular to accompany yours, and will write you about it.

Sincerely yours,

S. F. BAIRD

AGASSIZ to BAIRD

NAHANT, *June 21, 1855*

Do not direct to Nahant as our P.O. is not reliable.

My dear Baird,

I have this day returned the card of Prof. Henry to be added to my prospectus. I hope that the delay caused by my present residence in Nahant will not have prevented its returning in due time.

I have received your revision of the N.I. fishes with which I am well pleased. I shall be very glad to get originals. I suppose I already have your new *Pomotis,* though of course undescribed, as also your Cyprinoid *parvus. Hydrargyra luciae* I am afraid is only an old male of a common species! How does your *Centrarchis Pomotis* differ from *gulosus?* Is it not that very fish? I am particularly struck with your *Engraulus.*

I am now all Turtle again to complete my monograph which I shall make my first Vol. Have you the eggs of any species of turtles not found in Mass.? I would thank you for them, as I mean to figure the eggs of all species, if possible and *the young just hatched.* Have you some of middle states, southern or western States or N.W.? Any living turtle you could now send, except *Chel. serpentina,* would be welcome, especially *Muhlenbergii, rubriventris, Kynosternon pennsylvanica* etc. in fact all the middle state species, especially females, that I may ascertain from the ovary & corpora lutea, still now visible, how many eggs the different species lay, and eggs found in the field in any stage of development during the whole summer from any part of the country would be highly valuable. Can you secure any? or induce any body to send me some?

Yours very truly,

L. AGASSIZ

BAIRD to AGASSIZ

June 30, 1855

My dear Professor,

I enclose a copy of Prof. Henry's circular to accompany yours of which we shall distribute at least 3000.

In the fall I will send you a series of fishes to accompany my paper. The Foreign Exchanges take up my time absorbingly now and as soon as I get through I must take my poor invalid wife to Lake Champlain for the summer. She still continues very ailing and I scarcely ever leave her — only to go to the Smithsonian and back. I fear I shall not be able to get to the Meeting of the Association in August: though if Mrs. B. is well enough we may come home via Boston in September.

With the specimens you can examine the *Cottus* I describe. I think *Hydraspis lariae* will stick. I saw and caught thousands of all the other species found on the coast and this is very different. It is a very small species, only an inch long, yet very brilliant.

I wish you had spoken sooner about the turtles, I could have sent many species. I sent Mr. Dumeril many living ones a month ago which you might have had and welcome. There were *Emys rubriventris, Muhlenbergii, picta, insculpta, terrapina,* etc. It is now rather late. Still I have written around for specimens. I send on Monday the only living species we have: *Cistudo blandingii* which I hope will go safely. We have no young turtles whose parentage I can swear to which I suppose would be indispensable. Perhaps I can do something, I will try. Two months sooner, and I could have guaranteed 12 or 15 species living!

Sincerely yours,

SPENCER F. BAIRD

BAIRD to AGASSIZ

July 24, 1855

Dear Professor,

I enclose a subscriber, not the last I mean to obtain by a good deal.

Did you get the turtles, living and dead, I sent you? Are you going with Perley?

Yours ever,

S.F.BAIRD

AGASSIZ to BAIRD

Aug. 24, 1855

My dear Baird,

I shall not meet Mr. Perley until they have done with that part of their business in which I can feel no interest and it is probably not to be finished this year. You may depend upon finding me in Cambridge by the middle of Sept. The turtles were very acceptable. Dr. Hoy[31] writes the supposed eggs of *Emys Blandingii* were those of the snapper. Why did you not come to Pr.? We had an excellent meeting.

Yours very truly,

L. AGASSIZ

AGASSIZ to BAIRD

CAMBRIDGE, *Sept. 1, 1855*

My dear Baird,

I have just received the parcel of pamphlets for which I thank you. This is to me full evidence that you will not forget my other requests. Of the whole lot I had only 2 before and those I had received from their authors. I am just writing out my Chapter upon genera, families, orders etc. You shall have an early copy of it.

Yours truly,

L. AGASSIZ

AGASSIZ to BAIRD

CAMBRIDGE, *Sept. 7, 1855*

My dear Baird,

I received your note of Aug. 25th but no other memorandum of the eggs of C. Bl. except an outline. By the way what is the name *C. meleagris?*

Can you not forward me eggs of the turtles found about your place now? I need them very much. There is no use in attempting to forward them from a distance alive. All those I have so received have arrived shriveled or moulded. Put them in alcohol. Have you no correspondent who could before the close of the season procure either eggs or very young turtles of any kind in alcohol. I must have all our species if possible. At this season they are most instructive. In the spring the embryos look all alike for many weeks. In great haste.

Yours truly,

L. AGASSIZ

---

[31] Dr. Philo Romayne Hoy (1816–92), Racine, Wis., was an enthusiastic field naturalist and the first to explore the deeper waters of the Upper Great Lakes.

AGASSIZ to BAIRD

CAMBRIDGE, *Oct. 15, 1855*

My dear Baird,

The turtles have already been of essential service to me and I truly thank you for your promptness in forwarding them. In a hurry I will mention that your specimens have enabled me to ascertain that the *Trionyx* from Texas is a distinct species from the *spiniferus* and *muticus,* a fact I already suspected from the sight of a few eggs from Texas Dr. Holbrook had sent me and which had been collected by Dr. Heerman[n]. Have your specimens also been collected by him? Next the *Chelonura Temminckii* has yielded a splendid skeleton which shows this turtle not only to be specifically but even generically distinct from ours. The generic differences are as striking as those between *Chelonura serpentina* & *Sternothorus odoratus.* By the way I have now every species of turtle mentioned in the country except *Emys concinna.* Can you not procure that for me? Of nearly all I have skeletons and of some as many as 8 or 10 skeletons of different ages, recently made by one of my pupils. These skeletons have proved of immense service in identifying the genera. There is one species however with reference to which you could further help me. Of our common *Chelonura serpentina* I have over 50 specimens in alcohol; but it so happens that I have not one the shield of which measures between 5 and 6 inches; could you send me one of that size at once to make a skeleton to complete my series of that type. When the time comes I hope you will also not forget the *rubriventris.* Since it is so common with you I would like also to make a full series of that. Do not forget also in due time to call upon your correspondents for eggs of all our species. I look also anxiously forward for more *Trionyx,* as I wrote last to you. With reference to families I have also one more difficulty to solve. Wagler[32] and after him Duméril have divided the Emyda into those the neck of which may be withdrawn under the shield by retracting the neck into the sheath made of the skin of the neck and those which are said merely to bend the neck sideways under the shield. Of these latter I have not a single representative at hand; can you let me have some? They are very common in S. Amer. and as you have sent me a very beautiful *Test. tabulata* from Para it has occurred to me that you may have some which would answer my purpose from that quarter. Either *Chelys,* or *Hydrapsis,* or *Platemys,* or *Hydromedusa,* or indeed any

---

[32]Johann G. Wagler (1800–32), a former professor at the University of Munich, was an authority in vertebrate natural history.

A. M. C. Duméril (1774–1860), was a French physician and naturalist.

of the family Chelydida as limited by Gray would do and the more the better. I should also like any european, or asiatic or african land turtle you can spare me.

Yours very truly,

L. AGASSIZ

P.S. I have written to Prof. Henry about bibliography in the same sense as to you and I have no doubt he will speak to you about it.

L. A.

AGASSIZ to BAIRD

CAMBRIDGE, *Oct. 26, 1855*

My dear Baird,

I have received Gray & the Bibl. so I know you are not forgetting your promise. But I have an additional request to make, which Prof. Henry will transmit to you, having enclosed it with an answer to other matters. Pray attend to it as soon as possible; and also to the sending of the other specimens. Time flies and I must have my first volume out before next summer. Look carefully over your memoranda, to forget nothing.

Yours very truly,

L. AGASSIZ

BAIRD to AGASSIZ

Oct. 31, 1855

My dear Professor,

I should have sent your things long ago but for the desire to get in some parcels announced long since and which I hoped might contain some of your desiderata. Since receiving your letters of the 25th (to Prof. Henry) and 26 I have concluded to send off at once what I have had ready for several weeks. The invoice is enclosed. The specimens are contained in one large barrel and one box and go to the express . . perhaps a day later.

I send you all your desiderata as far as we can now supply them, and hope to get more soon, of some species we send small specimens as we have no large size. As to *Emys* I have done the best I could: [illegible] In order to have you receive fresh specimens in the field I will give you the names of those I rely most on and advise you to write also as they will be more likely to respond to the joint appeal

Names are:

    Prof. E. B. Andrews, Marietta, Pa.

    Robert Clark, Wayne Co. Mich.

    Dr. J. P. Kirtland, Cleveland

    Dr. Geo. Englemann, St. Louis

    Dr. S. B. Barker, Charleston

Dr. Englemann will perhaps be most reliable.

I send you an embryo bear which you wont easily get elsewhere.

We have no *Trionyx* larger or as large as those sent. You have the largest. Please send me your results as to names of all sent you by localities. I could raise a *Testudo polyphemus* and species from Para. Note that the last one came from Miss & St. Louis. *Emys concinna* has not yet come to market. Will send them alive when they come.

Yours truly,

S. F. BAIRD

List of specimens sent to Professor Agassiz Oct. 20, 1855

Larger specimens principally in keg

1	Chelonura temminckii		Miss.
1	Testudo		Para
3	Trionyx	large	——burg, Pa.
			Allegheny
1	"		unknown
1	"		Texas
1	"		near Rio Grande
3	Cistudo	3 toed	Mississippi
1	"	"	St Louis
1	"	"	" small
1	Emys		Mississippi
1	"		Western Missouri
1	"		Pensacola
1	"		Marion Co. Mo.

1 separate head of large Trionyx from upper Missouri

Smaller specimens   [list illegible]

AGASSIZ to BAIRD

CAMBRIDGE, *Nov. 1, 1855*

My dear sir,

Looking this afternoon over the books you have sent me I noticed that I had one volume of the Proceedings of the German Assoc. for Adv. of Sc. which is not in your list. As my series is not so complete as yours I send it to you.

Yours truly,

L. AGASSIZ

Please tell Prof. Henry I shall answer his letter as soon as I have found time to look over the Smith. Contributions in our library.

BAIRD to AGASSIZ

November 5, 1855

My dear Professor,

I received your acknowledgment of the books today, but cannot imagine what has become of the keg and specimens I sent you nearly a week ago. I also wrote a letter with invoice of the things. I earnestly hope that no mishap has occurred, as many of the specimens I could never replace.

I am glad to have been able to meet some of your wishes, as a failure in this always proceeds from inability not disinclination. Having now got well posted up in our books I will take care with Prof. Henry's kind permission to keep you supplied.

I wish you would tell me what you thought of the plan and execution of Girard's Bibliography. I think that the copy sent you was of the first edition and contains many omissions rectified on the second, of which there was no copy left. He has now ready in MS. the Bibliography for the years 1850–54. Five years at which he has labored very diligently and has made very complete. One point would be to know whether the lists of new species are desirable or not. I welcome to prefer them as they will often save the necessity of taking much trouble to make a reference.

Girard has had several indirect offers to publish this Bibliography in a condensed form although nothing has yet been settled. I would like very much to see it published by the Smithsonian as it was got up entirely from materials here, and its gratuitous distribution is preferable to the selling of other parties. If therefore you like the plan or think that the sample of the 1851 portion would warrant Prof. Henry's entertaining the idea and by receiving the MS. and submitting it to a commission. I wish you would guide him on the subject. There can be no doubt as to the abstract value of such a work. And the chief point would be to decide as to the execution of that particular one.

I am very anxious to have your ideas on classification as I should find them of great value to me in my Mammal essays. Dont forget to let me have them very soon after published.

Very truly yours,

S. F. Baird

AGASSIZ to BAIRD

Cambridge, <i>Nov. 8, 1855</i>

My dear Baird,

I do not know how it has happened, but I have only received this morning your barrel & box, the contents of which are particularly welcome. I value particularly the great *Chelonura* & the *Trionyx* from Texas, and all the young Chelonians. Unfortunately from their mode of packing the other embryos have more or less suffered by pressure. They are so delicate that for safe transportation they ought to be packed singly in jars. They will however serve some good purpose notwithstanding.

As soon as I have examined & compared the turtles I will report to you what they are, and how the southern *Trionyx* compare with the northern. You may be surprised at my voracity but I must say I have not yet a sufficient supply of *Trionyx* and all you can do to help me to more will be thankfully acknowledged. I want especially now large specimens; your largest are not any more full grown as mine were.

I shall not wait till it is *published* to send you my Chapter on Classification. The results are so practical that even my students of one years standing with these rules are able to trace for themselves in lots of unlabelled specimens of any class I put in their hands, the natural limits of genera and families and they actually do it better than our old practiced Zoologists. So you see it will tell in the progress of science.

As to an American Bibliography for Nat. Hist. I hold with you that it is a great desideratum and do not see why that collected by Mr. Girard should not be published by the Smithsonian Inst. if it be what such a collection should be. But I must at the same time say that the part I have lately received from you does not everywhere exhibit that direction particularly required for such a task, leading to discard what is superfluous from the essential; it also frequently discloses an ignorance of the subjects alluded to. Such deficiencies could however easily be remedied by submitting the MS. to a commission (not too limited in number) of naturalists practically acquainted with different branches of the science, with power to propose alterations, suppressions and additions. This lies however in the Character of the Institution. I hold that the less the Instit. as such undertakes to decide upon such questions, the more is it likely to secure the good will and cooperation of all.

Ever truly yours,

L. AGASSIZ

AGASSIZ to BAIRD

CAMBRIDGE, *Nov. 17, 1855*

My dear Baird,

Mr. Putnam[33] has put up all my Saurians for you. They will go by Express tomorrow. I shall enclose by the next mail a catalogue of the whole, which I cannot do today, as I have no one to copy now for me, that which I intend to send.

The Saurians are much fewer than the other orders. I will have these packed up next week, and whatever Saurians may have been overlooked in this first overhauling. I send only the reptiles found within the boundaries of the N.I. as I suppose you do not wish for any others. Moreover I have only isolated specimens of the latter, and no series.

I proceed very slowly with the turtles, for I find that a morning spent with them unfits me for several days, but I shall go on doing the best I can.

Very truly yours,

L. AGASSIZ

AGASSIZ to BAIRD

CAMBRIDGE, *Nov. 23, 1855*

My dear Baird,

By this time you have no doubt received my Saurians, and the duplicate Catalogue of what I forwarded. Instead of sending the Catalogue by mail, as I had directed him, Mr. Putnam has kept the box back two days, and enclosed in it the Catalogue with an empty can just fitting the box into which you may transfer the specimens as you go along and

---

[33] Frederic W. Putnam (1839–1915), naturalist, archeologist, and Museum administrator, was born in Salem, Mass. In 1856 he entered Harvard College, where his ability and enthusiasm attracted the attention of Louis Agassiz, who made him his assistant the following year. For eight years he was closely associated with Agassiz. Later he became associated in administrative capacities with the Essex Institute, the Boston Society of Natural History, the Peabody Museum, and the Museum of Comparative Zoology at Harvard. He was largely responsible for the acceptance of anthropology as a university study.

have time for whatever you mean to send me. To-day Putnam has gone over all the species, not from the United States, left behind. There is not one from Mexico among them. In general, I am very poor in anything from Central America, with the exception of Haiti whence Dr. Weinland has brought a general collection. As soon as Putnam can complete the labelling and packing of the other reptiles you shall have them.

Respecting Crustacea, I may say I have a very large collection of them, including beautiful species from the Sandwich Islands & from East Indes, and would be glad to let Stimpson[34] work them up. Two of my students however are just trying their hands, one at the Macrura, the other at the Brachyura, and it would be unfair to take them away before the end of the course. But Stimpson can have at once the Isopods & Amphipods. Tell him to write me if he cares to take them up now.

Very truly yours,
L. Agassiz

AGASSIZ to BAIRD

Cambridge, Nov. 27, 1855

My dear Baird,

My last letter to you had just gone to the post office when I received the box with the living turtles which arrived in excellent condition and were particularly welcome. Of E. *concentrica* I have now plenty for examination, I should like however one or two very large specimens to ascertain what kind of changes they may undergo in their oldest age and when the season permits young, and youngest specimens also. The *rubriventris* of which I had only one before you forwarded me some in alcohol and then the living ones have already given me much valuable information; but of this species I need a good many more specimens and if you can select such as vary most I would be much obliged. I need not repeat my request for their young and youngest. I have now nearly all I want of Chelonians; indeed I have every species described from America, though some in isolated specimens, except E. *concinna*. Can you procure me that? The collection of *Trionyx* has made me step; I have

---

[34] William Stimpson (1832–72), naturalist, was born in Roxbury, Mass. He was interested at an early age in natural history, received encouragement from Agassiz, and for nine years he was associated with Baird in the Smithsonian Institution at classifying the immense amount of material collected while serving as a naturalist to the North Pacific Exploring Expedition. Later he was called to the directorship of the Chicago Academy of Sciences in 1865. He assembled and borrowed much valuable scientific material which was all lost in the great fire of October 1871. From this blow he never recovered and died within eight months of this tragic event.

obtained some of the *ferox* from Georgia, but I have not yet had a chance of comparing them with the Texas one, as they only arrived today. At first sight they seem to differ both from *Tr. spinifer* and from the Texan. These three however agree in having a keel, whilst *muticus* is flat on the back. If you could spare me another somewhat larger specimen from Texas I would like to make a skeleton of it. One of my specimens from Georgia is rather large, and will be very useful to ascertain one stage more in the process of ossification, than I have yet traced.

If you have the following books in the Smith. library I would like to have them for a short time:

Fitzinger New Classif. of Rept.
Fitzinger Systema Reptil.
Bell's Testudinata
Gray Synopsis Rept.

Also Holbrook N. A. Erpetology first edit (The Chelonians only) and any other new work containing descriptions of genera of Chelonians.

There is much room for improvement in the characteristics of the genera of this order even limiting one's [one, in letter] self to the N. Amer. species. Will you be able to let me have the foreign ones I have asked for?

Yours very truly,
L. AGASSIZ

BAIRD to AGASSIZ

Nov. 30, 1855

Dear Professor,

I am very glad to learn that what I sent proved of interest. You may rely on my not relaxing any effort on your behalf. The *E. concentrica* and *E. rubriventris* will come soon. I have engaged a lot from a dealer here. I wish I could get you *concinna* but we have it not. We have no more Texas *Trionyx* but may get some this winter at your service. I have somewhere a skeleton of one with shell a foot long, and will send it if I can find it. It came from Western Pennsylvania.

I am glad to be able to send you some European turtles. They are:

2 *Emys lectaria* Dalmaria
1   "   *Siegrizia* Spanish

I also send some small *Chelonuria serpentina* of several sizes within what you want. The Holbrook 1st ed. I can send you: Bell we have not got: I don't remember about Fitzinger but will look when I go over. I will make a general examination for new ones on genera as you request. My own notes may throw some light.

We have not a single specimen of the side neck band of turtles from

South America. As to *Testudo* from Para we have only one from that region. Perhaps Wheatland at Salem can help you. He often gets foreign turtles.

Ever yours,

S. F. BAIRD

I enclose some extracts from Max. Reise including all his turtilians.

BAIRD to AGASSIZ

Dec. 21, 1855

Dear Professor,

I send by express today a package containing Holbrook's 1st edition. Please return as soon as convenient as I shall have occasion to refer to it.

Also I send one box containing the largest *Emys rubriventris* I have seen. Let me know if with the other specimens sent, your series of the *rubriventris* and terrapin is complete. [Illegible.]

Did you get those European turtles I sent you.

What is the name of that turtle found in Mississippi as also in Missouri with the wide elongate red patch on the side of the head?

What did you find in the extract from Maximilian?

Yours truly,

S. F. BAIRD

P.S. I enclose a head of a turtle whose name I want without the trouble of hunting it out. Please send me the name as soon as possible.

I enclose pouch for Wyman.

Please give it to him.

AGASSIZ to BAIRD

CAMBRIDGE, *Dec. 28, 1855*

My dear sir,

I have just received, this afternoon, the parcels of books and the box with the splendid *rubriventris,* for all of which I return my best thanks. The specimens for Wyman I have at once sent to his laboratory. I had also received a fortnight ago the european species and the young *Chelonura* which were exactly the things I wanted. Please express also to Prof. Henry my best thanks for allowing me this supply of living turtles without which many important points in my monograph would have been left unsettled. The 1st edit. of Holbrook[35] has already served a good purpose. From the

---

[35] Dr. J. E. Holbrook (1794–1871), Charleston, S.C., was the author of "Herpetology of South Carolina" and an associate of Agassiz when he was a professor in the School of Medicine of the University of South Carolina.

memoranda from Pri New Wied I had satisfied myself that his *E. elegans* and Holbrook's *E. cumberlandensis* are identical. I now find that *E. cumberlandensis* does not appear in the 1st edit. of Holb., but for the first time in the 2nd of 1842; whilst N. Wied's work is of 1839. The name *Em. elegans* having the priority must therefore be preserved, and so much as I love Dr. Holbrook I am glad of it; as Pr. N. Wied has done so much for the Nat. Hist of this continent, it is gratifying to restore anything to him. I have just received a letter from him and shall inform him of this when I answer.

Not to forget anything you ask I will proceed to answer your letter summarily point by point. You shall have Holbrook back in a fortnight. However numerous the supply of specimens you have sent me may have been, I have unfortunately not yet done with them. I have made so many skeletons that the other points I want to investigate remain pretty unsettled, especially one point which has come up since your last invoice. Have we only one species of Terrapin as Holbrook and LeConte maintain or two as Dekay would have it. The characters given by Dekay are of no value. I therefore would not warrant the distinction and yet I begin to believe he has figured two species. On comparing a dozen skeletons, osteological differences were noticed which cannot be ascribed to the changes produced by age. Among the differences the most prominent consists in the large blunt head of the one and the small pointed head of the other. Dekay's figures give the difference of the head well. Holbrook's fig. is of the large headed kind. Now going back to the specimens cut up, I find 5 pointed headed which upon direction prove to be all females. Should we then have among Chelonia anything like the differences observed between the cow and the bull? I thought at first this would solve the difficulty, but all other species show no such difference, moreover the only one large headed left is also a female. Here then is a new puzzle which a select new supply of this species can alone solve. Please therefore look over large lots in the market to ascertain whether the large and small headed are equally common & next send me a good supply of both, selecting thin females and flat bellied males, large and small of each kind. What makes me suppose these two will turn out to be distinct species is the fact that two specimens I have brought home from Mobile, agree with neither and will probably constitute a 3rd species. Have you any from the gulf states, or from Georgia? I should like to see more of the southern form which has the narrow marginal plates entirely turned up, making a deep furrow along the edge. About *rubriventris* I would wish a few more of the medium and smaller sized ones.

The eggs of *E. geographica* are very acceptable, as I had only a few broken ones from J. Thompson. They are further interesting as extending the range of that species to Detroit. I did not know it so far north, though I have it further west. This suggests another request. My revision of our Chelonians is so complete that I have gone into their geogr. distribution thoroughly, which is the more necessary as Dumeril and Bibron contain very grave errors on this point. Would you furnish me with all the data you have upon this topic? I shall of course give you due credit for every single statement, as I have already done for all the trustworthy indications I have collected thus far. I wish for the precise localities as far as possible. For instance your last but one invoice contains a precious fact in this respect, — a young *Chelonura serpentina* from upper Louisiana. I did not know that species so far south in the west, though I have it from the Osage. Do you know the river in Louisiana in which it occurs? This is important with reference to the distribution of *Ch. temminckii*. I know no place where they occur together; but this fact would bring them very near.

I am sorry I did not know before that you had neither *floridana* nor *mobilensis*, otherwise I would have kept some for you, but I made 3 skeletons of my largest *mobilensis*, and have only young ones left, of which you shall have your share; of *floridana* I have only one female left in alcohol, and that had been opened. *Troostii, cumberlandensis* and *serrata* you shall have in good condition. The latter I have now in numerous living specimens. Do you want it alive? The head you sent is *E. elegans* v. *cumberlandensis*. Of the only new species I have got from California, I have only 2 specimens, one in alcohol, the other made into a skeleton.

Yours very truly,
L. AGASSIZ

P.S. I just remember that the very young *Emys* from Texas you sent me some time ago differs entirely from all the other *Emys* I have seen. It may be *ornata*. Have you any grown specimens you could spare or lend for comparison?

LA

BAIRD to AGASSIZ

Jan. 4, 1856

Dear Professor,

I send by express today *in alcohol:*

2 *Emys* from the Missouri river in western Missouri, one large, other small, near *elegans.*

1 *Emys serrata?* Washington Miss.

1 *Emys elegans*   "   "

1 *Emys rubriventris?* Beasleys Pt. N.J.

Alive

1 *Emys rubriventris* smaller than heretofore sent. Wash.

3 *Emys concentrica*   "

I want all the alcoholic specimens above mentioned returned, as they are all we have of the kinds. Please let me know what you think of them. Note the blunt almost malformed snout of the smaller specimen from Missouri. I have frequently seen this in [illegible].

The points on the *Emys concentrica* mentioned by you I have not been able to follow yet, as the one I took is very small as preserved. I wish you would send me an outline of the features in the head and shell which you think distinctive, and I can better look after the outline: it may be necessary to send copies of the diagram to several points where they bring in terrapins more abundantly.

I have written to a dozen reliable persons on our Atlantic and Gulf coasts for live turtles in any number and am sure of getting something so look out before long.

I will give you the facts of geographical distribution with greatest pleasure. I will however, wait till I get your specimens kindly promised to help me in the determination. I have *Chelonura temminckii* from Pensacola. Also *Ch. serpentina* from Caleasicia, La. on the Gulf Coast west of N. Orleans.

If you cant send good specimens of any of the terrapins, let me have them in any condition, even a mere shell. I would like to complete our series.

I have found a skeleton of *Trionyx* from Miss. with the bony carapace about 7 inches across. Would you like to see it or have you one of your own?

Yours truly,

S. F. BAIRD

AGASSIZ to BAIRD

Jan. 4, 1856

Dear sir,

I return these volumes with many thanks.

Have you not Fitzinger N. Class of Rept.

    Fitzinger Syst. Rept.

    Bell's Testudinata

    Gray's Synopsis Rept.

Yours truly in great haste,

L. AGASSIZ

Have you any of the new Kinosternon's described by Maj. LeConte which you could spare or lend me?

LA

AGASSIZ to BAIRD

Jan. 13, 1856

My dear Baird,

Your note of Jan. 4th announcing an invoice of specimens has been for more than a week before me, but the specimens have not yet arrived, and as I am anxious to have them they may have been delayed by the snow storms I write a line to inform you of the case. Please see what may have stopped them. I shall send you the *Emys* you want with those you expect back from this last lot. I now enclose the outlines of *Emys concentrica* pointed and blunt nosed variety. When you have all please do not forget the geograph. distribution.

I feel truly obliged for your renewed efforts to get specimens. But they are truly needed. In the investigation they melt away like nothing. I have now 14 or 15 skeletons of the *C. clausa* type to make more of the value of the western 3 toed, the large southern forms etc. By the way did you ever see a 4-toed *Cistudo* from the west? and South W.? If you have *Chelon. temminckii* from Pensacola, I have him from Mobile. This establishes its range along the Gulf states and their rivers. Please forget no locality when you make out the geog. distr. for me.

You forgot to answer the following two questions: Have you adults of the Texas *Emys* to match and identify the young you sent me before. And have you *Kinosternum guttatum* of LeConte which he says he got from you? I am now well satisfied with nearly all true Emyda, though there are a few points which will be made more plain with a larger number of younger and youngest specimens, for it is most remarkable how almost every species has its peculiar mode of varying with age; but the type of *Kinosternum* looks still dark, I have exhausted all my specimens and do not come to any conclusions. What indeed a labyrinth when men like Temminck & Schlegel say we have a single *Kinosternon* in N. Amer. They not even considering *pennsylvanicum* and *odoratum* as specifically distinct, and LeConte has 4 within the boundaries of U. St. and several others besides! Can you now do for me with *Staurotypus* and *Kinosternum* as you have done lately with Emyda? Send at least all you can, and what you can not spare I will faithfully return. If good luck would make it possible let me say that I need very much a living snapping turtle, to compare its brain, with that of the young lately hatched I am now examining. Could the fishermen who bring Terrapins to market not also furnish one or two snappers? If younger in Aug. send them at once. To lose no time I write a few hints about the limits of our species that you may begin looking up their localities.

Have you all our Chelonii proper? I can spare some.

We have 1. *Sphergis coriacea*. It is beyond question identical with the european. *Chelys atlantica* LeSueur has no right of existence.

2. *Thalanochelys Caouana* (*Chelonia caretta* or *cephalo* auct.). Could you procure a european specimen. I have doubts left as to their difference from ours. Indeed thus far I lean towards considering the european and american as different, but want the means of a more direct comparison.

3. *Caretta imbricata*. Have you by chance a specimen from the East Indies?

4. *Chelonia Mydas*. " " " " " " for comparison?

The above genera are well characterized by anatomical characters and must be admitted.

5. *Chelydra serpentina* There can be no doubt about this species. Only the generic name *Chelydra* being older than *Chelonura* or *Emysaurus* must be restored.

6. *Gypochelys temminckii* Ag. (*Chelonura* Temm. Holbr.). Have a skeleton made and you will see how good a genus this is. I have never seen young ones, nor eggs.

7. *Terrapene odorata* (*Sternothorus* and *Staurotypus,* also *Kinosternum odor*) It belongs neither to the *Sternothorus* which is a *Pleurodère,* nor to *Staurotypus,* which has a sternum of entirely different structure, nor to *Kinosternum* for the same reason. I have another species from Alabama, but only two specimens, and wish therefore a better chance of comparison if you have many more from any locality. The western and southwestern limits of the two will require particular attention. Have you none from California? And what? (Gray has described but one). If the name *Terrapene* Merr. can be retained, it must be for this genus.

8. *Kinosternum pennsylvanicum*. Its western and southern range is also very important. From this genus I have a second species from Alabama which requires also further examination as to its range. If you have any specimens of the types of S. America I would like them also for comparison. *K. surpoides, longicaudatum & brevicaudatum* (By the way the length of tail indicates sexual differences. In the females it is always short, so also in *Trionyx!*)

In *Emys* I have made the most extensive changes as you will soon perceive.

9. Genus *Ptychemys* Agass. characterized by the serrated edges of the jaws and the pointedly tuberculated sheath covering inside of the mouth the alveolar margin of the jaws.

9. [sic] *Ptych. floridana*. (*Test. floridana* LeC.)

10. *Ptych. mobiliensis* (*Emys mobiliensis* Holbr.)

11. *Ptych. rugosa* (*Emys rugosa* Gr. Dum. & Bibr, *E. rubriventris* LeC & Auct., *E. serrata* B. Merr. *E. serrata* Say, Harl. Gr., *E. irrigata* Bell, Dum & Bibr, *E. rivulata* Gr.)

All these 5 species, three of which Dum and Bibr. still admit side by side or rather far apart in their work and in the new Catal. méth., while Gray admits three also in another combination of synonymy, are certainly identical. I had satisfied myself about the first 4 names. Your last lot has brought in *E. rivulata* in addition.

12. *T. concinna*. I have some misgivings about the generic affinities of this species, as I have only half grown specimens.
N.B. The young from Texas seems to be another species of this genus, perhaps *E. ornata* Auct. but without adults it must remain doubtful.*
*If you know anybody in N. Orleans who could collect the turtles in the market the Texas species could be obtained there, as I saw them the last day I was there, when I had not a way to take them home. Remember this and try to obtain them. *Trachemys* Agass. Differs from the preceding by the structure of the sheath of the jaws.

13. *Tr. scabra* (The true *scabra* of Linnaeus! which he described from specimens from S. Carolina, *E. serrata* Auct., *E. scripta* Gray) NB. There was a specimen of this in your first lot of alcoholic specimens of *rubriventris* said to be from Wash. Yet I have never seen this species North of Carolina before. Look out for it! *Emys decussata* Gray is described from a half grown & *E. vittata* Gray from a young specimen of the same!!

14. *Tr. Troostii* (Is the *Emys serrata* of Temm & Schleg. from Tennessee. It occurs only W. I have it from the Osage through Stolley)

15. *Tr. elegans* (*Em. elegans* N. Wied. *E. cumberlandensis* Holbr., *E. Holbrookii* Gr.)

Graptemys. Very broad flat mouth, sheath upon the jaws, covering the whole palate and inner surface of lower jaw.

16. *Gr. geographica* (The true *geographica* is the large headed species, with wedge shaped spot behind the eye. *E. megacephala* Holbr. 1st edit. *E. macrocephala* Gr. *E. reticularia* Temm & Schl. Have you ever seen it in Tennessee? Dr. Holbr. mentions it from that State on the authority of Halde. I have only seen western specimens!

17. *Gr. pseudogeographica* (The small headed geogr; without large spot behind the eye. *Emys geographica* Say; Temm & Schl; Griff. An. Kingd., *E. pseudogeogr.* Auct., *Emys Lesueurii* Gr., *Emys Bennettii* Gr., *E. labyrinthica* Dum & Bibr)

I have some doubts about this species. There may be two confused here, as I find some specimens with a very ornamented sternum, and other only ornamented upon the symphysis of sternum & shield. But I have not a sufficient series to separate them, or to be sure of their identity. Is there any body west from whom you could have plenty. I have two from Iowa, and three from Ohio and Indiana, and that perplexes me more, those of the same locality agreeing while they differ from the others.

18. *Gr. hieroglyphica.* A larger number of *pseudogeogr.* may modify the synonymy of this species, to which some of the above may belong. Genuine genus *Emys,* the type of which is *Emys europea* or *lutatria,* to this?

19. *Emys meleagris (Cistudo Blandingii).* I have looked up Shaw's description. LeConte is right about it.

The Genus *Cistudo* must be retained for *C. carolina* which by its internal structure is generically more remote from *Blandingii* than any other of our Emyds, notwithstanding the moveable sternum. The same *Emys* deserving to be preserved and having been applied by Canino and Wagler to the European type, the generic name of *Lutremys* Gr. becomes superfluous.

Deirochelys Agass. Sheath of Jaws very narrow and smooth. Though the sternum is immoveable, this genus is closely allied to the true *Emys.*

20. *D. reticulata. (E. reticulata* Auct.) It is the species of which you sent me a rather small specimen from Pensacola.

Malaclemys Gr. Very good genus. Comes nearer to *Deirochelys* & *Emys* than to any other genus.

21. *M. palustris.* Notwithstanding what I have stated about the differences in the head I can not yet make up my mind that we have more than one species of this genus. If they differ among themselves then we have at least three species; for you will find that the specimens from the Gulf States are smaller, and have a much thicker margin, with entirely turned up edges.

Chrysemys Gr. Equally good genus. This and the following three genera *Clemmys Melanemys* & *Glyptemys* have only semi palmate toes whilst in the preceding the web extends to the claws.

22. *Chr. picta (Emys picta* Auct.). How far west do you know it? I never saw it about St. Louis. Neu Wied quotes it in the Wabash! Have you it South W. Duméril quotes N. Orleans (Marcou); but Marcou never visited La.

23. *Chr. Belli (E. Bellii* Gr. & *E. oregoniensis* Harl & Holbr) I can find no difference between the *Bellii* I collected about St. Louis and which Pr. N. Wied saw high up the Mo. & *E. oregoniensis* of Harlan. I suspect therefore that Nuttall[36] did not collect his specimen in Oregon, but on this side of the Rocky Mts. Could this be ascertained in Philadelphia?

---

[36] Thomas Nuttall (1786–1859), botanist and ornithologist, was born in Yorkshire, England. In 1808 he emigrated to America and soon Benjamin Barton got him interested in plants. He was a good collector, having been a naturalist on several expeditions. For 10 years he was curator of the Botanical Garden of Harvard University. He wrote one important book in ornithology entitled "A Manual of the Ornithology of the United States and Canada."

Clemmys Ritgen & Wagler. (sensu strictione)

24. *Cl. guttata* (*E. guttata* Auct.) About this nothing is needed except the precise range of distribution W. and south.

Melanemys Agass. Differs from the preceding by the pholidons of the neck and the hooked lower jaw.

25. *M. Muhlenbergii.* (*E. Muhl.* Auct.) You would greatly oblige me to give me another specimen or two. I have dissected the three you sent before and have none left for my collection.

Glyptemys Agass. Pholidons, and sheath of jaws characterize this genus.

26. *Glypt. insculpta* (*E. insculpta* LeC., *E. pulchella* Dum. & Bibr. not Schweig. nor Schoepff, *E. scabra* Say, *E. speciosa* Gr., *E. Muhlenbergii* Temm. and Sch.). Holbr. is right in opposing the admission of the name *pulchella* for this species as the specimens of the [illegible] plenty were sent there after the date of Schweigger publication.

27. *Glypt. californica.* This is a new species unless it be identical with Hall. *E. nigra* which I have not yet had an opportunity of comparing directly. Have you no *Emys* from California?

Cistudo Temm. After a comparison of 14 or 15 skeletons I come to the conclusion that Gray's genus *Onychotria* for the three toed *Cistudo's,* is not admissible. Rudiments of 5 toes exist in the skeleton of the three toed as well as the fourtoed and the structure differs in no way. I can not even make up my mind to consider them as specifically distinct; I would not hesitate to unite them all if 4 toed varieties occurred also in the W. & S.W. which I have not yet seen.

28. *Cistudo virginea* (The name *virginea* is older than either *carolina* or *elaura.* It occurs already in Grew's Mus. of the Roy. Soc. of London) The *Testudo tabulata* from Para which you sent me has not only shown me that our *T. polyphemus* differs from that species contrary to the opinion of Temm. & Sch. but that they do not agree generically. The same is true of the Gallopago's turtle. This splits *Testudo* as far as I can study the species into 4 genera. I have not yet made up my mind what names to give them. For our *Polyphemus* I would propose the name *Cholochir* Ag. on account of the peculiar structure of the anterior feet without flat sole so entirely different from the posterior.

29. *Ch. carolinus.* (*T. polyphemus.* The name *carolinus* as Le Conte has shown has the priority. It was applied to this species before it was transferred to *Cistudo*) For Gallopago Turtle which is now grown in California, though not indigenous there, the name *Chersine* Merr. may be retained as *Ch. retusa Merr.* his first species, applies to it.

30. *Ch. indica.* (The name *indica* has the priority over 10 others nuder which it has been described!!) It differs generically by the structure of its feet, the ant. port. of which have the same broad flat sole. I have kept *Trionyx* for the last because I have some misgivings both about

the nomenclature and the species. At all events ours can not retain the name *Trionyx* as Wagler when subdividing that genus retained the name *Trionyx* for those species to which Dum & Bibr. applied afterwards the name *Cryptopus* and Gray that of *Emyda,* both of which being later must be given up. The genus *Aspidonectes* Wagl. corresponds exactly to *Gymnopus* Dum & Bibr. and having the priority must also be retained; but there come now Fitz. and Gray both of whom subdivide *Gymnopus* or *Aspidonectes* into several genera the validity of which I can only test from descriptions and not from specimens. If good or even partly so and ours can be separated from those of the old world the name *Platypeltis* Fitz. will devolve upon them but it remains even doubtful whether *T. ferox* and *muticus* are generically identical (You would be surprised at the difference of their skull). We would then have:

Amyda for *Tr. muticus* &

Platypeltis for *spinifer, ferox* etc. — Would it be possible for you to se-cure some eastern *Trionyx* for comparison. Have you none from the Nile from Mr. Marsh?[37] About the species of this last group the following re-marks are suggested. I find constant differences in the coloration of the north western specimens and those of Georgia. The latter are entirely white under the neck and the inner & lower surface of feet, whilst the northern are mottled upon these parts. Now a comparison of specimens from the middle and lower course of the Mississippi would settle the question of the specific difference or identity; for differences there are unquestionably be-tween the specimens of these two fields of distribution, and if they do not run into one another at their junction, they will prove specific dif-ferences. I have unfortunately no specimens either from Alabama or La. Those from Texas you sent me differ again from those of Ga. in the total absence of ornamental coloration upon their back which is entirely mono-chrom; so we have either three *Platypeltis:*

Pl. spinifer of the N.W.

Pl. ferox of the S.E. Of this I would like the skeleton you speak of.

Pl. texanus of the S.W. or only one *Pl. ferox* if they run together.

This, including the two new species of *Terrapene* & *Cinosternum* would make either 34 or 36 american Testudinata and if *Kin. sonoriense* and *guttatum* LeC. differ from mine again 36 or 38 species. I have this day written to LeConte to let me have a sight at the original specimens of his descriptions.

---

[37] George Perkins Marsh (1801–82), lawyer and diplomat, was born in Woodstock, Vt. He was a graduate of Dartmouth College, elected to two terms in the House of Representatives and appointed in 1847 a Regent of the Smithsonian Institution. One of his major contributions to the Smithsonian was perhaps his influence in having Baird appointed as its Assistant Secretary. While serving at diplomatic posts in Turkey, Greece, and Italy he corresponded with Baird and made extensive collections for the Smithsonian.

If you were publishing the Bulletin you intended what a fine chance the publication of these notes would afford to obtain information from every part of the country. Has that plan been entirely given up? Such a publication would greatly lessen the burden of your correspondence. This sketch will best show you where and how far you can help me still. There are still many of the western and southern species of which I have neither the eggs nor the young!! And without these the generic characters remain incomplete, as the peculiar mode of development of each type constitutes a very striking feature of the genera, as I have already ascertained for our northern types and for *Ptychemys* & *Trachemys* among the southern regions. When you get young of the *rubriventris* it will furnish I trust a very satisfactory confirmation of this statement if it agrees, with *mobiliensis,* which I know in all its stages, as well as *serrata!*

When I last wrote to Prof. Henry I forgot to make a proposition to him which I trust you will approve and second. You know how long Stolley has been collecting in the West for me and he has furnished me with highly valuable specimens. He is now in Texas and as I can no longer support him I sent him lately one hundred dollars to await further directions & to prepare for coming north, unless I could arrange something for him. He now writes that if he could receive three hundred more dollars and then sell out in the end the apparatus with which I furnished him, wagon, donkey, guns, nets etc. he could remain another year. Now I offer you to share in equal parts the products of this years collection, if you will give the three hundred dollars, I furnishing as my share all the equipment. and the means of returning north. I do not think that any thing like what we may get from him could be obtained otherwise for half the money. If you agree I will direct him to forward everything to Washington. You and he making the division when he returns. Is that not a fair offer? If you cannot I must write to him to sell out now and to return as soon as possible.

Truly yours,

L. AGASSIZ

The study of our Testudinata has satisfied me that it is impossible to characterize the genera of this order from dried specimens, not any more than Rodentia without looking at their teeth, and that species cannot be defined properly without comparing extensive series of specimens of all ages; color very seldom affords specific characters, not even the pattern of coloration always.

So I close for today

Wishing you a happy new year

Yours truly,

L. AGASSIZ

AGASSIZ to BAIRD

CAMBRIDGE, *Jan. 19, 1856*

My dear Baird,

I do not know how I managed to leave out the drawings of *Emys concentrica* I meant to enclose in my last letter. Here they are. In my hurry to add names to my new genera I also overlooked the fact that Gray has already appropriated the name of *Chersine* for another genus of Testudinata, so change mine in the notice I sent you into *Deinochersus*. [Ed. Note: Baird had crossed it out in last letter.]

I send by this day's express the following turtles to you:

3 specimens *Emys serrata*. It is the bulkiest roundest and largest from Charleston, S.C.

1 spec. *E. Troostii*. Large flat, blackish from Osage Mo.

1 spec. *E. elegans*. Identical with yours from Wash. Miss. — from Osage Mo.

1 spec. *E. Bellii*. Very like *E. picta*. — from Osage Mo.

1 young *E. mobiliensis*, wrapt up in a piece of cloth. — from Mobile Ala.

The others you may want I will send after my drawings are completed, as I have rather exhausted my supply.

I return also by the same opportunity:

1. Your *E. rubriventris* from Beesley's R. N. T. Unquestionably *E. rubr.*, also a new locality.

2. Your *E. elegans* from Washington Miss.

3. Your *E. serrata?* from Washington, Miss. Is *E. pseudogeographica!*

I keep for further examination the two specimens from Mo. which are unquestionably a very interesting new species, intermediate between *mobiliensis* & *floridana* and belonging like these to my genus *Ptychemys*. The four species differ in the following manner. *Pt. rubriventris:* equally strongly serrated in both jaws with double hook in the upper like this

lower jaw one prominent hook

Pt. mobiliensis Slightly serrated in upper jaw, with double hook

strongly in lower jaw with strong point; like this

Pt. floridana. Smooth upper jaw and slightly emarginate;

Slightly serrated in lower jaw with feeble hook.

Your new species has a marked sharp emargination in upper

jaw and lower jaw like *mobiliensis*

Give this a name that I may introduce it in my enumeration, but select a good one. I will take care of the description. If you have any more doubtful species send them on please, as soon as possible. You can easily do it while you go over the localities with my list. At the same time give me a list of your desiderata. All you send me which I have not already I will of course leave to you to name. Look my last letter carefully over that you do not forget anything. Can you tell me what are all the doubtful species of Col. Wailes in his report? Even those he names seem to me questionable. Is his *picta* not *Bellii,* his *serrata geogr.* or *pseudog.* his *terrapin* perhaps *elegans?* What of his other species? If you have any doubt about any of them, let me see them if you have them.

Truly yours,

L. Agassiz

We have sustained a very severe loss this week. Dr. Harris is no more. LeConte writes to me that Hallowell's *E. nigra* is in Washington; that it was in one of the collections from a pacific expedition. Can I get a sight of it, to make sure that mine differs or not?

LA

As I must go to press next month, you would greatly oblige me to do your best to let me have all this and my former letter alludes to as soon as possible. There will be time yet in early spring for eggs & young; as I begin with the revision of our species; and the numerous specimens you promise from the South & S.W. will give me the waiting information about the number of eggs they lay, for the embryology will next follow. I am still deficient in eggs and young of the species living West, in Tennessee, Ky., Ohio & Mo. I have some from Iowa from Dr. Rauch, among others, *pseudogeographica.*

I must close not to lose the mail.

Yours, LAg

AGASSIZ to BAIRD

CAMBRIDGE, *Jan. 22, 1856*

My dear Baird,

To increase the probability of getting in due time for my volume the young and eggs of those species I have not yet got, I subjoin the list of them.

Sphergis uriacea neither young nor eggs

Chelonia mydas " " " "

Chelonia imbricata " " " "

Trionyx muticus young but no eggs

Trionyx ferox neither young nor eggs (I mean the southern not spinifer)

Chelonura Temminckii " " " "

Testudo polyphemus eggs, but no young.

Emys Muhlenbergii neither young nor eggs. Can you not obtain this from Pennsylv.?

Emys rubriventris " " " "

Emys floridana eggs but no young.

Emys Bellii neither eggs nor young

Emys hieroglyphica " " " "

Emys elegans " " " "

Emys Troostii " " " "

Emys pseudogeographica eggs but no young.

Emys concentrica young but no eggs. I trust the eggs of this will be found

Emys concinna " " " " somewhere in the spring

Emys serrata " " " "

Emys insculpta eggs " " young, I have raised hundreds of eggs of this and unfortunately have not allowed one to be hatched.

The most important of these as you see could be obtained from Tennessee and along the Mississippi and Georgia. For the marine I have written to Key West.

Under young I mean here specimens just hatched; of many I have already younger specimens, sometimes half grown, sometimes even small; but I want all if possible in their embryonic form. As I have often only one of those in my possession, I mean not to say that I do not want more of them for skeleton etc. — x

Truly yours,

L. AGASSIZ

x There are indeed few species of which I have had a sufficient number of young to complete in every respect my series of skeletons and anatomical preparations, which I should like to make more perfect than anything of the kind ever done.

BAIRD to AGASSIZ

Jan. 26, 1856

My dear Professor,

You will not attribute my long delay in answering your letters to any but the true cause — want of time. I have been so busy for two weeks past that I hardly know where I stood at the end of each day. I have read and re-read the very interesting accounts of the species in your letters and turned to the collections over and over again but each time have been forced to abandon the effort. I have, however, at length found time to do something and send you a series of specimens and the list is enclosed.

In order to meet your wishes, I have sent you the whole of our Sternothaeroids complete, and trust that they may furnish a clue to the difficulties involved in your labor in determining the species. I became bewildered at finding *Sternothaeri* with *Kinosternum sterna* and vice versa. I attempted to separate by putting those with stripes on the sides of the head together and those with the head only spotted, but then in each I found species with keeled carapaces, narrow and broad sterna and had to give it up on that ground.

Please note particularly the two specimens from Tarboro.

You are right in supposing Wailes *E. serrata* to be what I sent you under that name. I had never seen the true *E. serrata* and only took the name marked by him by way of defining the species. But are you sure that this is the *pseudogeographica?* It looks so high and broad behind. Please compare No. 19. I already sent you a rather smaller one from same lot of Wailes. *Emys terrapin* is *E. elegans.* What is no. 21? Please let me know what you consider the characteristics of *Emys belli* compared with *E. picta.* I can then better look for it.

The drawings of pointed and blunt nosed terrapins have given me the idea about the species and I will make diligent examination for them. At present the markets are very poorly supplied, owing to the severe weather. We have scarcely had a thaw for four weeks: and good sleighing equal to Cambridge all the time.

In reference to *C. clausa* I send a 4-toed specimen from Missouri, St. Louis, the only one among a lot of three toed. All the Miss. specimens are 3-toed. The Miss. specimens (No. 22) you can keep.

I send our single specimen of small *Chelonura temminckii* for you to look at. It is very curious.

Kinosternon gallatus I dont have. The major took the largest of our specimens a year ago but returned them in considerable derangement, keeping a few. I do not know to which he refers — perhaps to the Upper Darby specimens.

I am sorry not to find any snappers alive. I have a large one buried under the ice of a large tank, of course, dead. When I can get it out you shall have it as well as any live ones from the market. Should the weather moderate, we ought to have plenty in market.

As to the Marine Chelonians we have absolutely none except a skull of *Chelonia mydas* from Florida. I wish I could have some from the old world for you. Neither have we any South American. Am promised shortly a couple of living "Mud Turtles" from Panama and look for them daily. You shall have them at once. I dont know what they are. I shall write to a friend at Panama to send me a large lot alive; may be I shall get them, but am not certain. I have written to N. Orleans with special reference to the Texan specimens.

How can I tell *Emys scabra* so as to look it up among specimens of *E. rubriventris?* By the way, is there any size (except smallest) which you still lack of this species?

The true *Emys geographica* is abundant on the Susquehanna and Juniata Rivers of Penna. I used to get it at Carlisle. It attains a large size (shell a foot long) and is abundant but excessively shy and hard to get. I used to secure it by creeping up within ten or twelve yards and shooting the head to pieces with a ball. It is delicious eating. Like a fool, I failed to get specimens there, and have only one young. I will try, however, to get some in the spring from there.

I doubt if Nuttall's specimen of *Emys oregonensis* is extant in this country. I never saw or heard of it. Harlan was just as likely to have given it to the Zoological Soc. of London.

Emys guttata I never saw from south of Washington.

I send you three more specimens of *Emys muhlenbergii.* In the spring I will try and get plenty alive.

Hallowell's *Emys nigra* I send you. It is different from your *G. california* I suspect. I send specimens which I suppose to be this last mentioned.

I am much obliged for the turtles you sent — which were very acceptable. I will give you a list of additions and deficiencies, in fact, I would be glad to have a full series of all your species to save as types of your article; those supplied you from our main collection will answer as far as they go when returned with names. The series shall be kept intact and complete as your types.

As to the two specimens from Missouri — you are very welcome to name and describe as you think best. If not exceptional in any way, I might suggest the name of Hoy as that of their collector, and an energetic and excellent naturalist. Use your pleasure, however, in this. The same with the other specimens belonging to the Institution which you will name in your own name, not mine. Do you propose to figure any sent you?

I believe I wrote you that we did not have the Bell's Testudinata about which you wrote. The Acad. of Nat. Sciences has it. I was under the impression that it was in the Harvard Library.

The last list (Jan. 22) will help me much in concentrating effort in your behalf. I shall do my best: with what result remains to be seen. I have never made a special effort in behalf of the turtles, not having felt the want of specimens, which for your sake I now do. Can I meet the same success as I did with Mammals last year? Even you would be satisfied: (We received 2500 mammals, either dry skins or in alcohol). So please believe that I am preparing for a grand campaign.

Professor Henry regrets very much that he cannot afford to join you in keeping Stolley in Texas for another year. We already have some small explorations in the field, not to mention that of Mr. Samuels in California. Perhaps the Academy of Natural Sciences would join.

By the way, have you any specimens of Hares from Texas, as the *Lepus bachmani, callotus, texensis* or any kind? Have you the *Zeomys pineti* or "Salamandor" pouched rats of Florida, skins or skulls?

Very truly and sincerely yours,

S.F.BAIRD

P.S. What Mammals, skins or skulls, have you received since I saw you? (or unpacked).

EXTRACT OF A LETTER FROM
S. F. BAIRD TO LOUIS AGASSIZ

Jan. (28?), 1856

I have been in a dilemma as to how I could let you examine the specimens of turtles brought home by the government expeditions without incurring official risk from their commanders. All the specimens belonging legitimately to the Institution are, as you well know, freely at your service. But there is such a precision and technicality in relation to the government collections, that we have to be very careful in our movements.

The following arrangement, if you agree to it, may make the matter perfectly practicable. It is: — for you to consent to prepare a report on these collections, to appear in your own name, of course, as the Chelonians, by Prof. L. Agassiz. This to consist of a description in full of all the species, with specific characters, synonymy, etc.

2. A list of the species, with characteristics of the new ones, to be published in the Proceedings of the Philadelphia Academy, in the same official way as I have published these, to be reproduced with a full description in the reports of the expeditions.

Having thus first published the species under official sanction and with especial reference to the government authorities, there will be no impropriety in your reproducing these same published remarks in your work. There would however be a difficulty in your doing (at first) more than this, as the officers would insist that the detailed descriptions shall appear in their reports first, which unfortunately are not likely to see the light for at least a year.

Of these expeditions there are seven or eight entirely different ones. It would be much trouble for you to prepare as many different reports; the best plan will be to make out a single one for all, putting each species with its specific characters on separate sheets. Send this to me, and I will make the assorting by expeditions and arrange the articles for publication in the proceedings of Acad. Nat. Sciences under your name.

It would be well also to present the new species of the Smithsonian collection in the same way, giving the specific characters in the Proceedings of the Acad. You will of course give these with any amount of additional detail in your book.

There is one objection to this arrangement, that these government collections will necessarily be sent out of the city. Still I presume you will not want them a great while, and could probably have them back here in a month or two; could you not?

In arranging some specimens, I have found a skeleton of *Trionyx* from Allegheny river, Pa. and one from Miss. which when alive were about a foot long in the shell. Would you like to see these?

Let me know at once what you think of the plan above proposed. There are many new and curious things in it; *Testudo* from the Rio Grande, but very puzzling; others from the Gila, Arkansas, etc., etc. *Emys* of Rio Grande, Brazos, California, and other things too numerous to mention.

Very truly and sincerely yours,

S. F. BAIRD

AGASSIZ to BAIRD

Jan. 31, 1856

My dear Baird,

Not to lose a moment I write in a hurry to say that I will gladly undertake to write out at once, within a month say, such descriptions of all the Chelonians of the different Government expeditions as will certainly satisfy those who made the collections; so send them at once. As to the publication of these descriptions I will agree to the necessities of the case cheerfully for the sake of the information I shall get; and introduce nothing more about them in my work than shall have been published before elsewhere. As I do not intend publishing figures of new species in my book it will rather suit me to have a chance of publishing them otherwise.

The collection your letter announces has not yet reached me.

Ever truly yours,

L. AGASSIZ

AGASSIZ to BAIRD

CAMBRIDGE, <i>Jan. 31, 1856</i>

My dear Baird,

I send a postscript to my hasty note of this morning to state, that it would be best, if you intrust to me the Chelonians of all the expeditions which have brought home any species of this order, to send all the species, whether known or new, that I may identify them beyond question, as I now easily can. I shall not mind the trouble and for the sake of getting a general review of their distribution over the whole continent I am ready to undertake any amount of labor for the reports of the gentlemen who collected them. Are there none from Oregon and Washington territory that the northern limits of the order on the western coast may be determined? None in the Salt Lake plains? Stansbury says nothing of them. How is it about the Colorado?

There is another point about which I forgot to ask you. How high up in the Alleghenies do any of the species go in Pennsylvania, Virginia and further South if you have any information. I can not find a single case of their presence in great altitude anywhere upon the whole surface of the globe.

I should like very much to have a sight at your two skeletons of *Trionyx.* I will gladly make your series of Chelonians as complete as mine. All my boxes etc. are now unpacking and arranging. I will let you know if anything interesting turns up of what you wish.

As soon as I am through with the Chelonians I shall take up the Naiades. I would be grateful if you will lay out your nets in time for alcoholic specimens from the South & West beyond the Ohio basin, which I have already very well represented, having brought together about 110 species in numerous alcoholic specimens. I want now chiefly those from Kentucky, Tennessee, and the Gulf and the Mississippi States. From the far West and the Pacific slope I have not yet any.

Emys Bellii differs from *E. picta* by having yellowish red marks upon the centre as well as along the margin of the scales, on the back and a large lyriform black drawing upon the sternum, like an ancient lyre. If you have got anything like *picta* from St. Louis, Mo. it must be *Bellii.* What is *picta* of Wailes? Is it not also *Bellii?*

Your question about *pseudogeographica* I will answer after I have received your last lot announced. You can never fail in distinguishing *scabra* and *rubriventris* by examining the sheath of the jaws, of which I gave you the outline for *rubriventris*. In *scabra* it is neither serrate, nor double hooked in the upper jaw.

My southern most specimens of *E. guttata* are from Baltimore and yet both Holbrook and LeConte say it extends to the southern atlantic states. It is worthwhile looking into this matter. I doubt its existence so far south. I shall write immediately to Holbrook about it.

As I have young *geographica* from the West a comparison with yours from the Susquehannah would at once settle their identity. I know *geographica* perfectly. I cannot understand how LeConte insists upon uniting with it *pseudogeographica* which is totally different. The question is more dffiicult between *labyrinthica, hieroglyphica* and *pseudogeographica*.

I will gladly dedicate your new *Ptychemys* to Dr. Hoy, for whom I have great regard, though I have not a personal acquaintance with him. His investigations seem to be made in the true spirit of an accurate observer.

Yours very truly,
L. Agassiz

AGASSIZ to BAIRD

Cambridge, *Febr. 2, 1856*

My dear Baird,

Upon reviewing all sorts of information to which I have access, I find not a single statement going to show that the Testudinata are found any where to any height above the level of the Sea. It is therefore a matter of considerable interest to ascertain how high any of them have been observed with regard to this general proposition. It does not matter much whether the species are identified or not, it would be a great step in this inquiry if you would ascertain from officers of the Mexican War whether they saw any about Mexico, or from the officers of the railroad parties whether they noticed any in the desert W. of the Mississippi upon the slope of the Rocky Mts. or between them and the Sierra Nevada. Ch. Pickering[38] says he saw none east of the Coast Range in the Pacific slope. None are mentioned anywhere from Tibet etc. It looks as if by nature they were excluded from regions not receiving the full pressure of an atmosphere, or nearly so. Pray help to make this out, beyond doubt. Every specimen

---

[38] Charles Pickering (1805–78), a naturalist, chief zoologist of the U.S. Exploring Expedition under Lt. Charles Wilkes, had made extensive contributions to the geographical distribution of plants and animals.

from western expeditions would in this respect be of the highest value from Santa Fe for instance etc.

Yours very truly,

L. AGASSIZ

Nothing could be more interesting than to obtain the species of Cuba to make sure of the species of Ramon De la Sagra, who has some as identical with ours, what I do not believe. By the way, have you that work? I have it not within my reach here.

BAIRD to AGASSIZ

Feb. 6, 1856

My dear professor,

I received your two notes a day or two ago respecting the expedition turtles and am glad to learn your willingness to undertake the work. As soon as I get a little time from an inordinate pressure of work, when I send I will write further on the subject. In the meantime let me know your views of the specimens sent a few days ago.

In response to your request in your letter of the 2nd ult., I have written to an intelligent friend in the Allegheny Mts. for information as to their turtles and their altitudes. I will also make the inquiries of explorers of the expeditions in the west and collect all the data I can.

As to West Indies and South American Turtles — I have set several traps for them. I have written most urgently to the correspondents at Panama, one at Aspinwall, and one at the city of Mexico. I will also write to Prof. Poey[39] at once. I have no doubt that a month or two will bring response from some of them. The "Mud Turtles" from Panama have not yet arrived, but are looked for daily. You shall have them at once.

I will with much pleasure work for you in this way of collecting Cinosternidae in alcohol. Some we already have at your service. I would rather wait a little while before beginning any stirring appeals until the previous application for turtles is responded to as I do not want one to neutralize the other.

As to new species there will be no difficulty in publishing any you may have in connection with one or the other of the government reports, even if somewhat out of the region, certainly for any west of the Mississippi.

If you will send the specimens here I will have them figured. Your California species occurs in several western collections and can readily be given.

Very truly yours,

S. F. BAIRD

---

[39] Felipe Poey (1799–1891), a Cuban naturalist, director of the museum at Havana, long a professor in the university, published important papers in ichthyology and entomology.

PLATE 5

Anderson School of Natural History.

CAMBRIDGE, MASS., June 26, 1873.

M.

I have at last decided to open the Anderson School of Natural History, on Penikese Island, at 12 o'clock, on the 8th of July next. The place is 14 miles distant from New Bedford, Mass., and the city is easily accessible by railroad from Boston or from Providence, R. I. Persons coming to join the school from a distance would do well to arrange their journey so that they may reach New Bedford Monday evening, the 7th of July. This place affords good accommodation at the Parker House, where information concerning the boat to the island may be had. A few miles to the east of New Bedford is a watering-place, Mattapoisett, where those reaching this vicinity a few days in advance may pass some time pleasantly.

It is necessary that all should remember that Penikese Island affords no accommodation for strangers, and that therefore nobody can be invited to visit the island during the session of the school. I have provided rooms and board for all, but made no allowance for supernumeraries. As it is, I am not yet able to say what the expenses will be. All the arrangements have been made upon the most economical plan. The dormitories have been built at the expense of the school, and no rent will be charged, beyond a percentage on the bedroom furniture. The board will be charged at cost. A caterer has been engaged who will provide for the table and keep the rooms in order, superintend the washing, etc., and the expense thus incurred will determine the charges.

It has already been stated that the instruction will be free. Aquariums have been provided which will take the place of books ; and cans and the other necessaries for the preservation of specimens will be ordered, and may be bought at cost. The preparation of these collections will not lead to any considerable expenditure, and is optional.

Very truly yours,

L. AGASSIZ.

P. S.—Should you be prevented from coming, give me early notice, as there are many waiting for a vacancy.

My dear Baird,

Whenever you come to Penikese you will find a warm welcome & tolerable accommodation. Peirce thinks that the School & your Department ought to share the advantages of the coast survey. What can I do to make the cooperation effective?

Very truly yours,

A. Agassiz

Circular distributed in 1873 by Agassiz concerning the Anderson School of Natural History

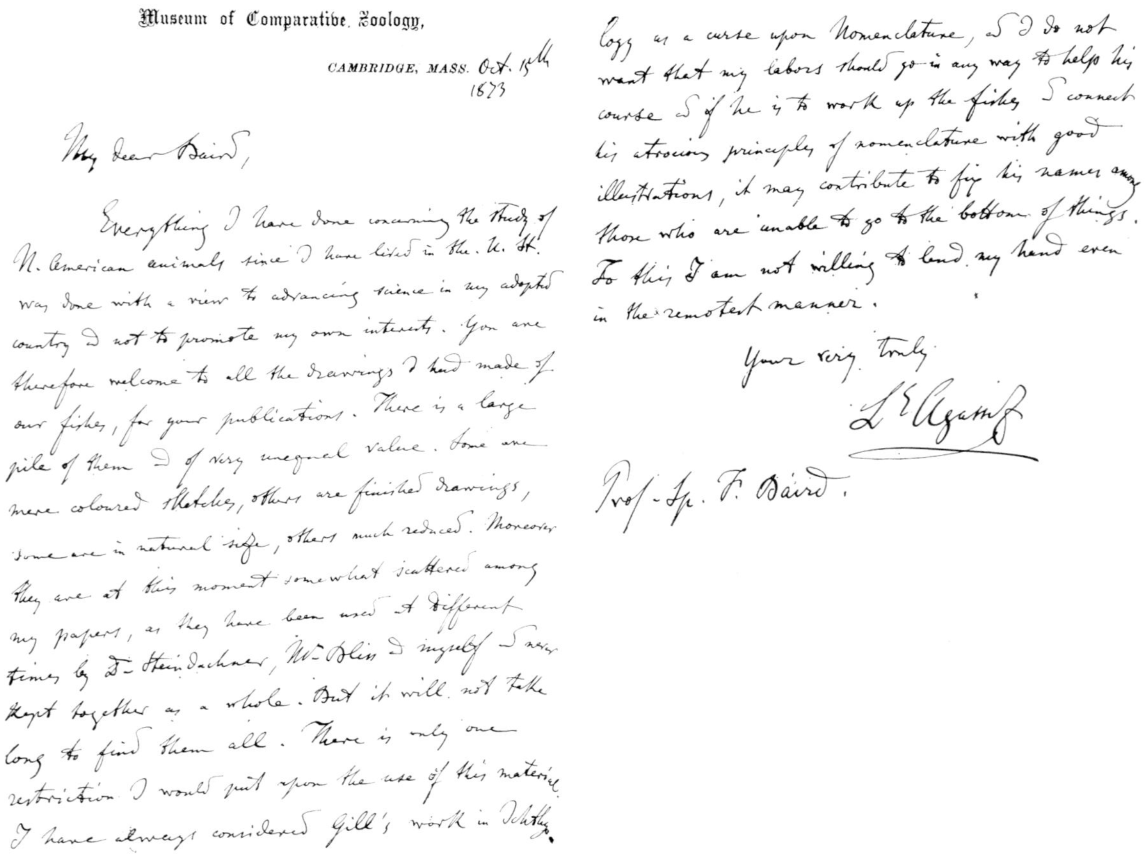

PLATE 6

Museum of Comparative Zoology,

CAMBRIDGE, MASS. *Oct 15th*
1873

My dear Baird,

Everything I have done concerning the Fishes of
N. American animals since I have lived in the U. St.
was done with a view to advancing science in my adopted
country & not to promote my own interests. You are
therefore welcome to all the drawings I have made of
our fishes for your publication. There is a large
pile of them. I of very unequal value. Some are
mere colored plates, others are finished drawings,
some are in natural [size], others much reduced. Moreover
they are at this moment some what scattered away
my papers, as they have been used of different
times by F—— Steindachner, M. Ortez & myself. I am
therefore not willing to [send?] [my hand?]
[...]

Yours very truly,
L Agassiz

Prof. S. F. Baird.

Letter from Agassiz to Baird, October 15, 1873

PLATE 7

Spencer Fullerton Baird about 1850, age 27

Spencer Fullerton Baird, from a daguerreotype taken
September 29, 1840

PLATE 8

Spencer Fullerton Baird with his wife and daughter Lucy

PLATE 9

MAMMALS

OF

NORTH AMERICA;

THE DESCRIPTIONS OF SPECIES BASED CHIEFLY ON THE COLLECTIONS

IN THE

MUSEUM OF THE SMITHSONIAN INSTITUTION.

BY

SPENCER F. BAIRD,

ASSISTANT SECRETARY OF THE SMITHSONIAN INSTITUTION.

With Eighty-seven Plates of Original Figures,

ILLUSTRATING THE GENERA AND SPECIES, AND INCLUDING DETAILS OF EXTERNAL FORM
AND OSTEOLOGY.

PHILADELPHIA:

J. B. LIPPINCOTT & CO.

1859.

Title page of Baird's *Mammals of North America*

PLATE 10

A

HISTORY

OF

NORTH AMERICAN BIRDS

BY

S. F. BAIRD, T. M. BREWER, AND R. RIDGWAY

LAND BIRDS

ILLUSTRATED BY 64 COLORED PLATES AND 593 WOODCUTS.

VOLUME III.

BOSTON
LITTLE, BROWN, AND COMPANY
1874

Title page of *A History of North American Birds,* by Baird, Brewer, and Ridgway

PLATE II

——— 672 ———

NATURAL HISTORY ILLUSTRATIONS.

PREPARED UNDER THE DIRECTION OF LOUIS AGASSIZ AND SPENCER F. BAIRD.
1849.

SIX SPECIES

OF

NORTH AMERICAN FRESH-WATER FISHES.

SIX LITHOGRAPHS FROM DRAWINGS BY A. SONREL.

———————

EXPLANATION OF PLATES BY DAVID STARR JORDAN.

———————

CITY OF WASHINGTON:
PUBLISHED BY THE SMITHSONIAN INSTITUTION.
1889.

Title page of the publication presenting Sonrel's lithographs of fishes, prepared
under the direction of Agassiz and Baird

PLATE 12

The National Museum Building (now the Arts and Industries Building)
of the Smithsonian Institution, erected during Baird's secretaryship

The "new" National Museum Building (now the Museum of Natural
History) of the Smithsonian Institution, completed in 1911

AGASSIZ to BAIRD

CAMBRIDGE, *Feb. 7, 1856*

My dear Baird,

Having received several days ago the cigar box containing *Emys nigra* and the stuffed *Sternotherus,* with the keg I began to be anxious about this. But it has at last made its appearance this afternoon. I had only a glance at its contents and yet I can already report a very unexpected pleasure. No. 17 *Emys* . . . from Red River La. is the young of a new species of which No. 21 *Emys* . . . Washington, Miss. is the adult. It belongs to my genus *Deirochelys.* This alone shows how important a direct comparison of the South Western species with those of the southern Atlantic States would be. Have you no more correspondents in La., Ark., and Miss., not to speak of Texas and then in Alab. and Flor. who could furnish more materials for comparison? I truly long for the specimens of the Western Expeditions. As I received dried specimens some days ago I have already had ample time to examine them. *Emys nigra* Holb. is identical with my San Francisco species. A worse name could not have been selected, as the highly ornamental *Emys* No. 25 from Monterey (in the keg of this day) is nothing more nor less than its young. It is a *Glyptemys* like our *insculpta* beautifully sculptured with colored radiation upon the scales when young & perfectly smooth when old, in which state it is Bell's *Emys speciosa.* I can tell you henceforth no one shall be justified in describing Chelonians from single dried up specimens. It will not do! The *Sternothorus* from Lake Concordia, La. is my new southern species, perfectly identical with my Mobile specimens. I shall call it *triquetra.*

No. 15 *Chelonura temminckii* is a perfect beauty of ugliness, a most acceptable addition to my illustration of the characteristics of that species.

So I have already disposed of Nos. 15, 17, 21, 25, and 26. As soon as I am through I shall return the specimens. Many thanks meanwhile for *E. Muhlenbergii* and the three toed *Cistudo* from Miss. I had it only from St. Louis before.

Yours very truly,

L. AGASSIZ

BAIRD to AGASSIZ

February 20, 1856

My dear Professor,

At length I have the very great pleasure of sending you one box and one keg of turtles as per accompanying invoice, belonging with few exceptions to the U. States. As we have to act with great formality where government things are concerned, I want you to return a copy of the list if you find it correct, with your receipt at bottom.

I trust you will be as much pleased in examining the specimens as I was in packing it up for you, thinking as I did how this specimen and that would strike you.

As heretofore, the numbers belong absolutely to the specimens and were not attached for temporary use. In referring therefore to them you can speak of such and such a number of the Smithsonian collection. Where I have a skeleton or a shell merely, it is entered among the osteological specimens of which the numbers run high — over (2100). Where the specimen is in alcohol or is a prepared shell or skin, it goes in the Reptilian Catalogue which as yet has not been filled out above 100.

I forgot to say that my delay was occasioned by waiting for some specimens just come in, and among the most important of the list, as No. 66 and No. 64 etc.

The better plan will be to give a complete list of all the specimens arranged systematically, characterizing the new species, or if you have time, all of them. Better give synonymy etc. briefly to each. Send it to me and I will cut it up into expeditions and have published in your name in Proceedings of Phila. Acad. and have extra printed. I dont bother you with the division as the collections belong to seven different parties.

No. 88 is a specimen of what B.&.G. described as *Emys marmorata* in October Proceedings 1852, Phila. Acad. It is the same Protean one you have, and we have sent before and now. So this anticipates *Emys nigra,* if they are the same.

The shell 2035 from the mountains between Oregon and California seems different from the others.

What a queer diseased specimen that from the Yellowstone is (55) I dont know the species.

Please put in the same paper for Proceedings notices of our new species from Mississippi and Missouri etc.

When you send back the specimens mark or indicate which should be figured for the reports and I will have it done in best style.

I send in same box my collection of turtle bones from the Carlisle Cave. Will you please assort by species and label for me. Of course you are at liberty to make any publication you please of these. Let me know what you think of them.

What do you make of that *Testudo* from Texas and Mexico? Is it not an important addition to our fauna?

I send a *Siredon* for Dr. Wyman. Please look at it and turn over to him. I have just put into his hands all my material towards the anatomy and embryology of the Salamanders. Get him to show you some of the queer Salamander skeletons.

Very truly and sincerely yours,

S. F. BAIRD

Feb. 23. Could not possibly get off the box and keg sooner than today.

List of specimens of turtles, the property of the United States, sent to Professor Agassiz for examination and description, to be returned in good order as soon as possible.

It is understood that the diagnosis of new species and names of old ones are to be published officially in the Proceedings of the Phila. Acad. of Natural Sciences, and fuller descriptions to be prepared for the reports of the several Expeditions by which the collections were made.

It is also understood that Professor Agassiz is at liberty to use in his work on American Chelonians any matter which may have been privately published as aforesaid in the Proceedings of the Phila. Acad. (Sent from the Smithsonian Institution Washington, Feb. 20, 1856)

In alcohol

47	Emys.	Fort Snelling Minn.		
48	"	Bet. San Antonio Fort Seger Texas.		
49	"	"	"	
50	Sternothaerus	"	"	
51	"	"	"	Rio Bl—a.
52	Cistudo	"	"	
53	"	"	"	
54	Emys.	San Francisco, Cal.		
55	"	Yellowstone		
56	" (elegans)	Upper Missouri		
57	Cistudo	Upper Missouri		
58	Trionyx	(Head) Yellowstone		
59	Testudo	Lower Rio Grande, Tex.		
60	"	"		
61	Sternothaerus	"		
62	Trionyx	"		
63	Sternothaerus	Guadalupe Canon, Sonora		
64	"	Medina R. Tex.		
65	"	"		
66	"	Tucson, Sonora		
67	"	"		
68	"	Camp Yuma (Gila R.)		
69	"	near San Antonio, Tex. (San Pedro)		
70	"	"		
71	"	"		
72	"	"		
73	Cistudo	Red River Ark.		
74	Emys.	(varies) Monterey, Cal.		
75	Testudo	New Leon, Mexico		

76 Emys.	"	(near Cad [illegible])
77 "	Steilacoom, Puget Sound	
78 "	Middle Fork of Amer. River, Cal.	
79 "	Dogtown Creek of Arkansas R.	
80 "	Guadalupe Mts. Tex. Pecos R.	
81 "	"	
82 "	Brownsville, Tex.	
83 Sternothaerus	Red River Ark.	
84 Emys.	(Head) Brazos Texas	
88 Emys. Marmorata, b	B. & G. Puget Sound	
85 Testudo	Monterey, Mex.	
86 Sternothaerus	San Antonio El Paso	
87 Cistudo	Arkansas River	

617 Trionyx	Skeleton. Allegheny River, Pa.	
106 "	" Mississippi	
89 Sternothaerus	Shell "	
2035 Emys.	" Lost River Cascade Mts. Oregon	
2155 "	" W. of San Antonio Tex.	
2166 "	" "	
2157 Trionyx	Skel. imp. R.Grande	
1529 Emys.	Matamores	
1532 "		
1528 Testudo	"	

One box of fossil turtles from Carlisle Cave Pa.
One Siredon for Prof. Wyman.

BAIRD to AGASSIZ

February 26, 1856

Dear Professor,

At last I have your desideratum of S. American *Sternothaerus* of which today I send two living specimens brought by Dr. I. Galov, from Panama. He is very glad to know that you will prize them highly. If convenient, I would like one back, but use both if necessary. There will be no harm in dissecting and cutting of the one to be returned, [illegible].

I hope you got the box and keg sent a few days ago and that you liked the contents. You shall have at once everything additional that comes in. I have laid the most extensive system for gathering turtles for you and feel confident of doing much. See if we dont have hundreds, from the south and west by May. I wrote particularly for very large *Trionyx*. Panama will probably furnish a good many, most of which I have requested alive.

Please give the *Siredon* to Wyman.

Anxious to hear soon, I remain,

Sincerely yours,

SPENCER F. BAIRD

I send an article on *"Gymnopus spiniferus"* written by Dr. Sager of Ann Arbor, Mich.

AGASSIZ to BAIRD

Feb 28 1856 CAMBRIDGE

My dear Baird,

I was beginning to be anxious about the keg and box of Turtles, when they at last arrived last night, with the two living specimens from Panama. As it is Sunday today and the whole was deposited in my laboratory I can only inform you without delay of their safe arrival, and shall tomorrow proceed to make out the receipt of the contents in due form as you wish me to do. I am delighted at the prospect and as much so to look forward for the southern specimens you are angling for. With such materials I hope to be able to do something worth having with the Chelonians of this continent. Many thanks meanwhile for your good offices.

Very truly yours,

L. AGASSIZ

BAIRD to AGASSIZ

March 18, 1856

Dear Professor,

I am waiting anxiously to hear your determinations in regard to the turtles.

I have a fresh installment for you, — some more Texas and N. Mexican specimens; a lot from Tennessee of very small critters, and a live *Emys decussata?* of large size from Cuba!!!

I am waiting to secure possession of a small *Chelonura temminckii* sent me and to ascertain its locality.

Yours truly,

S. F. BAIRD

BAIRD to AGASSIZ

March 21, 1856

My dear Professor,

I sent by express today a box containing 1 living turtle marked *Emys decussata?* sent by Prof. Poey from Havana. Said by him to be female of *Emys rugosa.*

Also in alcohol:

x 108 *Kinosternon,* San Bernadino Creek Sonora

x   94 *Trionyx* Texas

x   *Cistudo,* Indianola, Iowa

Miscellaneous turtles from several localities in Tennessee.

The specimens marked x, please return. The others do what you please with them.

Why don't you tell me something about the last lot sent?

It will soon be time to have the new lot of Southern specimens. I hope to get our Potomac species in large numbers.

Yours truly,

S. F. BAIRD

AGASSIZ to BAIRD

CAMBRIDGE *Mar. 21 1856*

My dear Baird,

My last lines were to acknowledge the receipt of the most instructive lot of turtles I ever saw; upon which I immediately set to work to identify them. I have done so I think with success, indeed there are only two which still trouble me. But the consequence of my exertion has been to be laid up for the past ten days. I am upon my legs again since yesterday and have almost felt like working again today; but I shall wait until Monday. I only write to inform you that every thing is as you would like it, progressing only more slowly than I could wish. The living specimens from Panama were the most valuable species yet received, as they cleared up the synonymy of *Staurotypus triporcatus* and should Bell's *Kinost. sparianum* to be a good species, would it be allowable to open one of the three specimens of *Kinost. sonoriense* LeConte, which are from the same locality? I shall be very happy to get your new accessions, especially the Tennessee youngsters and the Belle of Cuba. By the way *E. nigra* & *marmorata* are one and the same species and identical with my San Francisco species. Where have you described *E. marmorata?* I can not lay my fingers upon it. Is the name older than *nigra?* Both apply as far as meaning is concerned, very indifferently to the appearance of the animal; but *nigra* least of the two. The *Testudo* from Texas and Mexico is the most interesting land turtle I have seen, *very very* closely allied to *T. Polyphemus.* I have lately had *Testudo tabulata, radiata* and *gigantica* alive. No doubt *Testudo* must be subdivided into genera as Fitzinger has begun to do it. I know 6 genera of land turtles from personal examination.

Do not forget the eggs and young of *rubriventris* as soon as they can be had and the variety or species of *concentrica.* Think of my pleasure in receiving *E. Bellii* alive the other day. It was sent by Lapham of Milwaukee.

I think I shall leave only one species doubtful — *E. hieroglyphica,* from want of a sufficient series. The most troublesome is still *Cistudo carolina.* I have now examined hundreds and am as wise as when I began. I hope nothing will interrupt again my regular course.

Truly yours,

L Agassiz

AGASSIZ to BAIRD

Cambridge, *Mar 23 1856*

My dear Baird,

Adjoining you have the testified list of the specimens you last sent me for examination. You will perceive that with few exceptions all are at last identified. The questionable points I shall settle within a few days I hope. I have however sent already the names that you may more readily complete the list of localities you may have to add. Have you any wishes with reference to the naming of the new *Testudo* and the new *Kinosternon* and *Terrapene?* At last light has come upon the latter and I find it now as easy to trace their limits as in any other group. The fact is that the degree of moveability of the sternum is of little consequence, but the generic characters depend upon the structure of the sternum to which LeConte has rightly alluded in his last paper. Sternotheroids constitute a very natural family, first named by Bell, but to which he erroneously refers *Cistudo* and *Emys* proper (*E. Blandingii*). On removing these, the family consists of *Emys* like Chelonians with a sternum butting at right angles against the dorsal shield and not arched with it into a regular curve, the connection being made with few ribs, and the angles of the sternum at junction not projecting into the dorsal shield. No odd sternal bone; hence sternum dividing longitudinally into regular halves, lateral folding differently from *Emys,* head incompletely retractile. The first time you get a mud turtle see how very differently it draws its feet from the Emyds. Five genera: *Sternotherus* African. *Terrapene* Merr. (sensu strict.), what I thought of calling *Ozotheca,* but as it is possible to appropriate the old name of Merrem for them I prefer it. Type *T. odorata.* 2d species, my new southern species *T. triquetra,* of which you have a splendid specimen from L. Concordia, La. 3d, the new one from

Texas (Nos. 64, 65, 69, 70, 71 of the list above). *Staurotypus triporcatus* Wagl. — *Cinosternon*. To this genus belong the South American spec. described by Spix and Dumér. and Bibr. and the Central American species: 1. *Cin. sharianum* from Panama (*C. mexicanum* LeConte) 2. *C. sonoriense* LeConte. Our *pennsylvanicum* can not be united with them, but forms a genus by itself to which belongs also *C. cruentatum* Dum. and Bibr. and the new species from Texas (No. 50, 51, 61 and 83). I shall try to go to Philadelphia to ascertain whether as LeConte maintains *Cin. scorpoides* from Surinam truly differs from *longicaudatum* and *brevicaudatum* of Spix, and what is his *Cin. integrum* and Dum. and Bibr. *leucostomum* of which a specimen is said to be in the Museum of the Academy. It is a real pity that they have passed that law of not allowing specimens to leave their rooms. Can they fairly expect that other naturalists shall send them their specimens for inspections, when they deny that privilege to everybody? By the way, if you have Spix's Chelonia of Brazil, please send it to me, for a few days. I must once more to go to work with *Cistudo* and try to make out whether we have only one or several species; I can distinguish four forms, but so can a shepherd distinguish every breed in his flock. Differences are not necessarily specific differences and the more I study Nat. Hist. the more am I struck with the looseness of the admitted specific characters. *Emys picta* has become for me a very troublesome species, since I have got it from every part of the country. As long as I knew only the New England form I found no difficulty. So is also *E. elegans,* and *E. concinna.* If the young *temminckii* you have got is smaller than the one you had sent me before I would like it at once, as the young *Cinost, Terrap* and *Chelydras* are to come upon my next plate; otherwise send it with your next invoice. I have extended farther my comparison of our *Trionyx,* we have decidedly 4 species. The skeleton from Texas gave the last evidence wanting that the Southwestern species differs from the *ferox* of Georgia and the *spinifer* of the N.West. I first made it out from an egg sent me by Dr. Holbrook, next had the young from Brownsville you sent me to establish further comparison; now the skeleton shows it beyond question to be different. I am sorry I have not another year to complete my investigations; but I hope for another good lift as soon as the spring opens. Do your best for me.

Yours very truly

L AGASSIZ

P.S. A young artist of Boston, W. M. Wright who painted a beautiful portrait of Humboldt, when he was in Berlin, two years ago, has had his picture engraved and wanted to send a number of the engravings to Humboldt. I advised him to forward them to you, requesting you to enclose them in the next envoice of the Smith. Inst. I mention this as I told him I could use my name in applying to you.

LAG

I have only looked over the bones from the caves in Pa., without attempting as yet to identify them, though I recognized at once *Cistudo* & *Chelydra* among them besides the more frequent *Emyds*. What occurs with them, that has been already identified? Will it do to prepare also descriptions of the most interesting new species from my own collection to add to those of the Smithsonian for publication? I can not think of introducing them in my work which will be overfull with embryology. I have already very fine drawings of them and of some of yours. I have had so many turtles alive of late, that I can give them very natural attitudes; and you will see from my remarks above respecting the folding of the legs of *Sternotherus* how important this now is.

LAG

List of specimens of turtles, the property of the United States, sent to me by the Smithsonian Institution, for examination and description, to be returned in good order as soon as possible.

It is understood that the diagnosis of new species and names of old ones are to be published officially in the Proceedings of the Philadelphia Academy of Natural Sciences and fuller descriptions to be prepared for the reports of the several expeditions by which the collections were made.

It is also understood that I am at liberty to use in my work on American Chelonians any matter which may have been previously published as aforesaid in the Proceedings of the Philadelphia Academy.

No. 47 *Emys Bellii;* Fort Snelling, Minn.

No. 48 ⎫
No. 49 ⎭ *Emys elegans* or allied spec. Between S. Antonio and Fort Sage

No. 50 ⎫
No. 51 ⎭ *Kinosternon* nov. spec.   "

No. 52 ⎫
No. 53 ⎭ *Cistudo carolina*   "

No. 54 *Emys nigra* Hallow. San Francisco Cal.

No. 55 *Emys Bellii*   Yellowstone Riv. Nebr.

No. 56 *Emys elegans*   Upper Missouri

No. 57 *Cistudo carolina* Upper Missouri

No. 58 *Trionyx* (Head)   Yellowstone

No. 59 ⎫
No. 60 ⎭ *Testudo* nov. spec.   Lower Rio Grande, Texas

No. 61 *Kinosternon* nov. spec.   "

No. 62 *Trionyx* nov. spec.   "

No. 63 *Kinosternon sonoriense* LeConte Guadalupe Canon, Sonora

No. 64 ⎫
No. 65 ⎭ *Terrapene* nov. spec.   Medina River. Tex.

No. 66 ⎫
No. 67 ⎭ *Kinosternon sonoriense* LeConte Tucson, Sonora

No. 68 *Kinosternon sonoriense* yg of 63, 66, 67 Camp Yuma (Gila River)

No. 69 ⎫
No. 70 ⎪ *Terrapene* nov. spec. the same as No. 64 and 65 Near
No. 71 ⎪ San Antonio Tex.
No. 72 ⎭

No. 73 *Cistudo carolina*   Red River, Ark.

No. 74 Ovaries of *Emys nigra*   Monterey, Calif.

No. 75 *Testudo* nov. spec. the same as No. 59 and 60. New Leon (Mexico)

No. 76 *Emys concinna?*   New Leon

No. 77 ⎫ *Emys nigra* Hall. Steilacoom, Puget Sound
No. 78 ⎭   Middle Fork of American Riv. Calif.

No. 79 *Emys pseudogeographica* Dogtoura Creek of Arkansas River

No. 80 *Emys concinna*   Guadalupe Mts. Tex.

No. 81 *Emys Bellii* or new   ”

No. 82 *Emys elegans* yg   Brownsville, Texas.

No. 83 *Kinosternon* nov. spec. yg of No. 50, 51, 61 Red River, Ark.

No. 84 *Emys elegans* (Head) Brazos Tex.

No. 85 *Testudo* nov. spec. the same as 59, 60, 75. Monterey, Mex.

No. 86 *Kinosternon* nov. spec. the same as No. 50, 51, 61, 83 Between S. Antonio and El Paso

No. 87 *Cistudo carolina*   Arkansas River.

No. 88 *Emys marmorata* B & G = *E. nigra* Hallow. Puget Sound.

No. 617 *Trionyx* skeleton   Allegheny River

No. 1086 *Trionyx* skeleton   Mississippi River

No. 1089 *Kinosternon*   “

No. 2035 *Emys nigra*   Lost Riv. Oregon

No. 2155 ⎫ *Emys elegans*   W. of San Antonio Texas
No. 2156 ⎭

No. 2157 *Trionyx* nov. spec. same as No. 62 (Skelet. imperf.) Rio Grande.

No. 1529 ⎫ *Emys elegans* or allied   Matamoras
No. 1532 ⎭

No. 1536 *Testudo* nov. spec. same as No. 59, 60, 75, and 85. Matamoras

                                        L AGASSIZ

BAIRD to AGASSIZ

March 29, 1856

Lieber Herr Professor,

   I am very sorry that I was so imprudent as to send so many specimens at once so as to use you up in their examination. So please accept my humble apologies and the assurance that I shall do just so again whenever I have the chance.

I am delighted that you find so much to interest and instruct you in the lot. I hope to drop more of them in one lot or another so as to complete their history. Since I sent the live Cubans, the Tennessee youngsters and the Indianola *Cistudo* I have had another West Indian *Emys,* a fine old *Emys marmorata,* [illegible] like that shell from the Cascade Mts. or Klamath Lake or Lost river, I forget which. [Illegible.] *Emys marmorata* is long prior to *E. nigra* has been described in proceedings Phila. Acad. N.S. for 1852 or 1853 in an article by B. & G. in New N. Am. Reptiles collected by the Wilkes Exploring expedition (I write this at home and can't refer you to the exact place). I hope the *Cistudo carolina* question may assume new light into the 4 toed specimen from Texas. Scarcely one of our South Atlantic States reptiles is found in that locality. There seems from memory a resemblance between this specimen and those from the Arkansas and Upper Missouri, all somewhat different from the Eastern.

I have made all possible arrangements to get the young turtles and eggs you asked for, and shall be much disappointed if I don't succeed. By the way, why can't you have the desired species to lay their eggs in your limits. The adults are now abundant here in the market though somewhat costly.

I am much obliged for the notes on Sternothaeroids. They will be very valuable to me.

I have no choice whatever about the names of the new species although for the *Testudo* I would suggest the name of Berlandier, the poor unfortunate, unknown naturalist of Matamoras, who spent 26 years in investigating the Natural History of Mexico and Texas and died obscurely just as he was nearly done. He had collected specimens of this animal and given it a Mss name.

The new *Kinosternon* or the *Trionyx* it might be well to name after Professor Emory, the accomplished liberal head of the Boundary Commission under whose auspices some of the specimens of these species were collected. It would be a grateful tribute to his appreciation of Natural Science in having collections made.

We have not spare Chelonians of Brazil [illegible]. If you go to Phila. consult the specimens of the Phila. Acad., you must surely spend a day or else we shall never forgive you if you don't.

Of course, open one of the *Kinosternon sonoriense,* and any others even though unique, if necessary. You will of course not mutilate the specimens more than necessary.

Prof. Henry says he will with pleasure send the engravings for Mr. Wright. We send in June or July next, but can forward at once through the Prussian Minister here. Ask him to send one for that gentleman.

It will be very well indeed to describe all your new species of private turtles with the government ones. I am doing that in my own department. I would make also the communication for the Academy to embrace these diagnoses, as well as a list of all the species in North America with their localities; and one or two chief synonyms. Give first all the species collected by the government as a separate article which I will arrange for you, so as to classify by expedition. Then conclude by the list of species, and localities. We will have extra copies forwarded and distributed widely. Could you complete it to send to the Academy by the middle of April? We could then have it printed by the end of May and send copies abroad in June.

In your remarks and articles for the gov't reports put each species on a separate sheet or sheets with an index showing the systematics and distr. Enumerate all the specimens you have received by numbers and localities. Write out on one side of the page. I shall have to duplicate the same description sometimes so as to put into the different reports, where collected by the parties. This, however, will be mainly a matter purely mechanical or clerical.

The fossil turtles are probably all of recent species though some may not be found in the same locality. They are associated with remaining mammals, embracing nearly all our species with one or two that are extinct.

Very truly yours,
S. F. Baird

AGASSIZ to BAIRD

Cambridge 1^e April 1856

My dear Baird,

The Cistudo from Indianola has truly set me on the right track respecting the species of that Genus. You remember right this Texan species is the same as that of Arkansas and it differs specifically from ours. Good luck would have it that I received nearly at the same time 20 fine living specimens from Col. Wailes of the three toed form, so I trust within a few days I shall have mastered the difficulties of the genus. But who should have supposed that it required such extensive comparisons to determine a few species of turtles?

Since my last I have settled another troublesome point and ascertained that we have three and not only two *picta* like species; having received so called pictas from Dr. N. Miles in Flint, from Prof. Winchell in Ann-Arbor, from Dr. Hoy and from Mr. Lapham. Not a sign of *picta* in that part of the country but everywhere *Bellii* and a new species, both of which I have now alive before me with half a dozen of our *picta* kept alive since last fall. There is no doubt about their difference at all. In *picta* the vertebral and costal shields run nearly in a line with their margins, across which extends a broad yellow stripe so:

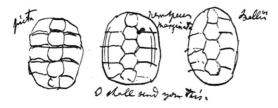

In the two others the costal shields alternate with the vertebral; *Bellii* moreover is an oblong species, the other broad like *picta* and even more so and with folds upon the marginal side of the costal shields. *Marginata* has a narrow, *Bellii* a wide blotch upon sternum. The length of claws varies, and is not indicative of species as Dr Hoy and Mr Lapham supposed when sending them. The youngsters from Tennessee were quite instructive, but there is a young *Kinosternon* of the type of *pennsylvan.* among them which differs from our eastern; can you not get adults? also of *picta*. It would be also very desirable to get the young & various ages of *pseudogeographica, geographica, heiroglyphica, Troostii* & *elegans* from there. By the way I believe I have hit upon the young of *elegans* among the specimens sent me a year ago from Brownsville Texas. But to make sure of it it would be well to have intermediate forms from some more accessible locality.

I shall follow your suggestion about having the *Testudo* and *Kinosternon* and *Trionyx* from Texas & do my best to have my synopsis ready by the time you mention. — I have found the reference to *Emys marmorata* and am glad it has priority over *nigra*, for that name would never do; *marmorata* is not exactly the thing either, but it is at least not so completely objectionable.

E. decussata I am happy to find is entirely different from any of our species. It comes nearest to *serrata*, with which it belongs to one genus *Trachemys*, differing however by its more elongated form and the more extensive sculpture of the shields which reach the vertebral shields. I should be glad to have southern turtles to lay here; but I have experienced that specimens which have been shaken will keep their eggs occasionally very long, so that you can only make sure in this way of the identity of the eggs, but not ascertain correctly the season of laying.

Ever truly yours

L AGASSIZ

BAIRD to AGASSIZ

April 5, 1856

My dear Professor,

Dr. Hayden[40] informs me that a gentleman in Rochester has two specimens of the curious *Siredon* of Fort Defiance sent for you by his son. You had better write him at once stating that you have learned that he proposes sending these things and indicate the channel. You will of course express your desire to possess so rare an animal. The address is:

Dr. H. I. Longworthy
Rochester, N. Y.

I was very glad to learn from your letter that the last specimens sent had enabled you to solve some of the vexing questions. I am a little dubious about the additional specimens from Kentucky; as that is now an unpredictable state. I will [illegible].

Perhaps if you are afraid of the risk of sending the turtles to Boston, I might pen them up here and collect the eggs. The dealers tell me these animals often drop their eggs in captivity and that the red bellies lay in June. We unfortunately have no open air enclosures at the Smithsonian, although I might make one in my own little garden. How shall I arrange a pen for them?

Are you finding any mammals among your collections as unpacked. I would be glad to have any from the South and West.

Very truly yours,
S. F. BAIRD

AGASSIZ to BAIRD

CAMBRIDGE *April 11 1856*

My dear Baird,

I have just had a nice pen put up in my garden for turtles, so that I am prepared to keep any number alive this summer. I have just put in a splendid *floridana*, 2 *elegans* and 2 *pseudogeographica*. I think on the whole best to collect together here all I can, as I see even those which I received from New Orleans are in good order.

I have received nothing new except turtles for nearly a year and not looked at any other part of my collection; but whatever turns up in the

---

[40] Ferdinand V. Hayden (1829–87), geologist, was born in Westfield, Mass. He was identified with many geological expeditions and wrote many valuable reports. One of his best known reports is the one which resulted in setting aside as a public reservation an area in northern Wyoming and adjacent portions of Montana and Idaho as Yellowstone National Park. Forty-four species are named after him.

Mammalian line shall be yours. I have immediately written to Dr. Long-worthy in Rochester. I would be delighted to have it in my power to give Wyman a chance to dissect that species as well as all other Ichthyoids.

I have lately received the blind fish of the Mammoth Cave from a well in Alabama.

Truly yours

L Agassiz

BAIRD to AGASSIZ

April 12, 1856

Dear Professor,

I will see that you have some redbellied turtles for your pen as soon as I can get some good ones. They will soon be plenty here.

Have you ever seen Auguste Dumeril's paper in the Archives du Museum of 1852 on Turtles [illegible] mentioned in Erp. generale? [illegible.] Have you seen Gravenhorst? There is some turtle matter there. I suppose you have had Schneider and Schoff. Perhaps you had better send me another list of desiderata in the book line, as we have received some works since you wrote previously for what we had new for you.

The paper for the Proceedings must be presented by title at least by Tues. (22) in order to go into the next number of the Proceedings Acad.

Did you receive some fossil bones from Augusta Co., Va. recently? If so, please let me know what they are, what parts, species, genera and condition of preservation. I want to know whether it is worthwhile to make further explorations there.

Yours truly,

S. F. Baird

BAIRD to AGASSIZ

Washington, *Apr. 26, 1856*

Dear Professor,

Did you get my letter asking whether you had seen Archiv du Mus; containing Dumerils paper on turtles, with descriptive figure of *Kinosternon orientatum leucosternum.*

Ever yours,

S. F. Baird

Do you want to keep the stones of Coral fishes done for the Inst. . . . .

AGASSIZ to BAIRD

CAMBRIDGE *April 27 1856*

My dear Baird,

I must be the first to disregard the critic I have made in my first volume of the manner in which species and genera are generally described and I find that to do it as I think it ought to be done it takes more time than I had expected. I could not by any possibility have completed my descriptions by the day appointed; but I am steadily at it, and as soon as done you shall have the whole. I trust it will when published in connection with all the old ones look well enough.

The two books you allude to Dumeril & Gravenhorst I have had for some time. Thanks nevertheless for the information. In a few days I will write again for some other works which you may have got lately.

I have a number of copies of my european works now on hand; if you can help me to sell them so much the better.

I have not received any bones from Va., so I can not tell you what is found there.

Two young *rubriventris* have reached me through Wyman, in very good state. Can you not obtain still younger ones?

I had a note from Dr. Brewer[41] asking me whether Sonrel could not draw some plates of eggs for him. I have seen Sonrel this week. He says it will take him to the end of July at least to finish my turtles and perhaps longer and he has for two months more work upon the corals. As soon as that is done he can do these plates, if it is not too late then. It is important that eggs should be represented with the utmost accuracy. I have now again *E. floridana* and *mobiliensis* alive, and a new species from Alabama.

Truly yours

L AGASSIZ

I have received the *Memobranchus* from Fort Defiance from Dr. Longworthy. They are very well preserved, but quite young, thus adding another piece of information respecting that remarkable species.

I had almost forgotten to mention, that I have received this week a few bats & mice & rats from California & from Texas. Do you want them now?

---

[41] Thomas M. Brewer (1814–80), ornithologist and oologist, was born in Boston, Mass. In spite of his devotion to business the greater part of his life, he developed as an avocation an interest in birds and became one of the leading ornithologists of America. He made the acquaintance of Baird while the latter was a professor at Dickinson College. He helped Audubon with one of his volumes on birds. In 1857 the Smithsonian published his work called "North American Oölogy" with eggs figured in colors. The entire biographical portion of the 3-volume treatise on "History of North American Birds" by Baird, Brewer, and Ridgway was written by Brewer.

AGASSIZ to BAIRD

CAMBRIDGE *May 2 1856*

My dear Baird,

I have no further use of the plates of my Coral paper after the number of copies you want and those you allow me are struck off.

Should like any *meleagris* you can spare.

My copies of european works are in the bonded warehouse of Boston, to save the duties which are $7.74 per copy, but will send you 2 or 3 sets. As I want badly to dispose of them I am willing to continue generally the half price plus duties, which makes $130.68 for complete sets, and stick to full price only for single works. If the Smithsonian keeps a copy send me an order from Prof. Henry to save the duty, I shall forward the copies next week; meanwhile enclose the prices. They are the half prices, so double them for each single work taken. I shall send the mammals from Texas and California at the same time.

As to the drawings of turtles, several are already done as I wrote you, and the attitudes taken from living specimens of closely allied species, so that if you have no objection I would prefer to have them all drawn so.

I truly long for the Cuban specimens. About *rubriventris* let me say, that I have left a place in a plate for a young *rubriventris* of smallest size and that plate is now finished, can you not have some of your fishermen look for one of the last years brood; those I may raise will not hatch before 7th or 8th and those now coming out, before they have fed are as small as when hatched.

I am very glad for what you write of Dr. Newberry.[42] Any assistance I can give him shall be cheerfully rendered.

Truly yours
L AGASSIZ

AGASSIZ to BAIRD

CAMBRIDGE *May 26 1856*

My dear Baird,

I now send the Rodents and Bats. All are from Texas, Williamson Co. except the large ones which are from San Francisco. I duly received the turtles, all highly welcome. Do your best for a youngest *rubriventris*.

My son Alex would like to spend his vacation upon some government

---

[42] John S. Newberry (1822–92), physician and naturalist, secretary to the western department of the U. S. Sanitary Commission in the Civil War, professor of geology at the school of mines, Columbia University, published numerous books and papers relating to geology, paleontology, botany, and zoology.

survey. He is in the first class of the Engineer Dept. of our Scientific School & could make himself useful, during the months of July, August & Sept. Of course he would expect no pay, and be happy to have the opportunity of improving himself in some serious work. If he can have his expenses paid so much the better. Do you know any survey going on which he could join on such terms.

Very truly yours

L AGASSIZ

AGASSIZ to BAIRD

CAMBRIDGE *May 29 1856*

My dear Sir,

I am truly delighted and thankful for the last envoice. It crowns the series, for it is really the young *rubriventris*. How wonderful these differences are! Do you think there is a herpetologist existing who from isolated specimens could identify any of our species? I say any for I have now specimens of *guttata* without any spots, *meleagris* entirely black, *picta* without yellow bands & so forth. Nothing tells but the proportions of the parts compared with one another, provided further the sexes be distinguished. I would gladly give a few more dollars to have some more young, and especially the age intermediate between those sent before & the youngest received this morning. How is it with the eggs; mine do not lay. I have now 12 *living floridana* in my yard. That species is found in Georgia, Alabama, Mississippi and La.; so much for its limitation to East Florida! The *Kinosternon* from Tarboro were most instructive, as they confirmed by a large set, all and every inference drawn from previous examination. The white mouthed are females, so much for Dumeril and Bibr. *leucostomum*, the short tailed are females, so much for Spix's *brevicaudatum*, the large headed are males, formerly I mistook them for a distinct species. No turtles can be well illustrated of which twenty specimens at least have not been seen. I am now really beginning to see my way clearly. I have received lately something like forty or more boxes of turtles, occasionally over 50 specimens in each. By the way I have mislaid the large rat of California. Among the heap of turtles I have delayed sending off the Texan specimens to add these, which must be forthcoming, as it is but a few weeks since they arrived and all the late arrivals are still in a heap together.

Many & my best thanks

Truly yours

L AGASSIZ

AGASSIZ to BAIRD

CAMBRIDGE *Aug. 20 1856*

My dear Baird,

Your two letters remind me of my promises. After the meeting of Albany where I did more than I ought to have done, I was laid up for a month and had to leave everything to take care of themselves. I have taken up my work again lately, but I am so pressed with the printing of my book to bring it out this year that I do very little else. I will however answer your questions one after the other by and by.

Today I enclose the Chapter on types, which I promised you should have first. The sheets I send are the first belonging to my work I allow to go out of my hands. I hope they may be useful in your present investigation of the Rodents. Make the most of it; but keep these sheets to yourself until I relieve you of the privacy. The notes on your turtles and the drawings you shall have next.

I would be glad to have Gray, which I have not yet been able to secure, notwithstanding my orders for it. It will not come too late to compare it with my arrangement, but this being already printed, I shall only be able to use Gray for an appendix.

I would thank you also for the Gopher, though I have had a dozen this summer, I have cut them up so fully, that I should be glad for some good specimens.

Yours truly
L AGASSIZ

AGASSIZ to BAIRD

CAMBRIDGE *September 1856*

My dear Baird,

I have duly received the book of Gray and the Smithsonian papers accompanying it, for which I return my best thanks.

I write a long letter to Gray by the next steamer, that he may learn from me, why I shall only be able to allude to his work in an appendix to mine. I am sorry for him, that he has made such an awful work of our species. I find that his *Ciromochelys carinata* is the only one not already noticed by Holbrook & LeConte. Our *floridana* he has under five different species referred to two genera.

I trust you have received my printed sheet. When I went to the printing office to get a set for you, I found it would be inconvenient for them to pick out in their storehouse, so I sent you my soiled copy, which is yet readable. In a few days I hope to send you drawings.

Truly yours,
L AGASSIZ

AGASSIZ to BAIRD

CAMBRIDGE *12th 1856*

My dear Baird,

Allow me to introduce to you Prof. Schmarda just on his way back to Germany after a 4 years journey round the world. You know his work upon the Geogr. distribution of animals etc. I need not say more to secure a hearty welcome for him. Please introduce him also to Prof. Henry.

Truly yours
L AGASSIZ

BAIRD to AGASSIZ

Oct. 8, 1856

Dear Professor,

It is some time since I have heard from and of you, and I write to be posted. Please let me know how you come on: how *the* book progresses etc.

Do you want any more turtles? I have living *Testudo polyphemus,* large, and some small ones in alcohol; one about 3 inches. Also a very large *E. serrata,* an alcoholic sp. of *Trionyx* from the coast of Georgia and perhaps some others. I had a *Chelonia mydas* about 10 inches long I caught at Beasly's point. I had it several weeks and then went into alcohol. I have maybe some other matters.

I have not yet had the small mammals from Texas-California. I would like any of these either skins or alcoholics; from any part of North America, especially Arvicolae, *Hesperomys.* Please let me have them at once as I am closing up my Monograph.

I have some interesting results among the Arvicolae, important [illegible] types and comparisons with European-Asiatic species, a large number of which I have had.

How comes on the report on turtles for the govt. reports? Please send on all the plates you want engraved; as many as you please of species west of the Misssissippi. Crowd the figures as much as you can in arranging them within the border [illegible] the size of that enclosing several Smithsonian plates. Ten won't be too many, or even more.

Have you the quarto Catalogue of Turtles of British Museum by Gray, 1855 or 56. It is of much importance to you. We have it at your service.

Ever yours,
S. F. BAIRD

BAIRD to AGASSIZ

Oct 12, 1856

Dear Professor,

Can I sell the Portfolio containing the drawings of the Salmonidae sepa-
rate from the Embryology, and at what price. I have several calls for it.
Have you many copies of this work: I think I can dispose of a good many.
Of what works can't you furnish any required number.

I find that of the three sets you sent, all lack Linnaeus 367 of [illegible]
families and 102 of [illegible] the Systeme Glaciare. There is only one set.
Let me know about the [illegible].

Yours truly,
S. F. BAIRD

BAIRD to AGASSIZ

December 6, 1856

Dear Professor,

About the 25th of October in sending you the last lot of living turtles,
among the *Testudo polyphemus* I enclosed a small glass bottle containing
a Lepidosiren, [illegible] packed perhaps in a small box. He writes me that
you have not been able to find that. Perhaps the mention of it and the circumstances may enable you to make a successful search among the vast
mass of materials in your collection. [Illegible.]

If you have any drawings of New European Emydae you want published,
please send them on at the earliest possible monent or it will soon be too
late to have them engraved.

When will you make out your report on these things. We have received a
few collections recently from Sierras and Yellowstone which might be of interest.

I read the introductory pages of your vol. with much interest and profit.

May I remind you that I have not yet had those small mammals of
Texas and California you promised me.

You have not yet said at what price you sell the Salmonidae apart from
the Embryology. I want to buy one set for a Christmas present to a friend.

Yours truly,
S. F. BAIRD

BAIRD to AGASSIZ

February 16, 1857

My dear Professor,

I enclose a letter from Prof. Poey of Havana, which I wish you would read and return as soon as possible with a short note in response to his questions about the turtles. Your investigations have doubtless put you in possession of all the facts for which he asks and the least we can do for his services is to give him the desired information.

What has become of you for so long. We hoped to see you in Washington and were greatly disappointed at your non arrival.

I have never received those small mammals from Texas and California you promised. Cant you send them at once as I am at work on the critters.

Yours truly,
S. F. BAIRD

BAIRD to AGASSIZ

July 4, 1857

My dear Professor,

It is an age since I have heard from or of you. I wish you would drop me a line and say whether you are in the land of the living.

Prof. Poey has sent us some more Cuban turtles of which he desires some information. If I send them will you answer his questions very soon? He thinks them different from the last.

When may I expect that Government article on the turtles? It is wanted now or will be in a few weeks for the Mss.

If there are to be any figures, I ought to have them at once.

When will Vol. 1 of *the* great work of the day be out? And what are you going at next. What can we send you or get for you?

I never received those Texas and California Mammals, much to my regret.

Sincerely yours,
SPENCER F. BAIRD

Has Wyman gone to S. America or not.

BAIRD to AGASSIZ

October 16, 1857

Dear Professor,

If not in immediate use, I would be much obliged to you if you would return our copy of Gray's quarto Catalogue of British Museum Tortoises, as I have occasion to make some references to it at the present time.

When may we look for the promised article on the tortoises of N.America
I sent you. It will soon be wanted to put to press for the Pacific R.R. Report.
When will your own vol. be out. I am very anxious to see it.

Have you ever been able to look at Prof. Poey's letter and to make any
memorandum in reference to his questions.

I wish I could hear from you. I have written a half a dozen times since
your last.

Truly yours,
SPENCER F. BAIRD

BAIRD to AGASSIZ

WASHINGTON *Jan 10, 1858*

My dear sir,

I am much pleased to learn that we may yet hope to have a memoir from
you to accompany the plates in the Institution. I feared that the immense
labor of preparing the work you have in hand would prevent us from real-
izing the anticipation of embodying in our series of Smithsonian Contributions — something from your pen additional to the paper on Classification
of Insects.

I regret very much that none of the works you mention are in our possession. The Transactions of the Institut Geneva's may be in a case at present
in New York. Should this be the case it will be forwarded to you immediately on its reception.

The Volume of British Museum Catalogues was duly received a few days
ago.

S F B

BAIRD to AGASSIZ

May 15, 1858

My dear Professor,

The Public printers are clamoring for the Mss. copy to complete the R.
R. Reports and I have been officially called upon by the War and Interior
Departments to say when the remaining Natural History Mss. will be delivered. All that is left unfinished at present is the Herpetological portion and
I write to ask you to please send on your turtle report as early as possible
as that begins the series. If I had it now I could get the printers to set it up
at once so that you could have copies to take with you to Europe and at
any rate it is important that you should have the opportunity to correct the
proofs.

It would be well also to send the specimens back as I shall want to have a tabular list for each species made out on the plan of that in the mammal volume. You can name them by reference to the numbers to be written off as you pack them up.

My report on N. Am. Birds is progressing very well. About 250 pp. are printed and I hope to have all done by the first of August. As all the reports are separately paged, however, this will not interfere with the putting your Mss. to press at once.

Hoping to hear from you soon, I remain

Sincerely yours

S F BAIRD

BAIRD to AGASSIZ

WASHINGTON, *June 11, 1858*

Dear Professor,

I write again to ask when you can let me have the MSS of your article on turtles. I am badgered by the people connected with the War and Mexican Boundary Offices to know when the reports are to be all in hand. And it is of very great importance to have all of the series finished up as soon as possible. The Mexican Boundary Report cannot go to press until all the MSS are complete for all the series and everything is ready but the turtles.

If you have not time to say much on the subject a simple diagnosis of each family, Genus and species will have to answer, although the more detailed the report the better.

When do you leave for Europe and how long will you be gone.

If you have time I would be glad to have your criticism on my Mammal Volume. I hope soon to be able to send you the plates.

I have printed 400 pp. of my report on birds and am within a few days of having the whole of my MSS. ready for the printer. I shall probably add 50 percent to Audubon's list.

Yours sincerely,

S. F. BAIRD

It has been a long time since I have seen your welcome chirography. Please let me look at it soon again!

AGASSIZ to BAIRD

June 23 1858

My dear Baird,

I am losing my eyesight so rapidly that until I know where it will stop I can do nothing, not even read my letters. I am going to Nahant tomorrow and I hope seabathing will stop the misfortune.

Truly yours

L AGASSIZ

BAIRD to AGASSIZ

July 30, 1858

Dear Professor,

I hope by this time that your eyes have sufficiently improved to warrant your preparing the report on the Turtles sent from Washington. It is of very great importance to have the whole series of reports finished and printed before the next session of Congress and nothing is now left but the Reptilia. Of these the Batrachia are done and the serpents nearly complete. I take the remaining material with me to Carlisle next week and hope then to finish before the first of October.

If you could certainly let me have the turtles early in October you would confer a very great favor, as I want to begin the report with them. Do not trouble yourself to make anything very elaborate. Recognizable diagnoses of the families, genera, and species will answer. With the synonymy a dozen quarto pages might include these, leaving the more elaborate portion for a separate and special memoir.

I am nearly through the press with my vol. on birds. About 700 pp. are in type and 200 more to come. In the land birds alone, I have 150 species not mentioned by Audubon.

Very truly yours,
S F. Baird

BAIRD to AGASSIZ

Oct. 11, 1858

Dear Professor,

I have sold for you one full set of your works (exclusive of Contributions); to the University of Havana but find the three series sent us all incomplete somewhat as noted when received in 1856. I want to make them perfect.

3 sets of Echinodermes fossiles part 3
3 sets of Old Red fishes Part 1.2. of text
2 sets of Systeme glaciare text and atlas.

To complete the Havana series I only want copies of the first: for the rest I want two each of the three.

Please have them sent at once by express as I wish to send off the books at once and get the money for them.

What can you do for the Turtle paper? The Pacific R. R. report must be all finished this year, and I would be much distressed at being obliged to omit this part for the reptilia. Can't you finish at least the diagnoses of genera and species with list of specimens of each. Do try to send something! I have finished the only unworked portion, the *Sauria*, and shall soon go to press. I make 88 good species of N. Am. Sauria in our collection, including new genera, and one new family. If you would like your species labelled, send them along. The total number of N. Am. reptiles exceeds 400.

My bird volume is nearly finished. It makes 1100 pp. I have about 730 species.

Sincerely yours,
S. F. BAIRD

BAIRD to AGASSIZ

Oct. 17, 1858

Dear Dr.

Never mind about the Set of Pacific R. R. reports for Martius. He can make it up some way or other. Let him send us any old Scientific Translations, periodicals or Monographs, not in our catalogue now in press. Make any disposition you please of your set.

Vol. 10 S. C. is not yet out, delayed by non-completion of Memoirs. Harvey is not ready to distribute. I will send your copies very soon.

I will enclose bills for the two packages of books for you from München, 6 each of part XXI and XXII of some palm (?) books. They came separately at intervals of a week. It was extremely stupid of somebody to send them so. They will go off to you probably tomorrow. I have only now returned from the North or would have attended to the matter before.

Sincerely yours,
S. F. BAIRD

BAIRD to AGASSIZ

Oct. 29, 1858

My dear Professor;

I do not wish to urge you beyond what is right and proper in reference to the report on the turtles, but it will be a sad disappointment if you are unable to furnish at least something on the subject. The whole series must be printed and completed at a very early day, as nearly as possible about the first of January. By beginning with the Urodela and leaving Chelonia to the last, the reception of the Mss anytime in December would answer, though I would prefer to begin with this order within a month. I would not dare to undertake the turtles, nor if I did would I have the time to study them up. So that if you cannot finish the report on them, they must be omitted entirely from what would otherwise be a very full account of North American Herpetology.

Still if this is to be done at the expense of your eyesight heaven forbid that I should be so selfish as to urge the matter on you; this sense is too precious a boon to be tampered with.

Could you not however without running any risk prepare a short account of the Chelonia even by taking one or two species daily and dictating the broad features to some one, the newer characters would recur to your mind. If you do not this now, you know how little chance there is of your ever finding time to take up what is even now fading from your mind, and giving an account of the many genera and species in your book. It will be impossible to identify these in many cases, and much confusion will necessarily result hereafter. It will not be necessary, however desirable, to give detailed descriptions of genera & species; short diagnoses of these would do, with a list of numbers of all of our specimens of each species, and any additional localities of yours.

When you send back our specimens, please complete the collection by duplicates from your stock, as we want to have the order perfectly represented.

Sincerely & affectionately yours
S. F. BAIRD

The parts of your work sent by Alex. have been duly received.

AGASSIZ to BAIRD

CAMBRIDGE Nov 1st, 1858(?)

My dear Baird,

Alex has answered part of your letter, and I have been considering what I can do with reference to the remainder. I have to husband with such parsimony, the little amount of time, during which I can daily look at anything, and I am so anxious to finish up the fishes of Wilkes that I have very little time for what you ask. But if its omission should be a grievance to you, I will contrive by dictation, to do it shortly. If I could only read the notes I took for that very purpose while I was working up my turtles, I could do what you want in a few days. As it is, it will be easier for me to take up the specimens, which are larger than handwriting and make up the necessary description. I think I have the objects still sufficiently in my mind to do it so. If I find my memory does not serve me well enough, I will let you know very soon.

I am truly amazed at the amount of work you have accomplished, and congratulate you hastily upon your achievements. I truly long to see your birds and reptiles, and the fishes also. My museum is increasing wonderfully from all quarters of the globe, and I have reasonable hopes of being soon able to put it in order. Meanwhile I amuse myself in bringing together things as they seem related to one another.

Truly yours,
L AGASSIZ

AGASSIZ to BAIRD

CAMBRIDGE *Nov 7 1858*

My dear Sir:

The rainy and overcast weather which has prevailed for the last few weeks has done me much good, and I have already begun upon your Turtles, and trust I shall be through by the time you want my notes. The specimens are so carefully stored up, that there can be no confusion about them, — at the same time, I will have all my reptiles packed for you, and would be glad to have them labelled in conformity with your recent identifications. I will send everything I have from North America, with the exception of the common species of this neighborhood, of which I have a large number of duplicates. I hope you may find something valuable among those of California. Should there be any species you have not, you are welcome to retain some specimens. I would even cede to you those of which I have no duplicates, if you will complete my collection by giving me all your species, even where you have only two specimens. I shall do the same for you with the Turtles and in course of time we may secure to me another fuller series.

Since the corporation of Harvard has granted me some means for the preservation of the Museum, I have made a beginning in the arrangement of my specimens. Among these, the Etheostomoids are in order. Besides those mentioned in the Catalogue of the fishes of the Tennessee River, I have 5 new genera and several new species. If you want yours labelled send me all you have. My assistant, Mr. Putnam, knows them well now and can label a gross in a day or two, and I shall give him directions to put up for you what you have not.

Yours very truly
L AGASSIZ

BAIRD to AGASSIZ

Nov. 13, 1858

My dear Professor Agassiz

I was truly glad to learn by your letter of the 7th that your eyes had improved sufficiently to warrant your undertaking the turtles and hope that they will not suffer in consequence. I shall be glad to have the MSS. as soon as you can prepare it, as it will come first in the report, and ought to go to press as early as possible.

I will be very glad to have the opportunity of looking over your reptiles and will label them as one group completing the series as fully as possible & returning them.

I will embrace the first chance to send you the Echinodermata of our collection to examine. As for our fishes, they are in confusion from having been transferred and not yet assorted. The transfer was made during my absence and what little arrangement there was before that has not been preserved. I hope in a few weeks, however, to have them more in order. I will then find the *Gasteropelecus*. Of *Mormyrus*, we have, I believe, no specimens.

Let me have your Saurians as soon as possible, as I am now at work on them and hope to finish them very shortly.

Sincerely yours
SPENCER F. BAIRD

BAIRD to AGASSIZ

Nov. 20, 1858

Dear Professor,

If you have any reptiles of Mexico, please send them along with the rest, as I take the whole North America as far south into Mexico as I can go. Single specimens may be of service in identifying described species of Wigmann and others and thus aid in determining allies for our own Southern borders.

In a few days I will send you my new list of N. Am. Birds.

Sincerely yours,
S. F. BAIRD

BAIRD to AGASSIZ

Dec. 4, 1858

Dear Professor,

I would have acknowledged receipt of your Saurians long since, but I gave your letter to Stimpson to answer in respect to the Crustacea (which he will be very happy to undertake) and he has not yet returned it, so I was without a reminder the way of an unanswered letter.

I do not find any new species in the collection of Saurians received, and I shall probably return it quite soon though I shall be somewhat delayed by waiting to add specimens from our collections. We can furnish a considerable increase to your stock. Our series of the Am. reptiles is pretty large for a beginning as it fills fully 4,500 jars, and amounting to at least 50,000 specimens.

I hope your eyes have enabled you to go on with the Chelonian report.

Truly yours,
S. F. BAIRD

BAIRD to AGASSIZ

Dec. 18, 1858

My dear Professor,

I have the pleasure of enclosing draft for $130.38, amount received from the University of Havana for Prof. Poey for a set of your works. Should you wish it, and will send me a form to copy and sign I will give any certificate that may enable you to receive back the duty which you can then pocket.

I had the set nicely bound before sending.

What is the price of the Zoological Atlas of the Fresh Water fishes, separate from the text and Atlas of Embryologie?

Yours truly,
S. F. Baird

BAIRD to AGASSIZ

Washington, *Jan. 6, 1859*

Dear Professor,

I enclose the certificate desired.

The copy of Fresh Water Fishes I wish to make a Christmas present to my brother in Reading.

I am very sorry I have not yet been able to pick out the Etheostomata of which we must have nearly 100 bottles. The fishes have been transferred from one part of the building to the other and the fishes all mixed up. I have no one to assort them but myself and I have not been able to work in this weather because it is very cold and the room is without fire so that the case does not look very promising. I will, however, do my best at the earliest moment of time.

Truly yours,
S. F. Baird

How come on the turtles?

AGASSIZ to BAIRD

Cambridge, *Feb. 2, 1859*

My dear Sir,

I have duly received your draft of $130.38, for which I return my best thanks. Let me know for whom you want the fresh water fishes. I shall put the price accordingly.

Ever truly yours
L Agassiz

AGASSIZ to BAIRD

CAMBRIDGE, *Feb. 9/59*

My dear Baird,

I introduce to you my young friend Mr. F. W. Putnam, — give him a good chance to see all you have, and listen to all his propositions and requests about the collections. Unable to write, I have talked the matter over with him. You will find him interested in the right way and you can fully trust him in anything you have to say.

Very truly yours,

L AGASSIZ

BAIRD to AGASSIZ

March 3, 1859

Dear Professor,

I am trying to see if I can raise money enough to send Kennicott to Hudson Bay, in the country north of the Saskatchewan early in the spring. Have you any funds you can devote to enabling him to collect fishes? He can go at moderate expense merely to collect dry skins, eggs, and insects. But to make alcoholic collections will require an extra cart to carry alcohol, nets etc.. Please let me know whether you can contribute and how much. The extra expenses to do good fishing would amount to $200 or $250.

Sincerely yours,

SPENCER F. BAIRD

AGASSIZ to BAIRD

CAMBRIDGE *March 11 1859*

My dear Baird,

Brilliant as my prospects are now for the Museum I do not think I shall have cash at my disposal before midsummer, and I have no way of anticipating my receipts — otherwise I would at once adopt your proposition to contribute the fishing part of Mr. Kennicott's expedition.

I feel however it would be very important not to let that opportunity pass unimproved. I would therefore make the following suggestion — that the Smithsonian Institution make the advance, and on Mr. Kennicott's return I will take up that part of the expense which you suggest.

Mr. Putnam told me that you are now collecting birds eggs largely and every where. Could you not provide your collectors with cans and alcohol to collect also specimens in liquor (spirits) that I may do for the birds what I have done for the turtles. I would of course repay all such expenses.

Consider this matter as very important for Ornithology. If the results prove only half as instructive as it has been for the turtles, I would consider that great advance had been made. Where as in the north an indefinite number of eggs can be obtained, several dozen of each species in every stage of development should be collected and the eggs cracked at the blunt end so as to facilitate the penetration of the alcohol. Of the rare species of course, I would be satisfied with whatever can be obtained. But of those which could be collected by the thousand, fifty at least representing every stage of growth should be put up.

Putnam told me further that Professor Henry still continues adverse to alcoholic specimens. If that be so let me make an arrangement not to lose any opportunity by which the Museum in Cambridge could supply all your expeditions with the means of collecting alcoholic specimens as well as dry ones. And when the time comes when you can relieve me of it, we may then divide the expense and the results in a manner which can certainly be made satisfactory. I want to secure in that way not only all our lower animals but also all our birds & mammals with the sole exception of the larger quadrupeds. But of these even embryos might be obtained from the pregnant females.

Could you not see that we get in this way buffalo embryos as well as those of the other western animals? I will write to Prof. Henry to try to overcome his opposition to alcoholic specimens. In that way only can we render our Museums superior to those of Europe.

Very truly yours,
L AGASSIZ

BAIRD to AGASSIZ

March 19, 1859

Dear Professor,

In preparing a new edition of our land animal pamphlet and a special off circular we call [illegible] allocating to the Soc. any embryos of birds we already have a few too many, and doubtless shall have more.

Whenever you can conveniently make the arrangements to please furnish at our disposal to enable us to invite alcoholic collections on a much larger scale than we can afford, we can have a vast increase of valuable materials. Opportunities of additions are almost daily lost because we can not embrace them in time.

We now have large numbers of mammals in alcohol at least 5000 specimens and the embryos of buffalo, antelope, deer, beavers and many others.

Very truly yours,
S F BAIRD

AGASSIZ to BAIRD

CAMBRIDGE *April 1, 1859*

Dear sir

Will you have the kindness to send me "Vetenskap Akademie Hand-
lingar" for 1844, which contains "Oversigt af Skandinaviens Echinoder-
mer" by Koren and Düben (page 239/—.?

Very truly yours

L AGASSIZ

We have already $220,000 for the museum subscribed and granted by the
State, but when the money comes it is not yet possible to say.

BAIRD to AGASSIZ

April 8, 1859

Dear Professor,

I send by express the book asked for & Crase Sys. [?] and return the accompanying receipt. Please send it back as soon as you are done with it.

I am very glad to hear of your success in the matter of Museum and
hope you may soon realize all your plans.

Truly yours,

S. F. BAIRD

AGASSIZ to BAIRD

CAMBRIDGE, *June 3, 1859*

My dear Baird,

It gives me pleasure in introducing to you my friend & pupil Mr. Theodore Lyman of Boston, whom you will find thoroughly posted up in the
Nat. Hist. of the lower animals.

How far are you with the Reptiles?

Very truly yours,

L. AGASSIZ

AGASSIZ to BAIRD

CAMBRIDGE, *Aug. 18th, 1859*

My dear Baird,

I am still under such a pressure of business since my return, on account
of the finishing of our Museum Building, the roof of which goes up this
week, to enable us to move into it next month, that I have no time to give
you now any account of my proceedings in Europe, except to say that I

have bought about 50,000 specimens of fossils among which splendid Ich-
thyosauri, *Mystriosaurus* etc.

I enclose a letter from Capt. Woodbury which needs no comment. Dr.
Wheatland who studies with me would have gladly gone, did not the
physician forbid his going on account of the present state of his health. So
you do the best you can with this excellent chance. Should you have no
means of providing the man who may go with alcohol, cans etc. I will
provide for them myself & divide the spoils with you in a fair proportion,
according to the arrangements you may make with a young physician to
go in behalf of the Smithsonian Inst. Be quick in the matter, for I suppose
the Dr. will have to leave from Charleston by the 4th or 9th.

> Ever truly your friend
> L Agassiz

AGASSIZ to BAIRD

CAMBRIDGE, *Sept 9th 1859*

Dear Baird,

I have just seen Dr. Holder, who called for information about the Tortugas. I have offered him a full supply of everything needed for collecting.
In case you should not be prepared to aid him in his outfit I will do all
the necessary & yet let you have a good share of the result.

> Yours very truly,
> L Agassiz

BAIRD to AGASSIZ

Oct. 22, 1859

Dear Professor,

Much obliged for the reference of Capt. Woodbury's letter. I have applied
to several gentlemen who may be available. We will gladly accept your
proposal about the alcohol and tanks if we find the men.

I am very anxious to see all the nice things you have brought from
Europe. I must try and get on next summer for that purpose.

I send to you today a few *Etheostoma* for Putnam's examination.

> Sincerely yours,
> S. F. Baird

BAIRD to AGASSIZ

Oct 24, 1859

Dear Professor,

Prof. Henry wishes me to enclose the accompanying letter and to ask you what you think of the proposition. He says we cannot buy the MSS although if the Memoir on the sheep etc. was finished complete in English without too many illustrations something might be done. How would Wyman take up the subject?

Please return the letter with your opinion.

Truly yours,

S. F. BAIRD

BAIRD to AGASSIZ

Nov. 6, 1859

Dear Professor,

Dr. Cooper, having concluded not to take the place of Surgeon at the Tortugas, I have offered it to Dr. J. B. Holder of Lynn, Mass., who I understand was somewhat versed in Marine Zoology, and a good surgeon [illegible].

I am every day almost obliged to let slip chances of furnishing alcohol, tanks and bottles to parties in various parts of the world, Central America, Mexico, West Indes etc, a large proportion of which would be productive of excellent results. Offers are being constantly made of assistance by Naval officers, consuls and others which almost breaks my heart to slight.

Sincerely & truly yours,

S. F. BAIRD

AGASSIZ to BAIRD

CAMBRIDGE *Nov. 8 1859*

My dear Baird,

If you decide upon sending me your *Etheostoma* do not think it superfluous to forward all the *E. olmstedii,* for I find that that species is by no means so widely distributed as we thought previously. If you will compare your specimens from Pittsburg, you will see that they have no scales upon the cheeks and throat, while those of Carlisle have. Again, there are others which have only a few rows of scales along the lateral line.

If you could send me any *Mormyrus,* of which I have not a single specimen, I think I could find out characters, by which to separate the

Scomberesoces from the other Pharyngognathi of Muller, which would be a great improvement in the classification. For the same purpose, I want also a specimen of the *Gasteropelecus,* which Wyman sent you, and of which he has not a specimen left.

Very truly yours

L AGASSIZ

BAIRD to AGASSIZ

March 14, 1860

My dear Professor,

I enclose a letter just received from Prof. Poey which explains itself. I have been in correspondence with him about the collection of types of his *200 new species of Cuban Fishes* and he wanted to know what size he is to send.

We have no room for large specimens; a foot in length being as much as we can accommodate. Shall I ask him to send the large ones for you at your expense? I am anxious to have these types here and dont care whether they are in your collection or ours so that they are in the country. He proposes to collect these fish, new specimens and old without any charge beyond the actual cost to him.

He is entirely at sea about bottles. Our Smithsonian [illegible] Tanks will be much better. These might be sent him filled with alcohol, and we might perhaps get the Spanish minister to have them entered into Havana free of duty.

He wants a good many species of our fish in exchange, some only of which we can supply. There are also a good many books which we have that he wants.

Let me know what to say to Poey for you or write him directly. Please inform me, however, what you tell him so that we may work together in the matter. If you greatly prefer it I will turn the whole exchanges over to you although I would prefer to have a series of the small specimens here.

Please return Poey's letter as soon as possible with your conclusions so that I may write him.

Sincerely & affectionately yours

S.F.BAIRD

March 23, 1860

Dear Professor,

Please send me some word in reference to my communication in regard to Prof. Poey.

Sincerely yours,

S. F. BAIRD

AGASSIZ to BAIRD

CAMBRIDGE *April 12, 1860*

My dear Baird,

It is not every week I can stand even so trifling a tax of my eyes as is required to write a few lines, so excuse my delay & laconism. As I have probably the largest collection of fishes of our southern coasts, it would be best if the Cuba collection was united with it, for the sake of facilitating comparison. Moreover I have the means of securing & preserving large specimens, such as sharks & skates to a length of five feet & more. Such large specimens being indispensible to characterize truly certain species. Again a large number of specimens of various sizes of all species are desirable and as I can go to the expense of securing them, if you will write to Mr. Poey to make such a collection I will assume the cost and when the whole is arranged and compared with what I have already, you may get from me what you want within the limits to which you restrict yourself, as to number of specimens & their size.

Not to write two letters would you be so kind as to present to Prof. Henry the claims of our Museum to a series of specimens of the shells of the Expl. Exp. I should like that the collection were made in the way I have expressed my wishes respecting it to Mr. Carpenter.[43] I am now progressing very satisfactorily with the arrangement of the Museum and hope before long to be able myself to send you something worth having. Alex has now been a whole year on the pacific coast and is constantly sending me splendid collections. He is now going into the interior of California and will remain there during the next summer.

Yours very truly

L AGASSIZ

BAIRD to AGASSIZ

May 2, 1860

Dear Professor,

I have written your wishes in detail to Prof. Poey and hope he will carry them out.

I send by express about a dozen species of Cuban Fish. Poey some time ago sent a small jar full and told me to send the duplicates to you. He promises to repeat the whole in fresher specimens, these being old.

Sincerely yours,

S. F. BAIRD

---

[43] Philip P. Carpenter (1819–77), born in England, settled in Montreal, bought a mass of California shells and subsequently became a conchologist.

BAIRD to AGASSIZ

May 11, 1860

Dear Professor,

I sent a list of fish forwarded from Prof. Poey some time ago. We out-
fitted a missionary to Japan some time ago with alcohol and bottles, this
amounted to about $20.00. He is enthusiastic and promises to do well. We
gave him other outfit worth as much more. Would you like to pay the first
bill and take half his collections?

Truly yours,
S. F. BAIRD

BAIRD to AGASSIZ

May 19, 1860

Dear sir,

We have this day sent by Adams Express a series of the larger duplicates
of the shells of the Exploring Expedition which I beg you will accept on
behalf of the Smithsonian Institution for the 1. Museum of Comparative Zoology. 2. Museum of the Academy of Natural Sciences.

They consist chiefly of the Indo-Pacific species of large size. The smaller
kind will be transmitted hereafter as also rare kinds from other localities.

These specimens are not labeled, but consisting of the commoner forms
which can readily be identified by any experienced conchologist.

AGASSIZ to BAIRD

CAMBRIDGE, *May 21, 1860*

My dear Baird,

I will gladly share the expenses and returns of an experiment in collecting
in Japan. I have myself already sent twelve cans to Amoor, where a Boston
merchant has a very intelligent agent.

Very Truly yours
L AGASSIZ

AGASSIZ to BAIRD

CAMBRIDGE, *June 8, 1860*

My dear Baird,

I enclose a check for $20.73 for supplies to the Japan expedition.

I shall have the cans for Prof. Poey ready in a few days; meanwhile
send me again his direction, for it is not readable in your note.

Ever truly yours
L AGASSIZ

P.S. I have duly received the two large boxes of shells, which Mr. Carpenter has informed me would soon come, but have not yet been able to

take care of them. Boxes are pouring in from every quarter of the globe and the arrangement of the Museum is progressing in a satisfactory manner. I hope you may come on this summer. I shall not leave Cambridge for a day, except to go to Newport.

LA

BAIRD to AGASSIZ

June 11, 1860

My dear Professor,

I have this day received your draft of $20.73 to cover your share of the Japan Exped. As soon as I get the receipted bill, I will forward it to you.

Poey's address is: Prof. Felipe Poey
Calle de L'Armistad 118
Havana

When you ship, advise him of the same. Do not send any alcohol on because with duty it will cost more than he can buy it for in Havana.

I hope to get on to see you this summer. I want to go over your great building and enjoy what you are doing. I only wish we had half the chance to do justice to our Zoological Collections. We are so hampered by our want of means to buy alcohol, jars etc and of suitable accommodations that I am often tempted to give up in despair.

Ever yours,
S. F. Baird

BAIRD to AGASSIZ

June 14, 1860

Dear Professor,

I have been just fitting up an outfit for Dr. Hayes[44] by direction of Prof. Henry. I believe he has nearly everything necessary including dredge, alcohol, Tanks etc. as far as he is likely to be able to use them but he will want some small collecting cans. Can you send him ten of the smallest size that can be carried by hand on the sledge parties? If so, please forward at once by Adams Express prepaid to Dr. I. I. Hayes, care Geo. N. Lawrence, 172 Pearl St. Corner Pine.

Sincerely yours,
S. F. Baird

As Hayes leaves in a few days no time is to be lost.

---

[44] Isaac I. Hayes (1832–81), American arctic explorer, accompanied the second Grinnell expedition (1853–55) under E. K. Kane as surgeon, Convinced during this expedition of an open polar sea, he solicited subscriptions which enabled him to outfit an expedition which sailed from Boston on July 7, 1860.

BAIRD to AGASSIZ

June 16, 1860

Dear Professor,

I enclose detached bill of Japan outfit. The explorer is Dr. C. E. Schimmel, a medical missionary in Japan.

Dr. Hayes sails for Boston or Newburyport and is now at Fremont House. Please send the little tanks to him there and not to New York, also any other equipment you think fit. We have sent one chest of tanks with probably 12 gallons of alcohol, also ass. bottles, or just dredge etc.

Sincerely yours,

S. F. Baird

BAIRD to AGASSIZ

June 22, 1860

Dear sir,

Mr. Theodore Lyman has in preparation a Memoir on the Ophiuroidae which he proposes to submit to the Institution for publication. Admitting that this work is perfect of its kind, and fully up to the requirements of Science, I would be glad to have your opinion as to the expediency of our publishing such works as this which I understand to be simply a description of certain species of marine animals.

Sincerely yours,

S. F. Baird

BAIRD to JOSEPH HENRY about AGASSIZ's letter to HENRY

July 27, 1860

Dear Professor,

I enclose a memorandum of reply to Prof. Agassiz's letter which covers a good deal of the ground taken by him. His whole mode of viewing the case is so queer that I hardly know how to meet it seriously. He might as well insist that a list of arrivals at a Hotel should specify the age, height, personal history etc. instead of the mere names alone as is usually given. A list for checking off and labelling is one thing: and a work on conchology with its synonymy is another. Each has its object and its uses: ours professes to be the first and lays no claim to the second although Prof. A. argues the matter as if it did.

Please talk with Mr. Gill[45] about this matter.

Very truly yours,

S. F. Baird

---

[45] Theodore Nicholas Gill (1837–1914), zoologist, was born in New York City. Through Baird's influence he was appointed a member of the group that was preparing reports on the zoological findings of the Northwestern Boundary survey. In 1861 he became a member of the Smithsonian staff and soon in charge of its library. When (in 1866) that library was placed in the Library of Congress he became senior assistant librarian there. He was highly esteemed as an expert in ichthyology.

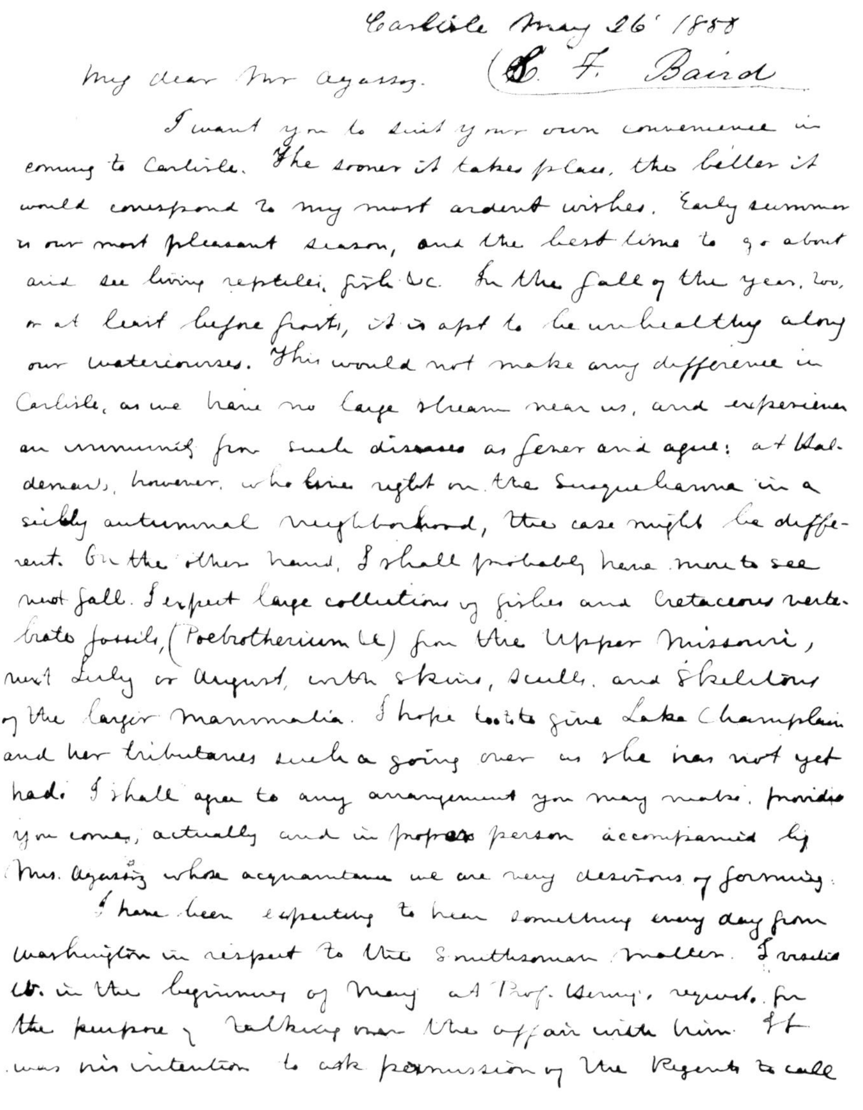

PLATE 13

Carlisle May 26' 1858

My dear Mr Agassiz.   S. F. Baird

I want you to suit your own convenience in coming to Carlisle. The sooner it takes place, the better it would correspond to my most ardent wishes. Early summer is our most pleasant season, and the best time to go about and see living reptiles, fish &c. In the fall of the year, too, or at least before frosts, it is apt to be unhealthy along our watercourses. This would not make any difference in Carlisle, as we have no large stream near us, and experience an immunity from such diseases as fever and ague; at Waldeman's, however, who live right on the Susquehanna in a sickly autumnal neighborhood, the case might be different. On the other hand, I shall probably have more to see next fall. I expect large collections of fishes and Cretaceous vertebrate fossils, (Poebrotherium &c) from the Upper Missouri, next July or August, with skins, sculls, and skeletons of the larger mammalia. I hope to to give Lake Champlain and her tributaries such a going over as she has not yet had. I shall agree to any arrangement you may make, provided you come, actually and in proper person accompanied by Mrs. Agassiz whose acquaintance we are very desirous of forming.

I have been expecting to hear something every day from Washington in respect to the Smithsonian matter. I visited it, in the beginning of May at Prof. Henry's request, for the purpose of talking over the affair with him. It was his intention to ask permission of the Regents to call

Letter from Baird to Agassiz, May 26, 1858

PLATE 14

me in, next winter, whenever the proper opportunity might arrive. I still look for something definite
on the subject within the next few weeks. It is quite
possible however, that the regents may deny Prof.
Henry's request. As to the Mnny fishes I have none
ready, I did not expect to get at, and work up my species
before getting more of them, as also those which you have
collected. I also wanted to have you here before hand, and
give me the benefit of your experience. Can't the plates
remain in Slates yus, until we are ready for them. None of your
plates have yet been executed, and it was the arrangement
to have our joint productions in one paper, was it not. Is
Sonrel to do any more of my fish? It would be a grand
thing for us to have all our present species, and those
to be procured this fall, together, and then examine
and confer respecting each. Cannot this be accomplished?

I have just finished reading "Lake Superior" and can
safely say that nothing ever instructed me more. Your
Botanical article is a model of imitation, and the Ethy.
ological not a whit behind it. I wonder if the day will
ever come when I shall be able to write such papers:
I fear not. I do not see how the men of diluvial currents
can stand after the push you give them with your glaciers. I have been finding some scratches on the sandstones
of our North Mountain, running north and south,
while the mountain chains go nearly east and west.

Any little help which I can render to your "Zoological
Journal" will be most cheerfully rendered. Such a periodical
ought to be supportable both in respect to articles and subscribers.
Will it be on the plan of "Annales des Sc. Nat.," "Wiegman's archiv"
or what.
                                        Very truly yours
Prof L. Agassiz Cambridge.   S. W. Baird

Continuation of letter of May 26, 1858

PLATE 15

Four naturalists, contemporaries of Baird and Agassiz:
Standing, l. to r., Robert Kennicott, Henry Ulke
Seated, l. to r., William Stimpson, Henry Bryant

PLATE 16

Samuel S. Haldeman, scientist and philologist,
another contemporary of Baird and Agassiz

John S. Newberry, physician and naturalist,
contemporary of Baird and Agassiz

BAIRD to AGASSIZ

Oct 14, 1860

Dear Professor,

I enclose a list of a very complete collection of European birds, 343 species and about 2900 specimens: many in large numbers, stunning varieties etc. The price 500 thalers ($375.00) is very cheap for a collection embracing so many rare species.

This list was sent by Prince Max. who endorses the accuracy of identifications. He does not mention name of owner but promises it if the purchase is concluded upon.

If you care for such a collection you may never have a better opportunity of getting a large series at moderate price.

If you dont take the collection please return the list to me.

I find many neat things among the accumulations here. Kennicott addressed 17 packages of rarities. He will sweep the region north of Slave Lake.

Please send on the tanks as soon as convenient as several opportunities now offer to use them to advantage. The new consul general to [illegible] Island is anxious to be supplied.

Prof. Henry has not yet returned.

Truly yours,
S.F.BAIRD

BAIRD to AGASSIZ

Oct 30, 1860

Dear Professor,

Mr. Drexler, our taxidermist, has just returned from a six months absence at the lower end of Hudson's Bay, having gone as far north as Fort Georgia. He made a very large collection of skins of rare northern birds, eggs, embryos in alcohol, fish (several kinds each of trout, whitefish, suckers etc.) marine and fresh water mollusks, Echini, Crustaceans, fossils etc, filling eight boxes and kegs. These have not yet been received, having been sent by way of London. But we hope to have them in November.

The expenses of this expedition have been met by private contributions chiefly of Dr. Bryant[46] and my own: the Smithsonian in view of the many other calls on its funds for exploration only giving up Mr. Drexler's time, he receiving his salary all the while. I find now on getting in the bills

---

[46] Henry Bryant (1820–68), an M.D. from Harvard, served for a time in the medical service of the army during the early part of the Civil War but was obliged to leave the service in 1863 on account of ill health. To restore his health he spent much time in the open air studying birds. In 1866 he purchased the LaFresnaye collection of birds, containing many original types of American species. This collection was finally deposited in the Museum of Comparative Zoology, Cambridge, Mass.

of expense that the amount collected falls short of the whole by about $125.00. The deficiency must be supplied someway, and I would be very glad if you could furnish it, as I do not want to peddle out shares of the collection in small amounts but would prefer dividing with you the entire lot after giving Dr. Bryant what he wants of skins and eggs.

Drexler had brought a few things among his baggage, all of which are new to us, skins of trout, *Lota, Etheostoma,* etc. all new to us. He found a considerable number of reptiles, snakes, frogs etc. as far north as Fort Georgia.

Please let me hear from you as soon as possible, as it is necessary to send the money to the Hudson Bay Co. as soon as possible.

Let me have a word in answer to some other recent letters and oblige.

Yours sincerely,

S. F. BAIRD

AGASSIZ to BAIRD

CAMBRIDGE *Dec. 6 1860*

My dear Baird,

Last October I expected at our business meeting of the board of Trustees of the Museum to receive a large appropriation which would have enabled me to do what you wished me to. I expected the more confidently that it should be so since part of the state grant has come in instead of which the Trustees have decided that the State money should be funded. This cuts me short of every resource for a year, though it eventually will secure the Museum an income of $9000 for active operations. I am therefore well satisfied at the prospect, though for the time being I am entirely crippled; This will explain why I have not answered your proposition respecting skins, eggs of Kennicott's collections. But now that our misery is evident to every body there has been set on foot a new subscription to give me the means of shifting over this year to the next were it not for the crisis I would probably have already what I want. Hope notwithstanding our troubles to get it before long. I shall then if not too late cheerfully accept the proposition about the collection of Kennicott. Now I am doubtful about the eggs. I don't much like the idea of a bird egg collected without the nests. My idea is that each nest should contain the normal number of eggs which the bird lays so as to afford an additional ocular information. Yet I know there are many which it will be difficult to get so if my means should permit I might yet change my view. Meanwhile I return the Catalogue & also the receipt for your last invoice. Very shortly I shall be able to send you more cans. When Prof. Henry was here I had a very long and satisfied conversation with him. From which I fully understood the difficulties under which you have been laboring in regard to the Museum and I want now to have as free a talk with you upon the matter as I had with him. I believe Prof. Henry is right in considering the collections as superfetation of the Smithsonian Institution as long as Congress does not make an appropriation for a National Museum. You may trust me to say so without the least reference to what I might get from you if his policy was at once strictly adhered to for as I promise it to you I shall set aside for you whatever I can spare whether I get anything or not and will keep it until you send for it. But it is obvious to me from the enormous expenditure which the increase of the Museum renders necessary that the means of the Smithsonian are inadequate to carry out together the publication system, build up a library, maintain a Museum, carry out the System of Internat. Exchange & support original researches. I am sure you would do for the country with your present means more good if you were heartily to join in the views of Prof. Henry & secure at the same time his hearty exertions in behalf of a separate Museum. Nay you may in the end have the whole Smithsonian building with Library for the Museum alone if you are wise. If I am able I propose to send during the vacation of January and February some of my young men to take out the specimens which I should like to have of which we spoke when you were here. Meanwhile please mention to Prof. Henry that Ordway is finishing up a Monog. of the Portunidae for which he wants specimens which Stimpson is willing to pack the moment he has leave to do so; so please settle this as soon as you can so that Ordway may finish his work before he goes to Washington. I should like to know whether the time during which I could send you the necessary help for packing the specimens I have been discussing will suit you. They could go from the 15th of January to the end of February.

Yours very truly
L AGASSIZ

BAIRD to AGASSIZ

Dec. 8, 1860

Dear sir,

Mr. Theodore Lyman, in returning the Smithsonian collection of Ophiuroidae which he has been engaged in examining, informs us that he has retained certain duplicates, which, with our permission, he proposes to place in the Cambridge Museum of Comparative Zoology. To this we readily consent and take pleasure in presenting them to the Museum under the usual conditions.

Sincerely yours,
S. F. BAIRD

BAIRD to AGASSIZ

Dec. 29, 1860

Dear sir,

In obedience to your request we sent you on Saturday the Portunidae of the Smithsonian Institution, selected and packed by Dr. Stimpson. As far as possible, we have forwarded said duplicate specimens which you will please present to the Museum of Comparative Zoology in the name of this Institution. This unique offer you will please take the utmost care of and return later. The list of specimens accompanying the box will indicate which may be kept and which are to be sent back.

Sincerely yours,

S. F. BAIRD

BAIRD to AGASSIZ

Jan 23, 1861

My dear Prof. Agassiz,

Your last letter was received just before it became necessary for me to visit Phila. with Mrs. Baird on account of her health and since my return everything has been in such a whirl of disunion, politics, pressure of official occupation, sickness in my family and personal indisposition that I have not known a moment when I could sit down and reply.

I am sorry to hear of your temporary monetary difficulties and shall be very uneasy in regards to the future of Mr. Kennicott's operation, as consequent thereon. Acting upon your proposition to contribute $250.00 annually during his absence, he was informed of the subscription and authorized to expand his operations by employing Indians to help him and also to remain one or two years longer in the country. He will receive this information in April and it will be another year before a countermand can reach him in the Interior of Russian America towards the Behring Straits. As it will not be necessary to put more to his credit before next year I hope you will be able to secure the necessary funds by that time.

His collections thus far returned have been of the highest interest, *Salmo mackenzie, Thymallus,* numerous trout and Coregoni, and all the fresh water species described by Richardson with additional ones: skeletons of *Antilocapra, Rangifer,* skins, specimens entire of numerous rodents, lemmings etc., many very rare arctic birds, eggs and embryos, insects too numerous to mention.

I am sorry you think there is any difference of sentiment between Professor Henry and myself in regard to the Smithsonian Museum. On the contrary I consider it a duty to maintain his policy as far as I understand it and

I shall always endeavor to do so. If he were to forbid the entrance of a single additional specimen of Natural History into the building and give me instructions to that effect I would unhesitatingly obey him and act accordingly. I am well aware that the present means and space of the building do not admit a vast and unlimited addition of materials such as you can have at Cambridge. All I do care for is to do full justice to the materials we are obliged by law of Congress to receive and keep in order, but I have no desire to make a show with these. I am much interested in the development and exploration of any new regions of North America and Mexico but will not restrict my views to Natural History and feel as much gratified when we get a batch of important Meteorological reports from a new arctic station, as with the birds and beasts accompanying them.

In accordance with Prof. Henry's policy and my own special predilections, I am anxious to see collected here [as] complete a series of the Vertebrata and alcoholic invertebrates of North America as possible, and such others from the rest of the world as are necessary properly to elucidate their study and such other closely allied species where we have collections from Government Naval Expeditions, [illegible] like to see materials from other places which may be necessary to elucidate them. When these are all determined, labelled and reported on, I am willing to let them stand as types only caring to prevent their destruction. All duplicates of elaborated and identified collections I wish to see distributed throughout the best museums, and have fresh materials come in. I look on these as additional means of usefulness in this respect where the distributees of duplicates have specimens equally of types to return. I, of course, want the Institution to possess the privilege of calling for them when it wishes. If they are bulky and require care, they may best be left undisturbed; if of small size and easily kept I see no objection in taking them and keeping in readiness.

If at any time Congress should authorize a National Museum of the first class and place money at the command of the Smithsonian Institution to extend its plans and embrace such an idea, I have no doubt Prof. Henry would cheerfully undertake its management. Or if the Museum were placed in charge of some other department he would willingly yield what he has now, on repayment of past expenses. I would be perfectly ready as far as I am concerned to see the entire Museum join with any other Charge if the right of Science and Scientific men were fully protected. Whenever such an extension of plan or change of supervision may be ordered the right of calling in corresponding museums for returns of such collections as were left in abeyance may be exercised.

What worries me now is the impossibility of acting in the interest of Natural History by taking advantage of the many opportunities presented for gathering materials from unexplored localities for the want of means of transportation and cost of alcohol etc. I don't ask to keep these for the Smithsonian: not even a single series if indivisible. I am willing to collect things for Cambridge, Boston, New York, Phila., London, anywhere so that they are collected. I was not a week ago obliged to decline an offer from the vicinity of Vera Cruz to collect largely of the marine animals of the coast under plea of poverty.

So strongly am I urged by the work to use passing opportunities that may never be renewed, that I have expended from my small salary in the past year over $200.00 without any expectation of ever seeing it reimbursed.

As I have already stated, the expenditures I would like to see on the part of the Institution are for exploration of unknown regions and localities. For this setting aside the great operation of Mr. Kennicott, five hundred dollars per annum would be an ample average, as much more for freight and $250 to $300 for jars, alcohol and incidentals would meet the main necessities of the case. Of course mounting specimens for show would be additional, but not bearing particularly on the question of scientific progress.

I am in despair about the Cambridge jars. I can really do nothing to speak of in the way of selecting duplicates until we have the means of assembling what we have now in bulk. I would have written you before about the coming on of some of your aids but that I wanted to have the jars. They can not help in the selection of the types as this is done by Stimpson and Gill, and will be completed in a few days. I will write Ordway a note on the subject by this mail.

Very truly yours,
SPENCER F. BAIRD

AGASSIZ to BAIRD

CAMBRIDGE *Jan. 28, 1861*

My dear Baird,

I have written Prof. Henry last Saturday asking him when I could send for the specimens I want from you, despairing to get an answer from you, which has however just come.

You need not be anxious about my promise respecting Kennicott. I shall pay it myself if the Museum does not get relieved before spring. What I am aiming now is to obtain an appropriation of $12–15000 for jars and alcohol to make thorough work with our alcoholic specimens. If I get it or anything I shall write to you again with reference to taking advantage of all the opportunities that are afforded for collecting in new regions.

I am very glad to learn from you that I was mistaken in supposing that there was a difference between you and Prof. Henry with reference to the Museum.

By the way the type specimens of Ophiuridae set aside for you by Lyman are at your disposal or may remain there until called for, just as you please.

Ordway tells me that your jars have gone to Washington. So let me know by return mail whether I can send my young men now. I would send Putnam to take the fishes, Ordway[47] for the Crustacea and Verrill[48] for the Corals & Birds. If they are welcome now I will send you a more elaborate list of desiderata. I wish they could go now, as we have a vacation to the end of February.

Very truly yours
L AGASSIZ

BAIRD to AGASSIZ

Jan 31, 1861

My dear Professor,

Yours of the 28th ult. was received today. I am happy to say that the bottles have arrived and that there will now be difficulty in the way of our assorting mixed lots of which there are so many. I will be very happy to have the young gentlemen of your museum come on, and I will be as attentive to them as I can under the enormous pressure of all kinds upon us. They will perhaps be in time to help us fight in defense of our Scientific treasures if invaded by the threatened mob.

Sincerely yours,
S. F. BAIRD

AGASSIZ to BAIRD

CAMBRIDGE *Feb 9, 1861*

My dear Baird,

In accordance with our previous understanding and having received last week a letter from Prof. Henry stating that you were ready for us, I send you today three of my young friends, Putnam, Ordway & Verrill to relieve you as much as possible in the work of putting aside specimens for our Museum. They leave for Washington this afternoon and I recommend them to your good will and friendly consideration. Of course I am anxious to get

---

[47] Albert Ordway, of Richmond, Va., was a student and assistant of Agassiz and was well known for his monograph of the genus *Callinectes*.

[48] Addison E. Verrill (1839–1926), zoologist, was born in Greenwood, Maine. He was Agassiz's assistant in the Museum of Comparative Zoology from 1860–64 when he was called to Yale University as professor of zoology. For 16 years (1871–87) he was associated with Baird in charge of the scientific work of the United States Commission of Fish and Fisheries in southern New England. Verrill was a painstaking investigator with an uncanny aptitude for close discrimination. It was once said that he discovered a thousand undescribed forms.

from you all that which you can possibly spare; but at the same time I trust you will in due time find that a liberal cooperation with our Museum will be no loss to you. Our accessions are truly extraordinary and if I get what I now expect from the friends of the Museum in Boston we shall be able to go on at as rapid a rate of increase as we can manage. I have given my young representatives full instructions as to what I should like to get from you, so that it would be best for your proceedings & save time if you would have at once a conference with them in order to agree upon a definite *modus operandi*. Should there be any point on which you want information after that, write me at once. Not receiving another letter from you, I took it for granted that you considered Prof. Henry's letter to me as containing all that need be settled before proceeding to work and now I commend once more the interest of our collections to your kind consideration.

Yours very truly
L AGASSIZ

AGASSIZ to BAIRD

CAMBRIDGE *Feb. 16, 1861*

My dear Baird,

I can only write a few words, as I am very busy; but I must thank you most heartily for the kind reception you have given to my young friends who feel very grateful to you. There is only one point respecting your policy with which I do not coincide; that of sending *type specimens* abroad without stipulating *returns of as many type specimens*. If you do so you will make it impossible for ten or twenty years for any american Museum to obtain such types and thus retard the progress of science in this country, and keep us all in a position of inferiority with reference to european Museums. The british Museum is the last I would thus favor as their policy is as narrow minded as that of the Academy of Nat. Sc. in Philadelphia. The truth is you can get nothing from them for comparison or examination, since they have only single specimens. As evidence I enclose a letter from Gray, to whom I had sent the choicest Echinoderms asking in return only duplicates of any kind of that class of species described by him. When he has your specimens he will serve you in the same way, if you dont look out. Please return this letter.

Ever truly yours
L AGASSIZ

I shall write to Prof. Henry

BAIRD to AGASSIZ

Feb. 21, 1861

My dear Professor Agassiz,

I duly received your letter of the 16th and shall not fail to urge the view it takes upon Prof. Henry's attention. It was an idea that had not occurred to me but I see the propriety of it.

I will return Dr. Gray's letter as soon as I can bring it before Prof. Henry.

Sincerely yours,

S.F BAIRD

AGASSIZ to BAIRD

March 4th 1861

My dear Baird,

The Bill granting $20,000 to the Museum has passed the Legislature, so that I can now move freely. How many days may pass before I can draw the money I do not exactly know, but I trust it will be in time to forward my subscription to Kennicott and to your egg man on Lake Winnipeg. The Boston Nat. Hist. Society has also been successful in its application for a reservation of land on the Back Bay grounds. It will be our fault if hereafter Zoology is not making progress in this part of the country. But if we would do the most that may be done with our means we should all come to an understanding in order not to attempt the same things and thus waste our resources in producing the same results over and over again, instead of advancing each in a special direction. Wyman, with whom I had a conference on that subject fully approves this suggestion and I wish I could come to a similar understanding with you. In this way the collections of each of our institutions would have a distinct character and all would be equally valuable and important in their specialty. If you approve of such a plan let me know what is to be your policy and your aim, that I may cooperate to the limits of my ability. As for myself I propose to pursue chiefly two series of investigations with reference to which all the collections in the Museum here will be arranged. 1. To represent the correspondence in the order of succession of the animals of past geological periods and the relative standing or rank of the animals now living and as far as possible also their embryonic growth. 2. To make faunal collections illustrating the mode of association and geographical distribution of animals upon the whole surface of the globe.

I do not propose to make general systematic collections of any one class of the animal kingdom embracing in a methodical order all the species known of the class. So that when arranged as I propose to arrange it in our

Museum will in no way resemble those which exist now. I am not appre-
hensive of interfering with any body or being interfered with; but I should
like to know what you propose that I may cooperate with you.

You can help me best now in aiding me to make local collections, as
complete as possible and in obtaining material for the embryology and meta-
morphosis of all common animals of which numerous specimens may easily
be obtained. I shall send Verrill to Lawrence next week to negotiate the purchase of W. Martin's California birds. I have lately entered into an arrangement with a backwoodsman for a collection of the fauna over which the
Buffalo roves. I have sent a collector to the Fijis to explore that group of
islands, and one of my students has gone to Zanzibar to remain there for
4 years to explore the seas between Africa, Arabia and the Deccan. This
will give me means for exchanges to obtain faunal collections from other regions. — For my "Contributions" only do I propose to go on working
systematically and critically at the principles of classification, but without
special reference to the general arrangement of the Museum since any results
so obtained can have reference only to one feature of the collections the rank
of the types in their respective classes.

By the way I have already answered your request about Echinoderms by
informing Stimpson that I would gladly let him have everything I possess
of that class, provided he gives me an opportunity of examining in my
turn everything he has. I want now only to call your attention to the
fact, that it would be worth his while to hunt up all the Echinoderms
scattered through your store rooms, of which Verrill tells me there is a
great quantity and to send them to me for identification. As I have all
the original drawings of the Expl. Exp. I could no doubt make out most
of them and thus recover the localities which are carefully noticed upon all
the drawings.

Very truly yours
L AGASSIZ

AGASSIZ to BAIRD

March 9, 1861

My dear Baird,

Strange as it may appear it has been impossible to have the copper cans
ready before this, owing to the pressure of business for southern exports. I
am promised to have them in a few days. Should it now not be better
to forward them at once to Chicago to avoid the delay of reshipment from
Washington. If you say so, send me at once the direction for Chicago and
write yourself on to give the proper directions about filling them with alcohol.

I hope in a week or two to have my appropriation from the Legislature, when I shall have all I can now wish for and then we can make our arrangements for a proper exploration of the North and such other places as you may have an opportunity of controlling.

Very truly yours
L Agassiz

I await Verrill's return to write to you about the visit of my young friends — W. and other matters about the Museum. Pray take up the question of supplying Europe with originals into serious consideration. A mistake in that respect may put us all back for years.

L Agassiz

BAIRD to AGASSIZ

March 20th 1861

My dear Professor

It will be best to send the cans here as they have each to be combined with other matters in larger cases, arsenic, bottles etc. They should be of the small sizes for the north, not over one and ten gallons each in a good box.

I would like the 250 for Kennicott as soon as possible as it ought to be in Montreal by the 5th of April if possible. The general appropriations for miscellaneous operations, there is not the same hurry about.

How about collections of birds, embryos etc. in Lake Winnepeg this spring. For about $150.00 we can have this done quite thoroughly by a resident correspondent.

Verrill left this afternoon. He has been of great service to us in assorting and naming our Corals.

I quite agree with you about the policy of distributing types, so as to produce a return of the same. It is certainly as incumbent on the Smithsonian and as important a seat in the increase & diffusion of knowledge to secure European types to Americans, as to place American types in reach of Europeans.

Stimpson is now working at his starfishes and wants materials for comparison. Cant you let him have yours by sections, & be returned very soon with series of what he has collected himself. Of course you dont care about naming species, and you will thus get our types much sooner for your comparative investigations. He will be obliged to work out his species quite soon, and unless he has large materials, will not do it as well. Copenhagen Museum has just sent birds, etc. unique and types for examination.

Sincerely yours
S. F. Baird

BAIRD to AGASSIZ

March 25, 1861

Dear Professor,

I return Dr. Gray's letter and have taken a copy of it for future reference.

We shall send off tomorrow a box of birds and another of nests and eggs which we hope will prove of interest.

Sincerely yours
S.F. BAIRD

AGASSIZ to BAIRD

CAMBRIDGE *April 2 1861*

My dear Baird,

In answer to your letter to Alex I would say that his claiming the cost of the cans must be a mistake arising from the fact that when I gave over to him the business of the Museum I probably did not explain everything with sufficient precision. Today he will enclose to you the amount of your expenses for us and the bill of Dr. Flügel.

I am very sorry I shall not be able to send you my subscription for Kennicott before a week or ten days. I am entirely *dry;* in fact I have already advanced about $5000 for the Museum out of my own means and do not know at this moment where to raise anything more; but I trust to be able next week to send you what you want for Kennicott. When I do it we may then make some general arrangement about collecting. I want very much to avail myself of your offer to have bird eggs and young collected about Lake Winnipeg & I shall add $50 for that purpose. I shall be very happy to have specimens from Mr. Xantus.

Very truly yours
L AGASSIZ

Our Museum bill before the Legislature, for a grant of $20,000 is likely to pass in a few days.

BAIRD to AGASSIZ

April 4, 1861

My dear Professor,

Yours of the 2nd just to hand. All right about the Kennicott appropriation. It will be on time I think even as late as May 1 if I can cable the Northern Brigade.

As you propose to take a share in the lumpy egg inc. I will forward a lot of bottles to preserve embryos and embryonic eggs in.

Sincerely yours,

S. F. BAIRD

BAIRD to AGASSIZ

April 20, 1861

My dear Prof. Agassiz,

Since the receipt of your letter we have been in such a state of excitement and uncertainty that I have not been able to find time for a quiet reply. And even now when the uncertainties of the future thicken around us, and we don't know but that the next day will see the Smithsonian battered down I have no heart to write at all.

I would be glad to have the balance of that Kennicott money when you can get it. If anything should happen to us here, I beg that you will send the amount of $250.00 to E. M. Hopkins, Hudson Bay Co., to be placed to Mr. Kennicott's credit. Next year a larger amount should be sent. If able, however, I would prefer to send the money myself.

I do not think it will be worthwhile to go into much detail concerning the plan of our Museum. Civil War will probably solve the matter. The principal part will be the exploring operations and funds are not appealed. Of course I should attend to it as long as I had the matter in my hands.

Truly sincerely yours,

S. F. BAIRD

P.S. *Ap. 24* No mails since I last wrote. We are all paralyzed here and can do nothing. If you get your money, please send $250.00 to Mr. E. M. Hopkins as desired above. And put the 50.00 for Mr. Gunn subject to my order, as I have sent him this amount.

BAIRD to AGASSIZ

May 11, 1861

Dear Professor,

In the wording are you still alive or not, the Smithsonian reply "I still live". Not yet have we been battered down, robbed or destroyed. And I hope the contingency now is a very remote one. We have got our bearing again, and are moving along in the even tenor of our way as before. The only sign of war about the Smithsonian is the constant presence in the Hall of hundreds of soldier visitors, busy in looking at the specimens. But without any disorderly or improper conduct whatever.

What has become of the funds you thought you could raise for explorations? What of the $250.00 for Kennicott? I am most anxious for the last. If you cannot in the present raise the above amount perhaps you can $100.00. It is not too late to put this to his credit with the H.B.Co. Please let me know about this.

Sincerely and truly yours,
S. F. BAIRD

BAIRD to AGASSIZ

January 16, 1862

Dear sir,

In compliance with your request made through Mr. Stimpson, I have authorized him to pack up the type specimens of Volutidae and Mitridae in the Smithsonian collection as mentioned in the accompanying letter and they will be sent at once by Adams Express. You will of course see that these specimens are carefully preserved, and returned in good condition at the earliest moment.

I have also to request that you will sign and return the enclosed receipt.

Sincerely yours,
S. F. BAIRD

Cambridge, Mass.

Mus. Comp.

Received of the Smithsonian Institution in good order and condition the foll. specimens

Mitridae and Volutidae of the Smithsonian collection corresponding to the following numbers, to be returned in good order and condition at the expiration of ————, unless an extension of time be authorized, or sooner if called for by the Institution.

Copy off numbers only.

AGASSIZ to BAIRD

CAMBRIDGE, Mar. 10, 1862

My dear Baird,

The bearer is Capt. Nath. Atwood, whom you know already for his extensive contributions to our Ichthyology & whom I take great pleasure in introducing to you.

Yours very truly,
L AGASSIZ

AGASSIZ to BAIRD

March 29, 1862

My dear Baird,

A young friend of mine, W. A. Hyatt,[49] a graduate of our Sc. School, now in Baltimore proposes to spend the summer in the Rocky Mts. and will call upon you, probably at the same time as this letter reaches you, to obtain all the information you can give him respecting his preparation for the journey. Please assist him as far as you can, for he is a very deserving student, entirely devoted to the pursuit of science.

I take this opportunity to request you to lend me the Catalogues of the British Museum relating to the Hydroids. I want to refer to some genera and families among the Tubularidae characterized by Gray which are first mentioned in these Catalogues and as I have them not, I would be much obliged to you, if you could forward them at once. I shall return them in a fortnight latest.

Ever truly yours
L AGASSIZ

I trust you have received the $50 for the egg excursion.

BAIRD to AGASSIZ

April 2, 1862

Dear Prof. Agassiz,

I have seen Hyatt and will do all I can to aid him.

There is no British Museum Catalogue relative to the Hydroidae as far as I can ascertain. Our set is nearly complete and I have seen Catalogues down to Dec. 1861 which makes no mention of the list.

$50.00 for Lake [illegible] was duly received and acknowledged to Alex. Can you send anything for Kennicott?

Sincerely yours
S. F. BAIRD

---

[49] Alpheus Hyatt (1838–1902), zoologist and paleontologist, was born in Washington, D.C. In 1858 he entered the Lawrence Scientific School of Harvard University to study engineering. Soon he became interested in natural history through the influence of Louis Agassiz. He was also associated with Baird. His talents were most notable in the field of science education for he was one of the founders of the Peabody Academy of Science, the Teacher's School of Science, the American Society of Naturalists, and the American Naturalist. Hyatt was also the first president of the Board of Trustees of the Marine Biology Laboratory at Wood's Hole, Mass., which is now one of the chief marine biological laboratories in the world.

AGASSIZ to BAIRD

Oct 18 1862

My dear Baird,

I take pleasure in introducing to you Wm. J. Shute of Woburn, who has made himself a thorough observer especially in the bird line. You will no doubt be pleased to hear of his observations on the breeding of our birds which he has watched with unrelenting care. Of all this he will tell you more than I can in a few lines; and when you have seen him my note of introduction would be superfluous beyond introducing him to you.

I have been much disappointed not to see you this summer.

Yours truly
L Agassiz

BAIRD to AGASSIZ

Dec. 26 1862

Dear sir:

If Mr. Putnam has the Mss of his Etheostomidae paper ready for press it will give us much pleasure to publish it at once, either in our quarto or octavo series. If illustrations have been prepared, we may be able to engrave them; if not it may be as well to proceed at once with the text leaving this to be a subject for future arrangement.

We are particularly desirous to see the Memoir in print, and we can make no use of the names supplied by Mr. Putnam for our Etheostomidae, either in labelling our own collection or in distributing its duplicates, until they have been published in connection with descriptions of new species.

Although several years have elapsed since the completion of the Memoirs by Mr. Putnam there will be little to do in bringing the synonymy up to date: nor perhaps in examining and incorporating the additional materials received at Cambridge and Washington since that time.

Yours sincerely,
S. F. Baird

AGASSIZ to BAIRD

Cambridge, *Feb. 7, 1863*

Dear sir,

I have this day sent you a can containing all our Bats, even the full number of our duplicates for Mr. Allen to examine. I think he may be able to make skeletons of those of which there are many. Should there be any which you want I will gladly send them to you, after the specimens have been returned. I hope in return you will let me have what we have not got whenever you have spare specimens.

In case hereafter specimens are wanted from our Museum for the use of the Smithsonian please write to me for them & not to the young men employed in the Museum. It may make difficulties which I want to prevent before there is an occasion that may require my interference in a way I may not care to be led into. You will receive the Catalogue by the next mail.

Very truly yours
L AGASSIZ

BAIRD to AGASSIZ

Feb. 7, 1863

My dear Professor,

Dr. Allen of the Army has just finished a Monograph of the Bats of North America to be put to press by the S. I. I wrote informally to Mr. Verrill asking if you would like to have your species identified at this time and now repeat the same question to you. He returns to his field duties in a few days, having obtained leave of absence to finish this work. If the bats get here by the middle of next week, it will not be too late.

Dr. Allen can also identify any exotic bat you may have. He has been studying the whole series for a long time with the Smithsonian and Academy collections before him.

Another point. I made the summer of 1861 a thorough revision of the North American species and found some ten new species, several of them, *Neosorex;* one entirely new group of American species with 20 cuts etc. This memoir I shall take up very shortly and finish and would be glad of the opportunity to examine your species, dried and alcoholic, especially of the genus *Neosorex.*

Another group which Mr. Kennicott is working at is that of the weasels; *Putorius,* especially such as the ermines etc; any of your specimens of this kind, please let us have.

Have you a specimen of *Spermophilus richardsonia,* especially from the Saskatchewan country. This would be of greatest importance as we are revising *Spermophilus* and lack typical *richardsonia.* We have fine new Rocky Mt. and arctic species.

Mr. Cope[50] is now making a final examination of North American Sau-

---

[50] Edward Drinker Cope (1840–97), zoologist and paleontologist, was born in Philadelphia, Pa. In 1859 he went to the Smithsonian Institution to study reptiles under Baird. At the age of 22 he was recognized as one of the country's leading authorities in reptiles. In 1870 he became associated with Joseph Leidy in the description of fossils collected by the Hayden Survey in Wyoming. He is perhaps best known for his work on extinct vertebrates of the far west.

rians for us. I cannot find time to finish the Monograph I prepared three years ago, and in despair begged Cope to do the whole either anew or use my MSS as far as possible. Shall I send him your N. Am. specimens and ask him to work them up for you.

Sincerely yours

SFBaird

AGASSIZ to BAIRD

Cambridge, *Feb. 10, 1863*

Dear sir,

Before receiving your letter of the 7th, I had already forwarded the Bats for Dr. Allen, though without the foreign species. In a few days you will have the rest and the other things you call for, including some spermophiles from Minnesota. As to the North American Saurians I should be glad to have Mr. Cope work them up with yours. He has already received some direct from us.

Allow me on this occasion, and after having thus shown you that I am ever ready to have the specimens of the Museum in Cambridge used for scientific purposes, without any limitation, to state that your remark in the last Sm. Report, regarding the specimens which I have retained for a very long time, was neither gracious, nor of that kind which promotes easy inter-course. If you wanted the specimens they would have been sent forthwith, while you know that I have never completed my Monograph of the Chelo-nians, not any more than you have yours of the Batrachians, the specimens of which from our Museum have been nearly as long with you as your Chelonians with me.

Very truly yours

L Agassiz

BAIRD to AGASSIZ

Feb. 15, 1863

My dear Prof. Agassiz,

I have received your two letters of Feb. 9 and 10th. I write now to acknowledge the safe arrival of the American lot. Dr. Allen left for the field before the box got to Washington but as he expects to be immedi-ately transferred to Washington on Hassler duty I will keep the specimens undisturbed till he arrives.

I am very sorry that you should have in any way been hurt about what I said in my report about the turtles. So far from having had any motive or malice in my expression, I would really as far as I am concerned, be very sorry to have the specimens back at the present time......

So far from implying any reproach to you in the matter of the turtles no one knows better than myself the consideration that should be extended to those investigators who are obliged to devote their time to general supervision and detail. I certainly need allowance as much or more than anyone else in this respect as I have several extended investigations and memoirs on hand so nearly finished that one months work in the institution uninterruptedly continued would permit me to complete them (the rough work having been done at Carlisle in my summer vacation).

Yet I almost despair ever of touching pen more to them. The Monograph of Saurians I have already turned over to Mr. Cope who in fact will do the work better than I ever could. The Batrachian memoir, I hope he will undertake likewise and I myself finish up the shrew paper and several ornithological monographs and Lamidae. It is almost as much as I can hope for in the future.

I hope therefore, my dear Professor Agassiz, that you should accept this explanation and not continue to feel hurt or aggrieved at what, if offensive or inadvertent in form, was not intended to be so or as implying any reproach, being merely the simple statement of a point in the history of the Institution. There is no one in this country whom I respect and esteem more nor whom I admire as much and I would be deeply grieved at anything which might come up to interfere with that feeling of cordial relationship and cooperation which I have been proud to feel existed between us from our first acquaintance.

Very truly yours,
SPENCER F. BAIRD

AGASSIZ to BAIRD

CAMBRIDGE, *Febr. 18, 1863*

My dear Baird,

I shall be in Washington about as soon as this letter. I write however to say that your last letter gave me much pleasure.

Ever truly yours,
L AGASSIZ

BAIRD to AGASSIZ

March 24, 1863

Dear Professor,

The day you left our invaluable Solomon was taken ill. (we fear with small-pox) and we have no one else to pack up the promised things. I hope soon to find some one to take his place while he is ill. I merely write now to explain delays.

Let me know what you can do about the Xantus matter.

Our Lake Winnipeg explorers broke down last Spring on the Journey and returned, having expended only part of the money. He hopes to try again next spring and I hope with success.

Sincerely yours,
SFBAIRD

BAIRD to AGASSIZ

May 13, 1863

Dear sir:

When here last week I understand that you examined Mr. Meek's[51] work on the fossils of the Upper Missouri. Permit me to inquire whether in your opinion it merits a place in the Series of Smithsonian Contributions to knowledge.

Yours sincerely,
SFBAIRD

BAIRD to AGASSIZ

May 26, 1863

Dear sir:

We send by express a box of specimens, Natural History, selected from the duplicates of Mr. Kennicott's collections, of which we beg the acceptance of the Academy Museum as furnishing valuable materials relative to the Zoology of the Arctic region.

Yours truly,
S. F. BAIRD

AGASSIZ to BAIRD

CAMBRIDGE Oct. 29, 1863

My dear Baird,

I am really distressed not to have a few hundred dollars at my command to relieve Xantus.[52] I have written most entreatingly to a friend to give me some money for that object and received no answer, as I had ex-

---

[51] Fielding Bradford Meek (1817–76), geologist and paleontologist, worked from 1848 to 1858 on geological surveys in Iowa, Wisconsin, Minnesota, and elsewhere. He is well known for his contributions to the knowledge of the fossils of Illinois and Missouri.

[52] John Xantus (1825–94), ornithologist, was born at Csokonya, Hungary. He was of Greek descent. His entry into the Hungarian national army in 1848 resulted in his arrest by the Austrians in 1849. In 1850 he escaped to the United States. During 1855–57 he made valuable collections of birds for the Smithsonian Institution. Later he was appointed consul at Manzanillo, Mexico, and led a scientific research party into the Sierra Madre. Many lots of specimens were sent from this area to the Smithsonian Institution.

pected & told you I was likely to receive in time. This failing I have made an appeal to Prof. Henry not to allow Xantus to come back before he has accomplished his task there. Prof. Henry told me it should be his first business on returning to Washington to attend to this. I represented to him, what is emphatically true that the Smithsonian Institution could not spend its money better & with greater certainty of important results. My next appropriation is not voted before the last Wednesday of this month & after that a few weeks pass by before I can cash the money & I do not even know how much I shall be allowed, otherwise I might borrow to help you. But I trust Prof. Henry will do the needful.

Very truly yours
L Agassiz

BAIRD to AGASSIZ

Nov. 5, 1863

Dear Prof. Agassiz,

I received yesterday the copy of your letter books for which I am under many obligations. I read the articles with much pleasure and profit in "Atlantic." Am much pleased to have them in this permanent form.

The draft for Xantus came just in time. I have saved both drafts amounting to 500.00 the Smithsonian furnishing the other 250.00.

The fauna in your box will all be distributed speedily.

Meek wants much to consult the books in accompanying list. If you have any and will send by Adams Express we will return them very soon.

Sincerely — truly yours,
S. F. Baird

AGASSIZ to BAIRD

Nahant, Sept 10th, 1864

My dear Sir,

I have been absent from here during the whole week and only got your note last night on my return. As I have caught a bad cold I may not be able to go to Cambridge for the whole week; but if I am better after this nights rest I shall go tomorrow, *Monday,* and would be glad to see you there, or here any day this week before Thursday, that is next Tuesday or Wednesday. Next week I shall again be in Cambridge on Monday. After that I have nothing binding before me, so that you may fix a day for yourself.

I hope Mrs. Baird is better. Prof. Henry told me she had not been

well. With best regards to her from Mrs. Ag & myself & to your daughter.

Yours very truly
L Agassiz

AGASSIZ to BAIRD

CAMBRIDGE, *Nov 25, 1864*

My dear Sir,

You shall have the birds you want to the extent we possess them, as
fast as they can be hunted up. Mr. Allen, who has taken charge of them
since Mr. Verrill left, is not yet quite *au fait* with the collection; so that it
may take him sometime to find out all we have. But I cannot do better for
you than to have everything overhauled by a new hand. I hope this alcoholic collection of our Museum, which is daily increasing by additions
from every part of the world will prove important for the progress of
Ornithology. I have now most species of Europe adult as well as embryos in
the egg, and I have sent out to the E. Indies and Australia, as well as Cape
of G. Hope for the indigenous species. From Brazil I have already large
numbers.

Very truly yours
L Agassiz

AGASSIZ to BAIRD

CAMBRIDGE, *Dec 12, 1864*

My dear Sir,

I enclose the report of Mr. Allen concerning the specimens you wanted.
If more are found as he progresses with the arrangement of the collec-
tion you shall have them. Alex will forward the specimens by express.
Each one here has his special business.

Yours truly
L Agassiz

AGASSIZ to BAIRD

STATE HOUSE BOSTON, *January 27th 1865*

My dear Baird,

I am extremely sorry I did not read your draft of a plan for the Ornithological Survey of Central America, before I left Washington; for had
I done so I could at once have told you that the basis of an arrangement
thereto proposed could never be considered satisfactory to the Mus. of Comp.

Zool. Analyzed critically the proposition amounts to our Mus. *providing for the means* of the expedition, the material results of which would be equally divided between the Mus. & the Smith. and the Scientific results to be all yours. Again the position of Mr. Drexler in the arrangement does not suit me. I had not rightly understood your statement that he was to receive a salary. My idea of a scientific collector is that he personally should have no interest in the collections, but that all his aspirations should center upon the institution for which he works, (for the sake of the scientific advancement he is expecting in that connection). Having lately reorganized the Mus. of Comp. Zool. upon this principle, I excluded from our institution all those who thought they should work for themselves, I would stultify myself in entering into such an arrangement, for distant explorations. With reference to your agency & the part assumed by the Smith. I may misunderstand your intentions and therefore the above remarks may be out of place. But at first sight it appears to me, as if our Mus. were to play not only second fiddle, but not even to appear before the ornithological world as having done anything for the progress of Ornithology. As Director of the Mus. of Comp. Zool. my first duty is to give that institution prominence among Zoologists by all possible honorable means & I know no more honorable means than that of promoting researches in regions thus far imperfectly known. Now do you not think that is too much for the Smith. to assume joint action, when its share consists simply to advise where the expedition should go? Is it not enormous for the Smith. to claim an equal series with the Mus. for that advice? Even a share in unique specimens? — Now I regret the more the unexpected difficulty, as on reaching Cambridge I find that I could at once make an appropriation from the Museum Fund for ornithological collections; but I do not feel justified in doing this in any way which shall not benefit the Museum to the utmost.

In sending a student on such an exploration, the expense of salary would be fixed and the exploration be proportionally extended. Moreover have we not something to do towards improving the mode of making ornithological collections? by adding specimens of young, half grown, eggs in alcohol in every stage of growth of the embryo etc. Now a taxidermist is not likely to do this; even if directed so to do especially if he is allowed a share of specimens. For all this I do not say that I am not going to begin an extensive ornithological exploration of some region, or other; but your plan does not strike me favorably. If you feel therefore still interested in what I may do, having Mr. Drexler out of the question, let us discuss this matter further & do something really handsome in Ornithology.

I have been deeply shocked at the misfortune[52a] that has befallen the

---

[52a] This refers to the fire in the Smithsonian Building which occurred on January 24, 1865.

Smithsonian. Write me please what is the actual damage to our scientific interests. Stanley's collection is no doubt a great loss to him but not to science, & the destruction of property a material loss for the institution; but I hope that neither the library, nor the Museum have seriously suffered.

Ever truly yours,

L Agassiz

BAIRD to AGASSIZ

Feb. 3, 1865

My dear Professor Agassiz,

I received your letter of the 24th some days ago but have been so much engaged in putting matters to right that I could not answer it earlier. I am thankful to say that, for the most part, our losses are such as money will replace. Neither museum nor library were disturbed. [Illegible.]

I think you misunderstood the plan which I proposed to you in regard to Mr. Drexler. It is precisely the same as that which I read to you in Mr. Meek's room the day before. [Illegible.] You were very favorably impressed with the idea. At your request, I had a copy made which you have and is precisely like the original in my possession.

You may perhaps remember how the whole idea first took, it arose from your saying that you desired to obtain for the M. C. Z. a general collection of birds which might enable your students to make investigations in ornithology as they were able to do in other branches of zoology already. You asked my advice as to how this could be done in the quickest possible manner and at the same time asked how the M. C. Z. could be placed on the first class of distribution of duplicate birds as it was already for nearly everything else. In regard to the latter point, I said that I have already sent duplicates in behalf of various museums that had sent many specimens of birds to us, and that the only way at our command to increase the value of our collection of birds and furnish the materials for the complete elaboration of the [illegible] to have duplicates to exchange for other species. And, in regard to the rapid increase of the ornithological collection of the M. C. Z., I advised sending a professional collector to some zoological point in Central or South America, have him collect a large number of first class marketable skins, have them properly labeled and authenticated, and exchange the duplicate series for corresponding series in the hands of naturalists and museums, which I said could be readily done to my certain knowledge; increasing a collection by nearly 500 species of birds and that, in return for such a collection, the Smithsonian could supply at least as many species or more from its collections, that all duplicates consisting of many individuals of few species could be disposed of to dealers and good returns obtained. The proposition thus enunciated seemed to meet with much favor from you, and, after much explanation on my part of the most desirable localities and offering to render any aid in carrying out the plan by use of the Smithsonian facilities of free freight transportation, you said, "Well, you find me the man to go, and I will furnish the means and place the whole matter in your charge." I accordingly drew out the proposition referred to and placed it in your hands.

In all this, I had not the slightest expectation or idea of having the M. C. Z. play a subordinate part for the management of the affair, had it been entrusted to me, I could have acted in the name and behalf of M. C. Z. I certainly did not suppose that the stipulation for a series of specimens, at least the next to the principal ones, was unreasonable. Considering that under the general conditions on which our distribution of duplicates has been made, we would be entitled to a complete series of such duplicates at the disposal of M. C. Z. in return for what has already been sent to it. In addition to which such a donation on the part of M. C. Z. was to place it at once in the front rank of all recipients of duplicates of Smithsonian birds from a collection of over 30,000 specimens. In addition to that, we were to throw into the affair all our influence and privileges to reduce the cost, among which were to be counted free freight to New York of all collections, and from New York outward of all the outfit: free transportation of collector to the Isthmus (already secured) with greatly reduced cost of living there and probably free transportation by British steamers east and west. The saving to be thus effected could amount at the very least to one third of the expense of operation, which as being on a gold basis would be a very considerable gain.

As to my proposal to prepare a paper on the subject, I made this in the interest of the enterprise: as the exchanges referred to could only be made advantageously on the basis of giving one type series of labeled specimens, illustrating some special research for another. I know of no one else in the country who would undertake to do the same for the collection — at any rate within the time required to accomplish the object of increasing the Cambridge collection.

I do not very well see how I could be supposed to claim half or an equal division of the results of such an expedition, when I only stipulated for a series. All the surplus after selecting two sets was to be exchanged with individuals and institutions having similar sets of duplicates at their disposal, the proceeds of which were to be entirely for the benefit of the M. C. Z. Supposing that 2000 specimens were collected in the year. It would be a fair estimate to deduct 750 to 800 for the two series, leaving 1200 to be exchanged almost skin for species. It is quite likely, that including the complete series of those collected by the operator and the exchanges of the duplicates, that 500 species could be acquired by one year's work for the M. C. Z., and all additional species by a continuation of the enterprise.

As already remarked, the problem presented to me for consideration was to supply as speedily as possible as large a number of species as could be procured and thus increase the range or possible study of the question of general ornithology. To do this workmanlike skins are necessary so they may command the best consideration and returns of other parties. No mere amateur or student work will answer in such cases: it must be a professional effort, both in regard to finish of skins and rapidity of workmanship, to command the results desired. Any side operations would only detract the party from what I presumed under the circumstances in question to be the main objective — to secure the greatest number of artistic specimens, in the shortest possible time.

The idea of giving a percentage on the number of birds collected was only included to stimulate the agent to excessive effort. As, unless he obtained 1500 skins, he got nothing whatever.

If a student can be found, zealous and capable, able to make skins rapidly and well, the object I presumed you had in view may be accomplished as well as if you sent Drexler. If one will go on the plan you propose, who will make the rough collection of alcoholic specimens, embryos etc. it will undoubtedly be an advantage to science, but it will not enable you to increase your stock of species to any great extent.

We have had great experiences in the efforts of amateurs as such to supply ornithological material for different regions; in fact, very few of our birds have been prepared by professionals. The consequences are that out of hundreds of duplicate skins, only a few are of slightest avail for ordinary purposes of exchange. I suppose the half of all we have after their data are recorded and entered might as well be burnt; and many are destroyed, some useless for exchanges. Few museums, public or private, are as accommodating as ours and yours, so ready to take anything, however defective, that furnishes any new material for study.

In conclusion, let me say that whatever plan you adopt, it will give me very great pleasure to aid in carrying it out to the best of my ability. Let me have your program in return for the one I have suggested which embodies a considerable amount of practical experience of such operations.

I shall be greatly relieved at any effort you can make in this direction, as apart from the abstract results to Science. We hope to be considered for the first series of duplicates, which you may be able to share for our museum, this being one of the very few specialties which we care particularly to have exchanges returned to us.

We received yesterday a very nice collection of birds from the table-lands of Mexico which will aid very much in clearing up the difficulties of identifying the species in Swainson's paper on the birds of Mexico, published in 1827. Today came a box of several hundred skins of Costa Rican birds — that rich place of ornithological novelties.

We are gradually clearing up the dirt of the fire and hope in a week or two to be able to open the Museum again to the public. I do not know whether Congress will aid us to rebuild the upper story and towers, but trust they will do so, to some extent at least.

Very truly & sincerely yours,
S. F. BAIRD

BAIRD to AGASSIZ

December 20, 1865

Dear Professor,

I beg to acknowledge with many thanks the arrival of the fine specimens of *Helminthopaga rufuspalla* advised in your letter of the 20. As soon as I have completed the desired examination, I will return them in good order.

Truly yours
S. F. BAIRD

AGASSIZ to BAIRD

CAMBRIDGE, *Oct 21, 1866*

My dear Baird,

While examining my *Anableps* from the lower Amazon, where the genus has not been noticed before, I came across the description of a species from the West Coast (described by Gill in the Proc. Ac. Nat. Sc. for 1861), which I would like very much to compare with those I found in Brazil & other I obtained from Guiana. Can you send me the specimen; it must be in the Sm. Inst. and was presented by Capt. Dowe. How about the fish books & the Report for 1865?

Yours very truly
L AGASSIZ

AGASSIZ to BAIRD

CAMBRIDGE, *Oct. 28, 1866*

My dear Baird,

Last night I was greatly rejoiced in receiving a large parcel of books with the Smithsonian card upon it, thinking it must contain the books on fishes you promised to send me soon. Upon opening, however, I find twenty copies of the Report of 1865. Is there not a mistake? & have not the books gone where the Reports ought to have gone & vice versa? Explain please.

Yours truly
L. AGASSIZ

BAIRD to AGASSIZ

October 30, 1866

My dear Professor,

Your first letter about the books came here before I got back. As soon as possible, I requested Mr. Gill to make out the list. His duties in the Library connected with the removal of the books have been very onerous, and it is only today that he completed and delivered the list. Let me know which of the works mentioned you wish to have us send you.

The copies of Smithsonian Report are for you to distribute among those interested.

We send by express a fine specimen of *Anableps dowei* which you can keep as being a duplicate.

Sincerely yours,
S. F. BAIRD

AGASSIZ to BAIRD

Nov. 1, 1866

My dear Baird,

Many thanks for the *Anableps*. Happily I have already got a good many of the papers quoted. I would be however much obliged for:

Canestrini Mam A. Torino XXI.

Dumeril Selachians.

McDonnell R. Irish Ac. XXIV 1854.

Molin, Instit. Veneto VIII 1859.

I need also Castelnau's Voyage the part on Fishes and if you have already received it the volume of Gunther's Catalogue which contains the Characini.

If you can procure the following, I should be greatly obliged:

Mettenheimer Disquisitiones Anat-Comp. de membro piscium pectorale, Berolini 1847.

Bakker, Osteographia piscium Groninger 1822.

Bruch, Vergleichende Osteologie des Rheinlachses 1861.

Wellenbergh, Observationes anatomicae de Orthagorisco Mola. 1845.

Henle Ueber Marine Berlin, 1834.

Busch, De Selachiorum & Ganoideorum Berlin, 1848.

If you have Bruch:Anfangtgründe der Vergleichende Anatomie Wien 1845

I should like the letterpress. I have the Atlas; but one of my students lost the explanation.

Please send as soon as possible.

Yours very truly

L Agassiz

BAIRD to AGASSIZ

Nov. 11, 1866

My dear Professor,

I am very sorry to say that of the long list of Works in your letter we have but three, which go to you by express. The [illegible] memoirs, monograph, and papers we do not have.

I hope for better luck with your next order.

Yours sincerely,

S. F. Baird

AGASSIZ to BAIRD

Cambridge *Nov. 14, 1866*

Dear Sir,

The first day of next week I shall pack up & return the shells you want. I am glad to hear that you are about arranging your skeletons etc. When you go at it, I wish you would set aside for our Museum as many skulls & skeletons as you can spare.

I have received the books & already read McDonnell. I thought you told me you had Dumeril; if so please send it, as I have not yet received the copy Alex ordered months ago.

Yours truly

L Agassiz

BAIRD to AGASSIZ

Nov. 18, 1866

Dear Professor,

I am very sorry that we have not Dumeril's work. I told you in speaking of it, that we did not possess it, but that it had been ordered. This has not yet arrived. The early copy I have seen in our business series whereby Mr. Gill has since returned.

Sincerely yours

S. F. Baird

BAIRD to AGASSIZ

Feb. 11, 1868

Dear Sir,

In compliance with your request we have had boxed up and sent to you by Express the crania mentioned in the accompanying list which please sign and return.

Ever yours,
SPENCER F. BAIRD

BAIRD to AGASSIZ

WASHINGTON *Feb. 17, 1868*

Dear Professor,

I write to comment and inquire after the "Bootherium" skull and am just informed that Mrs. Rote presented it last year to the Phila. Academy where I suppose you saw it.

Sincerely yours
SPENCER F. BAIRD

BAIRD to AGASSIZ

April 30, 1868

Dear Professor,

Dr. Ed. von Martens of Berlin asks our intervention to procure for his use a copy of Lyman Catalogue of Ophiuridea (Part I of Catal. Mus. Comp. Zool.). Should you be able to spare it, it will give us much pleasure to forward it at once in your name.

Very truly yours,
SPENCER F. BAIRD

BAIRD to AGASSIZ

June 6, 1868

My dear Professor,

We have advised you of the arrival of the boxes of exchanges sent by you for foreign distribution, but are not certain that we reported a charge exacted by the Express Co. of 13.45 freight from Boston. If this has already been paid by you to the Exp. Co. please request them to return the money to us, in order that we may close up our transportation account for the month of May.

Yours very truly,
SPENCER F. BAIRD

BAIRD to AGASSIZ

June 17, 1868

Dear Professor,

Your check for 13.45, amount paid by the Institution for freight on two boxes of books for foreign distribution was duly received and the amount returned to the fund in the hands of the disbursing agent for transportation.

B.

AGASSIZ to BAIRD

CORNELL UNIVERSITY, ITHACA, *Nov. 23, 1868*

My dear Baird,

I enclose a slip from the N.Y. Evening Express. Have you really seen the creature and is it anything but a basking shark (*Selache maximus*)?

Yours truly
L AGASSIZ

BAIRD to AGASSIZ

November 25, 1868

My dear Professor,

The "Sea Monster" is as you suggest, a Basking Shark, as I told the skipper is the same as I saw at Caleb's last summer. I did not remember the latest generic name for it. But promised to ascertain and report which I did. I feel like punching the man's head for bringing in my name.

Sincerely yours,
SPENCER F. BAIRD

BAIRD to AGASSIZ

WASHINGTON *Dec. 13, 1869*

Dear sir,

We duly received the box of corals, returned last spring by the Museum of Comparative Zoology, embracing the type specimens of the Wilkes & North Pacific Expeditions, borrowed in 1861, for Prof. Verrill's use in prosecuting certain researches at the Museum of Comparative Zoology. Expecting a visit from Dr. Stimpson from time to time, in whose charge these specimens more especially belong, we deferred opening & unpacking the boxes until quite recently, when this was done under the Doctor's inspection. A careful note was taken of the corals returned; & I now beg leave to inclose a list of the numbers receipted originally by Prof. Verrill, but which we do not find among those returned. We presume that these specimens have either been detained for further use in the Museum, or that they were overlooked in packing. If not needed any longer, we shall be pleased to have a search instituted for them, & such of them returned as can be found; as these are all types of new species of Prof. Dana & Dr. Stimpson, we are of course more particular in regard to them.

We regret to say that, owing to some carelessness in packing, considerable injury was done to many of the specimens, quite a number having been broken to pieces, & others very much mutilated.

Yours very truly
SPENCER F. BAIRD

BAIRD to Mrs. AGASSIZ

January 23, 1870

My dear Mrs. Agassiz,

I was very much concerned some weeks ago that the Professor had been quite unwell and have earnestly wanted further intelligence of his condition — hoping that I had been misinformed. Will you not kindly drop me a line? I hope this assures me that whatever the indisposition was he is now well again.

I have been looking forward to his annual visit to Washington with much expectation as I have much to talk about of common interest [illegible].

SPENCER F. BAIRD

I am myself far from well this winter, having a great deal of trouble with my head, and indeed am now under physicians order to go to Florida, but I dont much like to go if it can be put off.

Mrs. AGASSIZ to BAIRD

January 28, 1870

My dear Mr. Baird,

The professor has been seriously ill and is now living in absolute seclusion & quiet not even opening a letter & seeing even his own family only for a short time every day.

The physicians have been consulted. Several seem doubtful as to the exact nature of the attacks which at first alarmed us very much but they seem now decided that the symptoms were caused by excessive fatigue of the brain and may be put down to nervous disorders.

I think both Doctor Lyman & Doctor Tyler think he will recover entirely if he only allows himself rest enough.

This is as you know really difficult to get, but just at present he is compelled to inaction by inability to work.

He sends you his love and wants me to say (this great subject you see is his uppermost) that he would be very much obliged to you for any information you can give him concerning fauna of Bermudas, terrestrial, or marine of any class of the Animal Kingdom.

Pray give my affectionate regards to your wife & daughter and believe me with thanks for your kind notes —

Very truly yours,

E. C. AGASSIZ

I am sorry you should be driven off against your will but do go to Florida if you are needing rest and have trouble in the head. My horror now is overwork; it's so much better to take it in time and rest before you are actually broken down. I take the privilege of a friend you see & offer advice unasked.

BAIRD to Mrs. AGASSIZ

Jan. 30, 1870

My dear Mrs. Agassiz,

I have your note of the last week and was thankful to learn that the Professor was better, and trust that under your good care he may soon have the embargo in regard to company and correspondence removed.

As to the fauna of Bermuda, the best information is embodied in the volume of Mr. J. M. Jones, entitled "The Naturalist in Bermuda" and published several years ago, and in one or two supplementary papers by the same author in the Trans. Nova Scotia Institute of Natural History. With these, however, I presume the Professor is familiar. With love to him, believe me

Sincerely yours,

SPENCER F. BAIRD

BAIRD to AGASSIZ

Jan. 30, 1870

List of Crania sent to Prof. Agassiz Feb. 1868.

Buffalo skulls No. 2841, 2887, 2888, 2889, 2885, 2892, 2895, 2896, 7059, one not numbered.

Buffalo lower jaws 2840, 3817, 7060, 7061, one not numbered.

Buffalo fossil, Yukon River.

Musk Ox 5093 & 5094 ♀ : and horns from Greenland.

Rocky Mountain Sheep.

We are at present engaged in rearranging the osteological collections of the S.I. and are desirous of having before us all the specimens belonging to the S.I. in order to know what species to assign to the different genera and I wish to say that if you are not now using the crania sent you in February 1868 or likely to do so for some months we shall be glad to have them returned. Should you at any subsequent time want to recall these specimens, — they will be promptly placed at your disposal.

A list of specimens sent you is herewith appended.

An application has been made to me for the loan of the musk ox heads which we are desirous of granting.

S.F.BAIRD

AGASSIZ to BAIRD

CAMBRIDGE Feb. 25, 1870

My dear sir,

While I am not allowed to read & answer my letters I am equally unable to direct profitably this work of the Museum. It has occurred to me that at this time I could most conveniently do a good turn to Mr. Allen by sending him to Washington, especially if as I presume from Professor Henry's letter recalling the Buffalo skulls, you are now over-hauling all your materials for your new arrangement; whence Mr. Allen might have an opportunity of making himself familiar with all your collections of North American Mammals and birds. You might perhaps on this same occasion help us to fill our deficiencies. Please write me if there is a chance for Mr. Allen to find inexpensive board near the Smithsonian, and whether he would have any opportunity now of accomplishing the above objects. Dr. Maach to whom Professor Henry's letter has been referred tells me that he immediately returned the desired specimens and I hope they are by this time in your hands. There is another object which I should like to accomplish in order to relieve me in the same way of giving Mr. Bliss new instructions. He has lately made to my entire satisfaction a critical examination of the Cyprinidae from the East Indies in the Museum. If he could now undertake a critical revision of all the North American Cyprinidae which is so much needed he could be at work without me for many months; but I should not like him to undertake this revision unless he can have for comparison the Smithsonian Collection which contains the largest number of originals. Can you let me have them now? and if you have no one to put them up for this object and Allen can go to Washington he might pack them for you.

However I would prefer that the responsibility of the packing might rest upon your own man. If these two things can be accomplished it would be a real relief to me as the Museum weighs heavily on my mind.

I have heard from Mrs. Agassiz how kindly you have inquired after me and I thank you for your interest. *Please remember me very kindly to your wife and daughter, — warm regards also to Professor Henry & his family.

Very truly yours,
L Agassiz

* The Secretary wishes to pin in all the *un*official messages.

BAIRD to AGASSIZ

Washington, D.C., March 22, 1870

My dear Professor Agassiz,

You must not think me willfully negligent in allowing so long a time to elapse between the reception of your letter & my answering it. I have been for the most part of time out of town, having made three visits to Carlisle, Philadelphia & Baltimore on necessary business, & having been occupied in the intervals with matters requiring constant attention.

I hardly know what to say in regard to Mr. Allen's coming on at the present time. It will give me the great pleasure to make his personal acquaintance, & to give him the freedom of the collections of the Institution; but, unfortunately, the specimens which he will most wish to see & examine, especially the mammals & the larger birds, filling as you know a great many chests & boxes, are all packed away in tobacco, & I should be afraid to open & allow them to remain out at the present season, on account of the danger from the attack of moths. We are hoping to receive from Congress increased appropriation for the preservation of the collections of the government expeditions; & should these be granted us, we can then have anything we want to preserve, mounted & put in the cases. But unless unpacked for some such object, permitting us to distribute the surplus at once, to parties who can take care of it, I am afraid to disturb the present order of things, for fear of the consequences.

We are also clearing our decks here, preparatory to making our usual transmissions of parcels to Europe, which promises to be of enormous magnitude & to require all our time & attention for several months. This we desire to get done, by the end of May, since Professor Henry now contemplates making a visit to Europe, for the benefit of his health, which has, as you know, been very poor since last fall. So that, under the circumstances, it would be quite impossible for me to give to Mr. Allen that supervision, attention & assistance that he will require in order to make any headway in the work contemplated, & I would therefore suggest that it will be better for him to defer coming until the ensuing fall, when we shall be much less pressed for time & better off as to space, than we are at present; while the boxes can then be opened & the contents left lying around for some months without any fear of injury.

Of course, Mr. Allen could have ready access to the mounted specimens at any time; but as far as making any selections of duplicates for the Museum & the study of the extended series of objects are concerned, it would be very inconvenient at present, if not impossible.

My chief regret, personally, in view of the immense increase of our routine work, is in the impossibility of giving any satisfactory amount of time to natural history work. I frequently go to my office & directly thence to Professor Henry's, without having an opportunity in the entire day of getting down stairs among the specimens. Consequently, I am obliged to put off a great deal that ought to be done until a more leisure opportunity presents itself.

As to the Cyprinoid fishes, these have already been taken up by the Professor Cope who has made formal application to the Institution for them, in view of his contemplated study of the series. After he has completed his labors there will of course be no difficulty about Mr. Bliss's[53] having full access to them. At present the portion of the collection, not in Mr. Cope's hands, is stowed away in a dark basement where it will be extremely difficult to see it. I am very sorry indeed to have to present so unpromising a picture of our present facilities for investigations. But you can appreciate better than most persons the difficulty arising from an over crowded state of the Museum, & the difficulty on the part of the director of finding time to superintend even the necessary work. I hope to hear before long that you are improving in health & freed from the restrictions laid upon by your physician & friends. Will you not be able to come on to the session of the National Academy, on the 12th of April? I do not know how much of a meeting we shall have, but I presume equal to the average.

Very truly & sincerely yours,
S. F. Baird

Mrs. AGASSIZ to BAIRD

March 22nd 1870
Cambridge

Dear Sir,

As the time is approaching when the Professor must lay out new work for Mr. Bliss he wishes to know whether you can send him the Cyprinoids which he asked for through me in a previous letter.

---

[53] Richard Bliss, a student and long-time assistant of Louis Agassiz, was especially proficient in ichthyology.

He is improving very slowly but not yet allowed personally to attend to anything requiring application.

With warm regards to your wife & daughter & kind remembrance from the Professor.

Very cordially yours,
E. C. Agassiz

Mr. Allen may be with you the Professor says about the middle of April. Mr. Agassiz hopes you will be able to give him the names of petty deficiencies at the Museum in Mammalia & Birds. He would also be very grateful for any embryos you have—which are in great demand for the purpose of the Museum.

BAIRD to Mrs. AGASSIZ

Washington D. C. *March 28, 1870*

My dear Mrs. Agassiz,

The day after my tardy reply to your first letter had been mailed, I received yours of March 22nd. I am very sorry indeed that I was obliged to beg off at present from Mr. Allen's visit. As the pressure upon me increases every day in consequence of the immense numbers of visitors to Washington who prevent me from doing my regular work, & will require & perceive every minute of my time to get ready for the forthcoming sending of books to Europe. It will, therefore, be quite impossible for me to give Mr. Allen any facilities, such as he would require if he came on. If he can as well visit us in the coming fall I will promise to do all in my power to facilitate his mission. I am truly thankful to hear that the Professor has shown improvement in health & shall soon be able to talk with me concerning matters of mutual interest. With best wishes to him as well as to yourself, believe me,

Very sincerely yours,
S. F. Baird

Mrs. AGASSIZ to BAIRD

March 30, 1870

My dear Mr. Baird,

The Professor begs me to write you that it is all right about Mr. Allen and he will gladly come in the fall. He is some disappointed concerning the Cyprinidae because he has himself such rich material of that family. He now begs that as soon as you are relieved from the pressure of work about the books, you would send to the Museum for Mr. Bliss, the Fresh Water Percoids of your Museum. He does not care for the marine representatives of the family but would like all your fresh water species. He will put that family into the hands of Mr. Bliss instead of the Cyprinoids, as it requires, he says, about as much, a thorough revision.

Mr. Agassiz sends his best regards to you and yours, — he is better but still obliged to live the life of an invalid by the physician's advice.

I suppose he will be fortunate if next fall he is able to return, however moderately to his usual occupations. He laments his inability to attend the coming meeting of the Academy but it is out of the question. I am sorry to see by your letter that you are so overwhelmed with work, — I feel inclined to warn all my working friends away from that pitfall.

The Professor adds that he has directed the Museum pamphlets to be sent to you this week; you will probably receive them by the same mail with this letter. He trusts you will find them in some "orderly" condition, as he says, than those of previous years, & that they will give you no trouble.

With kind remembrances to Mrs. Baird.

Believe me always
Cordially yours,
E. C. Agassiz

BAIRD to Mrs. AGASSIZ

Washington, D. C. *July 1, 1870*

Dear Mrs. Agassiz,

I owe you a great many apologies for my neglect to answer your letter in which you ask from the Institution, in behalf of the Professor, for some of its specimens of fishes.

I have been hoping to have the means of responding to his request in the course of the present summer, & of advising, on the transmission of a portion at least of the desired collection. Unfortunately, about a year ago, our alcoholic collection was necessarily transferred from the old Library room in which it had been arranged into a basement room, in order to fit up the former for another purpose, & the worst having been done, in my absence, the entire series of some ten or fifteen thousand jars, was placed in a dark basement, & mixed up indiscriminately, so that reptiles, mammals, & birds are side by side on the same shelf. I had expected, however, in time to have this collection rearranged, & in bringing together objects of similar characters, to be able to act accordingly; but I am sorry to say that the first of July has come & no progress whatever has been made in that work. Prof. Henry's absence has devolved upon me the sole charge of the Institution, & with his desk &

my own to attend to I have not found time for any extra work. I hope, therefore, that you will excuse both the discourtesy of my silence & the neglect to meet the Professor's wish, when you learn how good a reason I have for the same.

We leave about the middle of the month, to spend the summer at Woods Hole, & I hope there to recover that measure of health that has been somewhat less than usual during the last six months. Returning, as we expect to do by way of Boston, I shall hope to meet the Professor whose genial countenance has been so little before me for many years past, & to find, for himself, as I am thankful to learn from various sources, that he is entirely himself again, & fully restored to the ranks of hard workers.

You are aware, of course, that the Henrys left the first of June. They had a delightful passage across, & both consider themselves entirely well again. The Professor is having a pleasant time in the Scientific circles of London & will soon leave for the Continent. We expect him back at the end of October, & hope to find that he has recovered at least ten years of his age.

Very truly & sincerely yours,
SPENCER F. BAIRD

AGASSIZ to BAIRD

DEERFIELD, Oct. 13, 1870

My dear Baird,

Allen wrote me some time ago that you had offered to him to agent yourself in his behalf to secure the place of Naturalist to the Arctic Expedition for him. I am glad he did not fancy the proposition, for his constitution could not stand the hardships of such a voyage. If the place is not already filled I would recommend Dr. Stähli, who for three years has been anatomical assistant at the Museum of Comp. Zoology. He was a practical physician before he came to Cambridge which would be an additional recommendation on such a trip. The chief work in an Arctic voyage would consist in collecting the large Marine animals, their skeletons, embryos etc. & birds, eggs, embryos etc. for all of which his previous occupations would particularly fit him. As he is a married man arrangements should be made for him that his salary be paid to his wife, during his absence.

Excuse my laconic way of writing, but I can not apply myself long.

Very truly yours
L AGASSIZ

BAIRD to AGASSIZ

Oct. 15, 1870

My dear Professor,

I was much pleased to find by your letter of the 13th, that you had recovered your health sufficiently to write autographically, & I trust that by this time you have recovered your former good health.

I regretted very much not to meet you in Cambridge last summer, as it is now several years since I have had that pleasure. I hope we shall see you in Washington in the course of the winter & be able to show you what we have been doing since you were last here.

Prof. Henry & Mary have just returned from their visit to Europe, both greatly improved in health. The Professor had every attention paid him abroad, & only regretted the necessarily limited period of his stay.

It will give us a great deal of pleasure to suggest the name of *Dr. Walker* as naturalist to the Arctic Expedition provided the place has not already been promised to Capt. Hall. Dr. David Walker, however, who, as you may remember accompanied McClintock on the voyage of the Fox, has volunteered his services as naturalist & surgeon, & has received the endorsement of General Grant for the place. I do not know whether the salary that Capt. Hall will be able to pay will be sufficient for Dr. Walker. I presume it will hardly exceed $50 or $60 a month. I will, however, bear your letter in mind, & let you know as soon as anything definite can be ascertained on the subject. If Dr. S. goes, there will be, of course, no difficulty in having his salary paid to his wife during his absence.

Very truly yours,

S.F.BAIRD

AGASSIZ to BAIRD

CAMBRIDGE, *Nov. 21, 1870*

My dear sir,

As I resume gradually my supervision of the Museum work, I find that Mr. Bliss has nearly completed his Monograph of the Helichthydon (*Pomotis, Centrarchus*) and I therefore reiterate my request that the Smithsonian Institution might lend its specimens of that family to the Mus. of C. Z., that nothing should be neglected to render it as complete as possible. I trust you may find the means of granting this request. Of late years the Mus. of C. Z. has not been highly successful in its applications and I wish now it could derive some aid in this matter from the Smithsonian.

Very truly yours,

L AGASSIZ

BAIRD to AGASSIZ

Nov. 29, 1870

My dear Professor,

It is very trying to me not to be able to respond promptly & fully to your request for the use of the fish mentioned in your letter of the 21st, as nothing gives me greater pleasure than to meet your wishes as far as possible. The difficulty in the present case is much the same as that which prevented us from furnishing some of the specimens you wanted before; namely, in the first place, that in the great increase of our collections in Ichthyology it became necessary to place all the alcoholic specimens of fish in a dark basement room, crowding them upon broad shelves. The removal was made hastily, during my absence from the city, & in such a manner as to run altogether all the orders, in the most promiscuous way. Second, to pick out the specimens referred to would involve a weeks labor on my part, in a damp & very unhealthy basement, in which a fire is not permitted, & in which I am afraid to venture for any length of time, in consequence of a persistent & at present aggravated bronchial affection. There is no one in the establishment upon whom I could call for this service, Mr. Gill not being employed by the Institution, & being occupied during the day at the Congressional Library. I have been hoping for several years, to find time to superintend a systematic rearrangement of the entire series of fishes during the warmer season of the summer & still look forward to the accomplishment of this purpose. But nothing can be done till some time in May or June next. If, however, Mr. Bliss himself feels inclined to come on, & overhaul all the collections, taking all the risks, it will give Prof. Henry & myself great pleasure to afford him the opportunity, & allow him to take away such specimens as he considers absolutely indispensible to his further researches as we have, at present, no room suitable to their prosecution here.

I am,

Very truly yours,

S.F.BAIRD

AGASSIZ to BAIRD

CAMBRIDGE, *Dec. 6, 1870*

My dear Professor,

I enclose the receipt for the books forwarded by the Smiths. Inst. to the Mus. C. Z. & myself; and take this opportunity to say that you need not trouble yourself any more to secure a place for Dr. Stähli in the Arctic Exp. Exp., as he has gone back to the more profitable business of medical practice. You would however oblige me by giving me the direction of Capt. Hall and telling me what that expedition is properly to undertake. I would like also to know when you are likely to be able to send me the Pomotidae for Mr. Bliss. I write abruptly as I am not able to sit long at my desk.

Yours truly,

L AGASSIZ

AGASSIZ to BAIRD

CAMBRIDGE, *Dec. 12, 1870*

When do you send books *abroad*.

My dear sir,

Much obliged for the information concerning the Arctic Expedition. I have of course nothing to suggest concerning the collections to be made to improve our knowledge of the Fauna. You are more familiar with it than I am. I want only to request you to urge the collection of large numbers of specimens, that our several museums may have a share. There are only a few final points connected with the work done at the Mus. of C.Z. to which I would call your attention. Collect embryos of *all the Arctic Animals,* Birds as well as Mammalia, in very large numbers, i.e. eggs in alcohol with young in every stage of growth and young in the nest for birds & young from the womb down to the very young & embryos preserved with the amnion at least for the Mammalia. Large numbers are indispensable as it is otherwise impossible to study successive changes and all must be preserved in alcohol, in *separate jars* to prevent pressure & alteration of natural form.

Young animals half grown are also very desirable. The Cetaceans & Pinnipedia ought in this respect to receive special attention. No Seal, no Porpoise, no larger Cetacean ought to be killed without examining the uterus, if it is a female. In this way the Expedition can do a great deal of very good work. The Musk Ox, the Reindeer, the Polar Bear etc. ought to be next considered. Perhaps that a search for *Alca impennis* is not yet hopeless. — Next to Embryos, the skeletons of all the northern animals (Birds & Mammalia, and larger fishes), ought to be collected in number, enough for distribution. A complete series of the Seals in every stage of growth is now more than ever a desideratum, once we know how greatly the representatives of that family vary. If I were with them I would fill the hole of the vessel with Walrusses and their skeletons. The success of this expedition will truly depend upon the naturalist. If he is only a *Skin* man, I would not give a sixpence for what he may bring home. A subject of much interest would be the lice and fleas of all the northern & Arctic animals and their intestinal worms which I believe have never yet been thoroughly collected. The expedition ought to be largely provided with alcohol for all this and with cans & jars (copper). Dr. Newberry will no doubt remember how rich a harvest of fossils may be collected in an Arctic expedition, not only of fossil plants but also of large Mammalia and if any of these should be detected in the ice, the naturalists of the expedition should take care to preserve any soft parts, skin, hair, muscles, that may be detected and any traces of the contents of the stomach & intestines.

I avail myself also of this opportunity to answer your statement concerning the collection of fishes of the Smithsonian Institution. I know full well that it is inaccessible and moreover that it has been so for a great many years and you will agree with me that it is a great pity, that it should not be so and that if it remains so long there is serious danger of a large part of it spoiling altogether. Now I will make to you a proposition, which I beg you will submit to Professor Henry for approbation. Do for the fishes what you have done for the Crustacea. As you have allowed these to Dr. Stimpson, let me take charge of the whole of your collection of fishes. I will arrange, label & take care of it at the expense of the Mus. of C. Z., until you want it back. I have now *three* assistants entirely devoted to the arrangement of our enormous collection of fishes; Dr. Steindachner,[54] formerly in Vienna, Mr. Bliss and Mr. Lockwood, two students of the Museum; not to speak of what I, myself, may be able to do for Ichthyology yet. I will send Dr. Steindachner to Washington to pack the collection; so that you shall have no trouble about it, except perhaps to help reading the faded labels. I will do all this simply to have on hand the originals described in the various government expeditions, that I may identify my own specimens by direct comparisons. And one more proposition; if in the end you will allow me to retain specimens of the species which are not represented in the Museum in Cambridge, I will return to you twice the number I receive from you.

I will make only one condition to my proposition; that you decide at once; for otherwise I propose to send Dr. Steindachner on an ichthyological exploring expedition during this winter and the season is already advanced.

Very truly yours
L AGASSIZ

---

[54] Dr. Franz Steindachner, of Vienna, spent two years in America to put in order some of the collections of fishes.

BAIRD to AGASSIZ

WASHINGTON, D. C. *Dec. 20, 1870*

My dear Professor,

I am much obliged to you for the suggestions in regard to Arctic matters, contained in your letter of the 12th, & shall certainly take pains to embody their substance in the instructions prepared for the naturalist of Capt. Hall's expedition. It is not impossible that Bannister[55] may go in this expedition. He is a good naturalist, a conscientious man, & has had large experience in Arctic work during the year he spent at St. Michael's on Norton Sound.

You ask when we send books abroad. Dr. Mack made this inquiry of us some weeks ago, which was promptly answered. At that time we had opened several boxes for England & Germany, which have, however, since then been closed & forwarded. If you have a small number of special packages that you want distributed to any prominent point on the continent or in Gt. Britain, we can send them for you at anytime. What we call our clearance of consideration on your part. Since I wrote you it has become necessary to make sundry repairs in the basement of the building, that will involve a great deal of confusion for a time in the vicinity of the rooms in which the fishes are stored. The repairs, however, will be completed in about a month, & we shall then have a much better place than before in which to arrange a great part of the fish collections. If, when we are ready for him, you could send Dr. Steindachner, to remain with us sufficiently long to arrange the collection, so as to have it in proper condition, he then can select such special groups as you have written for, & pack them for the use of the Museum. We shall then have the benefit of his work, & the arrangement may be convenient to all parties. A considerable portion of the collection is still unpacked, remaining in jars & kegs. We will order at once glass jars sufficient to accommodate these specimens, & as we have plenty of alcohol there need be but little delay in putting that entire department in good condition.

The suggestion I make informally, transmission will take place about April next.

And now, in reply to your suggestion in regard to the fishes. We can-

---

[55] Henry M. Bannister, long an associate of the Smithsonian Institution, was an assistant to Robert Kennicott on an exploring expedition in Russian America (later Alaska) to determine whether communication could be established between Europe and America by way of Bering Strait and Siberia. As soon as the Atlantic cable was laid the project was abandoned. Bannister made the meteorological observations and did a lot of collecting for the Smithsonian on the exploring expedition.

not very well part with the collection in this department, as Mr. Gill has under way a number of investigations which he has commenced, & will renew & continue as soon as the collection is brought in order. He is also engaged to make some articles for the report of the Agricultural Department, that will require their presence here. Mr. Cope also depends largely upon the collection for reference in his extended field of research. I shall, myself, have occasion to use it for the purpose of properly identifying & determining the collections I made last summer at Wood's Hole, which were quite extensive, & embrace a number of species new to the fauna of the State.

The uncertainty as to when I can find the time for a rearrangement of the collection, I mentioned in my last letter; & a suggestion presents itself, which may be worthy & it will, of course, require Prof. Henry's sanction; but as soon as I hear from you I will present it for his consideration. In this way, perhaps, Dr. Steindachner might proceed on his exploring expedition, & arrange matters so as to come round to Washington in the course of a month or six weeks.

Have you ever known of the occurrence of the Green Turtle on the coast of Mass.? And, if not, would you care to have a specimen, taken by myself in Buzzard's Bay last summer? It will be more interesting to you on account of its peculiar geographical relationship, than to us; & you are very welcome to it, if you do not already possess a specimen from Mass.

Among the prizes made last summer at Wood's Hole, were several specimens of a species of *Galeocerdo*.

Yours very truly,
SPENCER F. BAIRD

AGASSIZ to BAIRD

CAMBRIDGE, *Sept. 18, 1871*

My dear Baird,

Unless the fine weather of this morning turns to a storm within 24 hours I shall be with you tomorrow evening. During the whole summer I have hoped to pay you a visit, but my engagements combined with the state of my health have been such that I have never until now seen my way clear to do it. I only hope you are still in Woods Hole and as I have no time to ascertain it, I shall anyhow run down for the day.

Very truly yours,
L AGASSIZ

AGASSIZ to BAIRD

CAMBRIDGE, *Sept. 23, 1871*

My dear Baird,

I send today a male and female *Raja erinaceus;* but to my great surprise I find that among the many *Acanthias* I have stored there is not a single male. You must therefore be satisfied for the present with a female. I ask now myself whether I have ever seen a male and whether these come on shore with the females? If I can have access at my old barrels before leaving I may find some in one of them and you shall have it.

I reached Cambridge very much delighted with my trip to Woods Hole and with everything you have shown & told me and was also very glad to meet Hyatt & Verrill there.

If you have any means of communicating with Dr. Bessels let him know that he should not neglect to collect birds eggs with embryos in alcohol & also nestbirds in alcohol. I find no mention of these items in your instructions to him. I have already such a splendid collection of these that I would consider it a great treat to be able to add the arctic breeders to my present possessions.

Do not forget to inform me about the plates of *Astrangia* and I beg you will communicate to Prof. Henry the result of our conversation about casts & my request for the originals of the fossils in the Smiths. Inst. which I want to have cast here to save expenses, reserving to send Mr. Kappeler to Washington to do the brittle species & your ethnographic work. Hoping to see you soon.

Very truly yours
L AGASSIZ

AGASSIZ to BAIRD

CAMBRIDGE, MASS., *Oct. 9, 1871*

My dear sir,

I take great pleasure in introducing to you Mr. Hartung of Heidelberg. Though especially devoted to Geology, he takes great interest in every branch of Natural Science & the state of the country generally and you would greatly oblige him by procuring him some of our public documents.

Very truly yours
L AGASSIZ

AGASSIZ to BAIRD

Oct. 11, 1871

My dear Baird,

Do not forget to return Dr. Dohrn's[56] letters as I have not his directions, which he gives below his signature. I look forward with great interest to learn the result of your negotiation in my behalf in Philadelphia. It is time that we should put all our scientific institutions upon a right footing towards one another. Partly what I have already complained of, there is another point concerning which the Smithsonian has undue advantages over other scientific establishments. You get alcohol without duty and we have to pay full price when we do not do government work. Congress should relieve working scientific institutions of the whole country from such a burden.

Very truly yours,

L AGASSIZ

AGASSIZ to BAIRD

CAMBRIDGE, *Oct. 18, 1871*

My dear Baird,

I duly received this morning your note & Dr. Dohrn's letter, for both of which I thank you much. I hope you will find time to send the Mast. bones without delay, as it now appears that I may sail in about a fortnight. Do not forget also the information about the *Astrangia* plates.

I now write to say that Mr. Sohn, formerly a pupil of mine, and afterwards one of my willing companions & aid in Brazil has come to Cambridge a few days ago, with the finest collection of fossil Fishes from the Carboniferous formation gathered during many years in the Iowa Geol. Survey & obtained besides from all the Paleontologists in the West, which he intends to work up under my supervision. I have already placed a lot of other fossils of the same period in his hands for comparison, besides specimens & skeletons of living Chimeroids & Platostomes, and among others 5 specimens of *Cestracion Philippi* & *zebra;* which by the way do not seem to be congeneric. I wish to add to his means of comparisons the *Cestracion* of San Francisco & beg you would now send it for his use, and I shall be responsible. It would be most useful to show both

---

[56] Anton Dohrn (1840–1909) was born at Stettin, Germany. After studying at Konigsburg, Bonn, Jena, and Berlin he became known as a naturalist. In 1870 he founded and directed the great zoological station at Naples, Italy, which in 10 years became known as one of the most noted laboratories of natural science in the world.

your specimens & if you have received additional ones, all of them as I learn from *C. Philippi* that the dentition varies greatly.

Do not forget also the jaws of sharks & skates of which you promised me labelled specimens. My jaws of these families are not identified with precision, having mostly been procured by themselves, without an opportunity of seeing the whole fish.

Very truly yours
L AGASSIZ

AGASSIZ to BAIRD

Nov. 19, 1871

My dear Baird,

I find the enclosed in yesterday's Advertiser & send it as evidence that I remember your request. You shall have something from me as soon as I have myself seen our outfit. It is not probable that I shall have a chance before we reach St. Thomas. The Mastodon remains are modelling & will be returned shortly. Please send next any of the fossil Vertebrates you have that are worth multiplying in that way.

Yours truly,
L AGASSIZ

AGASSIZ to BAIRD

CAMBRIDGE, *Nov. 22, 1871*

My dear Baird,

I have directed Dr. Steindachner to show Mr. Bliss how he has arranged the fishes, so that by writing to Richard Bliss, Mus. Comp. Z., it is not likely that he may fail to find anything you want.

Yours truly
L AGASSIZ

T.I. Do not expect anything worth having before we have made St. Thomas.

AGASSIZ to BAIRD

CAMBRIDGE, MASS., *Nov. 23, 1871*

My dear Baird,

I have to wait another week for our start. If you could send me the Shark & Skates' jaws at once, I would be able to have them worked up, or at least give directions for the proper work upon them before I go.

Yours truly
L AGASSIZ

BAIRD to AGASSIZ

WASHINGTON, *Nov. 29, 1871*

My dear Professor,

I have just packed up & sent you as complete a collection of the teeth of the sharks and rays collected last summer as we can spare. Of *Cereparodon* & *Galeocerdo* I obtained but a single specimen, and these I can lend you, however, for a time if you desire. I have not sent either species of *Eutaenia,* as although there are plenty of specimens, a stray assistant forgot to mark them as they were prepared, & I can only determine them now after a comparison of skins, which are not yet unpacked. As soon as I can be certain as to the names, I will send on both species.

Very truly yours,
SPENCER F. BAIRD

AGASSIZ to BAIRD

CAMBRIDGE, *Nov. 11, 1872*

My dear sir,

I trust the Council of the Academy has decided to hold a meeting in Cambridge next week. In that case I want you to come to my house, with Mrs. and Miss Baird, if both can accompany you. Mrs. Ag. is equally desirous with me to have you make our home yours on that occasion; and I have so many things to talk over with you that unless you grant my request there may be no opportunity for a proper discussion of the matter, in the pressure of the meeting. You may like also to see some of the things we have brought home from the recent voyage of the Hassler.

Ever truly yours
L AGASSIZ

BAIRD to AGASSIZ

November 14, 1872

My Dear Professor,

I was delighted to see your familiar writing once more and to know that you have returned from your long journey in improved health.

I greatly wish it were in my power to accept your very kind invitation for myself and family on the occasion of the approaching meeting of the National Academy, but I find so much work on hand as to render it absolutely impossible for me to leave home for a single day. I would delight above all things to be once more in your house and renew that familiar intercourse that I prized so highly when I enjoyed it, & trust that the pleasure is only delayed for a time. I want to see you & see how you look, & know something of your doings of the past & your plans for the future. [Illegible.]

I was actively occupied during the past summer in my work as Commissioner, spending the season at Eastport & vicinity. I made some important observations in regard to the natural history of our food fishes & think I can supply an interesting report.

Woods Hole continued to furnish interesting novelties in the way of fish, my assistant there having forwarded a specimen of *Exocoetus* & two species of *Gastropterus*.

Sincerely yours,
S. F. BAIRD

AGASSIZ to BAIRD

CAMBRIDGE, MASS., Dec. 5th 1872

My dear Baird,

I have much regretted your absence from the meeting of the Academy and still regret it, as I wanted to talk over with you some important matters. One which is now pressing I write about. We have organized a course of practical instruction in Nat. Hist., chiefly to fit teachers to introduce the study in our schools. A building has already been secured in Nantucket and some of my young friends have agreed to unite with me in this plan, which was originally suggested by Prof. Shaler,[57] now in Europe. The plan is to be carried out under my supervision whether Shaler comes back in time for it, or not. But I want it should be known that the first suggestion was his. We propose to extend the course to the three summer months, say middle of June, July, August to middle of Sept., and to cover the whole field of Zoology, Comparative Anatomy, Microscopy, Embryology & Hydrography. The men who have thus far agreed to take a part are — Alex. Agassiz, Pourtales, Packard, Wilder, Morse, Putnam, besides myself & Shaler. Prof. Peirce has promised to delegate Mitchell or Whiting to give some lectures upon the sea, currents, tides etc. Now I want to ask if you feel inclined to join and give us a few or many lectures upon your experience concerning fisheries and Economic Ichthyology. It has occurred to me that this would be a

---

[57] Nathaniel Southgate Shaler (1841–1906) was first professor of paleontology and later professor of geology at Harvard University. Besides trying to interest Agassiz in a course of instruction in natural history in the Massachusetts coast area he was also interested in Baird's plan for a national seaside zoological laboratory in the Woods Hole area.

good opportunity for you to show to the public at large that the work you are doing is of great practical value and thus to secure its continuation. As I want to issue our circular soon, I beg you will send me your answer soon. With kindest remembrances to your ladies.

Very truly yours,
L AGASSIZ

BAIRD to AGASSIZ

WASHINGTON D. C.
December 10, 1872

My dear Professor Agassiz,

I can assure you that my own regret at being unable to spare the time for the Cambridge meeting was very sincere, as I wanted above all things to see you & talk over the experiences of your journey. I hope this pleasure, however, will not be long delayed.

I have taken a great interest in Shaler's project in regard to a Summer Field School of Natural History, & when he came to Eastport on purpose to discuss it with me, I at once gave it my hearty support. I will gladly do whatever I can to make it a success, & if you think that I can tell anything worth hearing I will be very glad to take part in the active exercises, should my arrangements permit. I have not yet decided what to do another season, should I be spared; but probably can take Nantucket in my way for a part of the time at least.

My report upon the Fish and Fisheries of Vineyard Sound & Buzzards Bay is now nearly through the press, & I hope to have the pleasure of sending you a copy in the course of a month or two. It will be quite profusely illustrated in various ways, & I think will be of service to Natural History students.

Have you anyone in your establishment who could compare some North American turtles, principally shells, & name them from your types? Most of the collection has been in your hands, but it was not named before returning, & I have therefore no means of determining many of your species. As I am arranging these specimens at present, I would like to have them returned in a few weeks if sent; & therefore ask if this can be done, though I would be sorry to put you personally to any trouble in the matter.

Very truly yours,
S. F. BAIRD

AGASSIZ to BAIRD

CAMBRIDGE, MASS. *Dec. 15, 1872*

My dear Baird,

As any identification of your turtles made by others would not with certainty represent my nomenclature, which is, I suppose, what you want, I will do it myself for you and engage even to return your specimens within a week after they have been unpacked in the Museum. I will do this to show you how much I appreciate your willingness to help in the plan of a course of instruction in Nat. Hist. in Nantucket. As to your field of action for next summer, I do not think you could select a more useful one both for practical purposes and for the advancement of our knowledge, than the region of Cape Cod, North & South of the Cape, as that promontory has been regarded as the dividing line of two fauna, but thus far without sufficient consideration of the animals living in deeper waters. The view is mainly owing to Dr. A. A. Gould's study of the Mollusks, *collected along shore and in the stomachs of fishes;* that is all. Will it hold good upon an enquiry into the animals in deeper water?

Very truly yours,

L. AGASSIZ

BAIRD to AGASSIZ

WASHINGTON, D.C. *Dec. 17, 1872*

My dear Professor,

I have, as you know, taken a very lively interest in the expedition of the Hassler, & have published in Harpers Weekly repeated notices of its movements as supplied by the correspondents accompanying you. I am now preparing my Annual Record of Science & Industry[58] for 1872; which consists in a measure of articles reproduced from the Weekly & Magazine. In cases like that of the Hassler, where the work is continuous I propose to cut some paragraphs, & simply make a statement in a condensation. I will be very much obliged if you will have someone prepare a condensation of one or two octavo pages & allow me to have it. I can, of course, make up a current article from my own notes; but I would greatly prefer to have something from yourself which would be official & embody the most reliable information.

What I want in the first place is the current history of the expedition, when it started, the dates of its successive stops on the way & of

---

[58] The Annual Record of Science & Industry included nearly all the articles which Baird either wrote or edited for Harper's New Monthly Magazine and Harper's Weekly during a year. Eight of these volumes were published 1872–80.

its arrival in San Francisco, the more positive results of the expedition, in the way of observations on the glaciers, deep sea temperatures, soundings, etc. & some indication of the magnitude of the collection & its general character. Can you not help me in this, sending it at farthest within two or three weeks.

Very truly yours,

S. F. BAIRD

BAIRD to AGASSIZ

Dec. 20, 1872

My dear Professor,

Many thanks for your kind offer to label the turtles. As soon as I can conveniently get them together, I will gladly avail myself of it & send the specimens to you for identification. There are a great many circumstances to be taken into account in reference to selecting a sketch for the next summers work, the most important however, being the necessary appropriations! Should this not fail me, I shall then be able to give the subject a serious consideration.

I am greatly interested in the work done on the Georges last summer & hope to see that continued on a new and more efficient scale next summer.

Very truly yours,

S.F.BAIRD

AGASSIZ to BAIRD

Dec. 30, 1872

Dear sir,

I send this to ascertain whether you have anything to add or change and to request you to give me your ideas about the kind of help you may be able to extend to us, besides giving some talks to the assembled teachers.

P.S. When you send the turtles, I would be much obliged to you to add the two specimens of *Cestracion* (*C. Francisci*) you have from California. It is of the highest importance for me to compare them directly & not merely from descriptions with specimens I collected in Tayta & at the Galapagos. In a few days you shall have the Report of the Hassler's voyage.

Yours truly

L AG

BAIRD to AGASSIZ

Jan. 1, 1873

Dear Professor,

Your circular is at hand, and I can only say that it will give me much pleasure, if I can make it practicable, to take my part in the course of "Field Instruction" that you have so cleverly laid out. The title of my lecture should perhaps be "On the Preservation of our Sea Fisheries," as that is a subject upon which I could talk indefinitely. The assistance that I can give, as Commissioner of Fisheries will probably consist in the use of some apparatus for collecting or dredging, & in whatever other way the circumstances as they are may suggest.

I hope in the course of a little while to have all our alcoholic collections arranged, having two or three persons at work in that direction. I shall then hope to discover the Astracionti you ask for, & will gladly place them in your hands. I was under the impression, when you wrote, that they were still in your possession, we having forwarded them to Cambridge I know, at one time, for your use. Are you certain they were actually returned to us?

I shall be most happy indeed to receive the report of the Hassler voyage, so as to introduce it into my "Annual Record."

Very truly yours,

S. F. Baird

AGASSIZ to BAIRD

1501 H. St., Washington, *Jan. 26, 1873*

My dear Baird,

But for your note, I would have carried the enclosed sheets back to Cambridge, as I had completely forgotten them. Finding myself too much fatigued Friday evening to start Saturday, I have tried to rest and here I am still shut up in our hospitable mansion. We go, however, tonight, as I must be in Cambridge Tuesday morning.

My wife is greatly disappointed at my corrections of her copy of my notes and wants to keep the MSC. back to make a clean copy; but I am afraid she too is not fit for work and so I must allow her to appear to great disadvantage by the side of the neat MSC. you get from your good wife, to whom I beg you will give my kindest remembrances.

Every truly yours

L Agassiz

BAIRD to AGASSIZ

WASHINGTON *Jan. 28, 1873*

My dear Professor,

I was quite worried in returning home Sunday to find your letter stating that you were still in Washington, as I wanted very much to see you again, & would have made every effort to do it.

Professor Henry wants the privilege of using your article in part for the purpose of enlarging your address to the Board of Regents: but this will not interfere with my purpose. Before printing, I shall have the article copied very carefully.

With many thanks for your kindness, I remain,

Sincerely yours,

S. F. BAIRD

AGASSIZ to BAIRD

CAMBRIDGE, MASS. *Feb. 9, 1873*

My dear Baird,

Mr Charles D. Gibbs, of Santiago, Chile, with whom I have had a correspondence for some time is returning to Chile and is now desirous of making an attempt to introduce Salmon in the mountain streams of that country. It would be a splendid result if you would bring this about. I have written to him that I would ask you to do the necessary for him, if possible. We will leave New York between the 20th & 28th of this month and you might write to him directly now, to save time. Write Ch. D. Gibbs, care of Charles Pratt, 108 Fulton St. New York. I do not believe that he is particularly well informed concerning the care to be taken of the spawn and young. But even a few eggs successfully hatched would prove the practicability of the attempt and lead to further efforts.

Yours truly

L AGASSIZ

AGASSIZ to BAIRD

CAMBRIDGE, MASS. *March 18, 1873*

My dear Baird,

Of course I can have no objection to your request, I only regret that I did not know sooner that you wished me to *cooperate;* for in that case I would have given more extensive accounts of the voyage etc. All I thought you wanted was correct statements of a few leading results.

Yours truly,

L AGASSIZ

The Mastodons have been cast; but are not yet dry enough to be painted and so you must wait a little longer before I can send them.

The Nantucket plan for a Naturalist's School is likely to be permanently *endowed*. About it more soon.

AGASSIZ to BAIRD

CAMBRIDGE, MASS. *Apr. 5th 1873*

My dear Baird,

Penikese Island will afford a favorable location for experimental parks to breed fishes, Crustacea & Mollusks as well as domesticated animals. I am now preparing plans for the marine department and I hope you will make any suggestion that your past experience may prompt. We should neglect nothing which may give practical value to the institution, and your work as fish commissioner must have prepared you for the consideration of all the questions involved. Let me have the benefit of your information on the subject.

Very truly yours
L AGASSIZ

BAIRD to AGASSIZ

April 8, 1873

My dear Professor,

The receipt of your letter of the 5th makes me sure that the newspaper statements in regard to your health were not well founded. I was much concerned with the announcement that you were unable to finish your course of lectures, & trust that such after all is not really the case.

You may readily imagine my gratification at learning through the papers of the magnificent donation of Penikese Island, made by Mr. Anderson. I am, of course, very familiar with the locality & am free to say that no better spot could have been selected in the entire extent of our coast for that very object than Penikese.

I shall be glad to know from you when your plans assume a definite form, what they are to be, so that I may make some announcement in reference to them in Harpers. I will think over the marine farming, & write you hereafter. Among the apparatus for the ready capturing of fish, with little or no trouble you will need one or two fyke-nets, these serving well in fish pounds and portable [illegible] set in one place and another by means of which you can secure great numbers of old and young fish.

Very truly yours,
SPENCER F. BAIRD

AGASSIZ to BAIRD

MUSEUM OF COMPARATIVE ZOÖLOGY

CAMBRIDGE, MASS.

April 13, 1873

My dear Baird,

It is unfortunately true, that I had to stop in the middle of my lecture, a fortnight ago, as I felt the blood rushing to my head; but it has passed without serious consequence and I have already given two more lectures since. I am greatly exercised with the unexpected amount of work which this great donation of Mr. Anderson throws into my hands, in addition to the anxiety about the grant of the Legislature, which has passed the Senate, but hangs in the House. I have to meet the Finance Committee tomorrow and the members of the House the next day and God knows what more, so that it is impossible for me to go to the meeting of the Academy.

You may not agree with me, but I think Gill and some other candidates before our body are not fit to be made members, while men of such versatile attainments, and solid comprehensive knowledge as Pourtales remain outside. Two years ago, I caused Pourtales to be nominated, and I am at a loss to understand why his name is not even upon the list now.

I am giving as much time as I possibly can to the organization of the School on Penikese, which shall be called the "Anderson School of Natural History." I have discussed with Mr. A's agent the basis of a deed, all the provisions of which are particularly acceptable to me. It is to be a sister institution of the Museum of Comparative Zoology, to work hand in hand with it; in fact to stand as the Educational Branch of the Museum, with an Independent estate. Instead of being organized as a Summer School only, Mr. A. has consented to make it a general School of Natural History, with a summer session on Penikese and a winter session in Cambridge. We must now look to the founding of ten or twelve regular professorships covering the whole range of the Natural Sciences, with special reference to their practical application to Agriculture, the Industrial Arts, Medicine, as well as to the progress of science itself. I am now working at the plans for laboratories, so that we may from the beginning make experiments upon every question bearing upon the breeding of stock, the raising of fish, bees, silkworms, oysters, lobsters etc., while our students shall be taught what they ought to know in order to teach successfully. I trust the school may go into operation by the first week in July. Teachers who have already been engaged in giving instruction in Nat. Hist., and feel that they need further training shall have the first claim to admission, without examination and free of all charges for instruction; so that the whole of their expense will be reduced to their board. Next students who intend to become teachers will have the preference and be admitted on the same terms. As only fifty can be accommodated this year, I suppose these two classes of applicants will fill every available seat. I depend upon you to advise me as to the best mode of securing daily a large supply of fresh specimens of fish, mollusks, crustacea etc., as it will be necessary for each pupil to have a specimen of some kind or other before him, in place of books, which I shall completely exclude from our working rooms.

Ever truly yours
L Agassiz

P.S. Where can I get two Fyke-nets? Will you please order them for me.

Do you know Mr. Rudolph Hessel well enough to tell me whether he would be the proper person to engage to put up our aquariums and fish farms?

LA

BAIRD to AGASSIZ

Washington April 17, 1873

My dear Professor,

I was very glad to find by your letter that whatever might have been the cause of your temporary indisposition you have recovered your lost ground & only hope that the labor consequent upon the Anderson donations, may not tend to break you down again. I presume, however, that will involve considerable outdoor exercises and less trying than severe closed work would be.

I sincerely hope that you may obtain the appropriations from the Legislature, for which you ask, & I only wish that I were nearer Boston to speak a good word in your behalf, if the occasion offered.

As to the best methods for securing materials for instruction & investigation, two or three fyke nets set in suitable places in the vicinity of the island, will do a great deal; & a large trawl of about 10 feet-beam which can be worked from a sail boat of 8 or 10 tons, will probably cover the ground required. Mr Stowe, of the American Net and Twine Company of Boston, understands perfectly the making of both trawl & fyke nets, having manufactured them for me. All you need is to tell him to duplicate the apparatus he made for me.

I presume you will make use of the same Steamer for communication with New Bedford that supplies the adjacent island Cuttyhunk. This makes three trips a week, I believe, carrying mails & passengers.

You can probably secure its assistance and perhaps obtain its help occasionally for dredging & trawling. You can work the trawl to much better advantage from a small steamer than from a sail boat. Indeed it would be desirable to have a small steamer yacht and launch at your disposal.

I do not know what wharf conveniences there are for such a steamer, but I am under the impression that there is quite a serviceable wharf at the island. I am quite familiar with its appearance, having spent many days in its vicinity.

I cannot advise you fully in regard to Mr. Hessel's ability to take charge of the construction of aquaria or fish ponds; but it is my impression that he would be an extremely competent person for such work.

Have you yet ordered your alcohol? I have found a distiller in Washington who offers to me copper double distilled spirits, perfectly clear & limpid at 30 cents a proof gallon. He has made a quantity for us which rates at a strength of 140, which would be equivalent to 70 percent of pure alcohol. The cost of this strength would be 42 cents a gallon, free of government tax which would be equivalent to 52 cents per gallon, currency, for 90 per cent alcohol, as furnished us by Lauman and Keimper. This is much cheaper than anything we have been able to procure; and it is possible he might be willing to manufacture anything you wish. You are probably as well aware as I am that it is always best to use spirits without diluting, and while this man cannot conveniently make anything above 70 per cent, he will give any strength of distillation up to that figure.

Very truly yours
S. F. BAIRD

BAIRD to AGASSIZ

May 15, 1873

My dear Professor,

I am about putting to press a very interesting & important work upon the fisheries of the Great Lakes embracing numerous novelties in the way of biographical notes of the species. I desire to include a series of wood cuts of the principal species mentioned therein, & I am extremely anxious to establish with precision the characters of the various species of *Grystes*. Our own collection not being adapted to this subject, I would like very much to borrow from you a full series of specimens of this genus from Carolina, Florida, the Ohio River & from Tennessee, especially your illustrations of your *G. nobilis*.

If you can spare these I will overhaul them at once & return to you without delay. If you have yourself had any final criticism made in regard to the species of this genus, I would be very glad to know what the results are, with the ascertained synonymy of the species. In any event, I would be glad to examine the specimens referred to.

I have about concluded to select an island in Portland Harbor as the center of my fishing investigations for the coming summer, & hope to have facilities for gathering numerous facts as well as many specimens. If at all practicable, I will try to visit Penikese during the season & see for myself the grand works that you will doubtless be then carrying on.

I look forward with great interest to the results of the great expedition to the Yellowstone, of which you so kindly permitted Allen & Konopicky to form a part. The opportunity is a grand one in view of the facilities for transportation, & the novelty of the field, & I hope that the proceeds will be greatly available to the interest of Science. I need not say that as good a series of specimens collected as possible, shall be reserved for the Cambridge Museum.

Very truly yours,
SPENCER F. BAIRD

BAIRD to AGASSIZ

May 17, 1873

My dear Professor,

I replied by telegraph your dispatch respecting Konopicky. Please have him get up whatever he finds necessary for the proper discharge of his duties, including color brushes, sketch books, etc. I am particularly anxious that he should have the means of making colored sketches of the fishes, reptiles etc., that he may encounter. The cost of these will be refunded by the Quartermasters Department which has charge of the outfit, & if a memorandum is sent to me I will see that it is properly attended to.

Very truly yours,
S. F. BAIRD

AGASSIZ to BAIRD

CAMBRIDGE, MASS. *May 20, 1873*

My dear Baird,

I would gladly answer your question about *Grystes,* if I could. All I know is that I have noticed characters which ichthyologists look upon as generic to be present or absent in specimens of the same species, or what

I think to be the same species; so that I am unwilling to express an opinion in a matter that can wait, as far as I am concerned. If I ever reach the Fishes again, in the manner I propose, I hope I shall leave them in a very different condition from what they are now. It is because I see Gill & Cope do such poor work with this Class that I have so little confidence in their scientific efforts. Why for instance does not Cope *describe* & *figure* and *illustrate* in a proper manner some of his interesting fossils instead of carrying on a most contemptible controversy & why does not Gill write *observations made from specimens* instead of his everlasting nomenclature.

But I meant to answer your letter. You shall have the specimens you want & you are welcome to make the most of them. And now that it is done, let me tell you that it was no small sacrifice for me to let both Allen & Konopicky go; for I want them both on Penikese very much this summer, Allen as instructor & Konopicky as draughtsman. I trust you will remember that when you divide the results of the Yellowstone Expedition. I have given Konopicky special instructions what to do & how to do it, as I believe I understand what you want of him & also with reference to his outfit.

I shall direct Bliss to pack the specimens of *Grystes* at once.

Very truly yours
L AGASSIZ

BAIRD to AGASSIZ

May 22, 1873

My dear Professor,

I do appreciate your kindness and liberality in yielding the services of Allen and Konopicky, knowing full well how useful you would find these gentlemen at Penikese. Indeed, I hardly expected a favorable response to our offer for Allen.

You may be sure that, as far as we can control results, we shall not fail to take this into account in the distribution of duplicate matter.

Rest assured that the party will all work so diligently as to give us a unique opportunity of favoring you with a large collection.

I shall be very glad indeed to examine the specimens of *Grystes,* & will take good care of them.

Very truly yours,
S.F.BAIRD

AGASSIZ to BAIRD

CAMBRIDGE, MASS. *May 30, 1873*

My dear Baird,

I have today forwarded two large boxes of casts to you, chiefly our Mastodons, which I trust you will consider an ornament to your collection and an additional inducement to send me all your most valuable fossils for casting. When they arrive please show them to Prof. Henry. I want him to see what you get from us.

Very truly yours

L AGASSIZ

BAIRD to AGASSIZ

June 4, 1873

My dear Professor,

The two boxes of casts announced in your letter of the 30th ult have come safely to hand, & for this extremely valuable addition to our collection we are a thousand times obliged to you.

As I expect to leave in a few days for Portland, I shall not be able to unpack & shelve them in proper style; but as soon as possible after my return I shall take occasion to display them where they can be appreciated.

I shall probably be in Boston between the 15th and the 20th of the month & hope I may have the pleasure of seeing you as I pass through & discussing matters and things in general.

I hope the parties who have gone to the Yellowstone will have a good time & bring back crowds of nice collections.

Very truly yours,

S. F. BAIRD

BAIRD to AGASSIZ

June 15, 1873

My dear Professor,

Knowing how important it will be to your inquiries at Penikese, I send you herewith the shells of Verrill's portion of my report on the Fishes of Vineyard Sound, so far as printed. I hope to be able to supply the remainder in a few weeks.

I will, of course, send you several copies of the completed book; but I give you these in advance thinking they may come into use at once in your operations.

I hope to leave Washington so as to reach Boston about next Monday to remain there one or two days before going to Portland & if you are in Cambridge, & I can possibly find time, I will run out to see you.

Very truly yours,
SPENCER F. BAIRD

AGASSIZ to BAIRD

CAMBRIDGE, MASS. *June 18, 1873*

My dear Professor,

I am very much obliged for the advanced sheets of Verrill's Report; and will be truly grateful for a number of copies of the whole to distribute among my Class at Penikese. There will be about 50 teachers from the West and from our Normal Schools here and no set of men are likely to be more greedy for information than these people will be, judging by their letters.

Very truly yours
L AGASSIZ

AGASSIZ to BAIRD

June 26, 1873

My dear Baird,

Whenever you come to Penikese you will find a warm welcome and tolerable accommodations. Peirce thinks that the school and your department ought to share the advantages of the Coast Survey. What can I do to make the cooperation effective?

Very truly yours,
L AGASSIZ

AGASSIZ to BAIRD

PENIKESE, *August 2, 1873*

My dear Baird,

We have already had two specimens of *Diodon* (*Chilomycterus*) *geometricus,* from a pound on Naushon. Last week I got another at Nahant. I also got an *Elacate atlantica*, 4 *Palinurus perciformis*, 2 *Alecteres* etc. if I had your complete list I might begin reporting what we find.

You asked in a former letter in what way you could help us? I think you might render the Anderson School very material service by sending us about one hundred specimens of each of the common species of any animal you may secure in sufficient quantity to give away such supplies, for our private collections to be carried away by the teachers present. Send either dry or alcoholic specimens as most convenient.

Yours very truly

L AGASSIZ

BAIRD to AGASSIZ

PORTLAND, *Aug. 5, 1873*

Dear Professor,

I wrote you yesterday expressing the pleasure it would give me to send you lots of the common objects of this coast; but forgot to ask whether you wished me to do this irrespective of their occurrence in great numbers at Penikese.

If you wish me to make collections and send many things, without reference to circumstances, will take pleasure in doing so.

Some might readily be sent, packed in ice, if you wish it or if you will tell me, and send small tanks, with alcohol, I can fill one up every day or two & forward.

Very truly yours,

S. F. BAIRD

Penikese via New Bedford, Mass.

AGASSIZ to BAIRD

PENIKESE, *August 6, 1873*

My dear Baird,

The day before yesterday two specimens of *Physalia arethusa* were caught here. One found on the north side of the Island was very fresh and active and could be studied to great advantage. Yesterday two specimens of *Tetrapterus rurus* were brought in; both males, the largest 7' 1" long. I wish I had a full list of what you have obtained to compare with our daily captures. We have already had three species of *Echeneis, naucrates, albicauda & remora.* Yesterday the dredge secured several specimens of *Alcyonium carneum.* Today we have 4 species of flounders; two of *Trygon* etc.

AGASSIZ to BAIRD

PENIKESE, *August 9, 1873*

My dear Baird,

As the season is so far advanced I do not think it worth while to send cans & alcohol for the specimens you may collect for us; but I should be much obliged for a good lot of *Echinus* of which we have none here, of *Holothuria pentacta* and any other characteristic species of Echino-derm you may get. One Ophiuran would be highly valued. Of Mollusks I would be glad for *Terebratula, Pecten islandica* and any of the Mytiloid except *M. edulis,* also *Cyprina islandica* and *Mactra solidissima, Buccinum undatum* & its egg cases.

Yours very truly,

L AGASSIZ

AGASSIZ to BAIRD

PENIKESE, *Aug. 24, 1873*

My dear Baird,

I am ever so much obliged to you for the fine lot of specimens you were kind enough to send me for the school. Unfortunately owing to the big storm of last week they were detained four days in New Bedford and were all dead, if not decayed when they reached us here. However the ladies and gentlemen were very thankful for the hard parts and truly happy to get a *Brachiopod.* I close the School this week. I am completely over-worked and must seek rest somewhere. Pourtales will pass a part of the next month on the eastern coast and pay you a visit. I have requested him to collect largely the common things for the winter work of our students at the Museum and would be greatly indebted to you, if you will help him and begin now to set aside about 150–200 specimens each of everything that can be obtained without much trouble. You may keep an open barrel for this and fill in everything that comes along.

When the Reports of your last years work come out, please do not for-get the copies you promised me for the pupils of the Anderson School. If you will forward the whole to Cambridge, I shall see that each gets his copy. Our first session here has been a complete success.

Very truly yours

L AGASSIZ

BAIRD to AGASSIZ

PORTLAND, *Aug. 25, 1873*

My dear Professor,

I sent you a week or two ago at Penikese a large batch of living inver-tebrates, but so far I have not learned whether they reached you. If they came to hand, will you kindly inform me of the fact, as I should be sorry to learn that they had gone astray.

Very truly yours,

S.F.BAIRD

BAIRD to AGASSIZ

PORTLAND, *Aug. 27, 1873*

My dear Professor,

I am very sorry that anything occurred to prevent the prompt delivery of the specimens sent you, as I had hoped they would go to enrich the collections made by your pupils. If I had known sooner your wishes in this respect, I could have sent earlier in the season & in successive batches so as to secure their receipt.

I shall be most happy to have Pourtales visit us here, & to give him every facility for making up a large collection. If he comes in his yacht we can show him the best dredging grounds; & if by himself we will help him with our own apparatus. I am sorry that our stay here will be so short, as we can probably not do very much in securing the quantities you ask for, of many species. We shall close operations here about the end of next week. If, however, you think proper to send one or two of your collecting boxes, with alcohol, we will fill them to the best of our ability, taking it for granted that you want anything we can furnish, such as Echini, Starfishes, Northern Crabs, etc.

I am sorry we have nothing more of the report than I have already given you. Verrill's occupation here has prevented his finishing his portion and I presume little will be done in the way of completion until he leaves the island. If at all possible, I will send you copies enough for all the members of your school, & if not, will let you have as many as I can. Verrill has ordered 500 extras for his own use, some of which I presume will be available.

I looked upon your experiment at Penikese with great solicitude, not as to its success, because of that I feel assured, but of its influence upon your own health. I sincerely trust you may not have overworked yourself in any way, & that after the present fatigue is past you will be better for it.

Very truly yours,

Penikese   S.F.BAIRD

P.S. Will Rudolph Hessel ever join you, as expected?

AGASSIZ to BAIRD

CAMBRIDGE, MASS. *Oct 10, 1873*

My dear Baird,

I have just had a look at Mr. Konopicky's drawings, which he sends to you today. I am ashamed at their number considering the short time he was in the field; and as to their execution it is truly splendid, so natural, so effective. I know nothing better, or equal, not even the plates of Prince Neu Wied and I trust the government will order them published in handsome style.

In conformity with my promise I shall from time to time send you a notice of what is going on in the Museum. I begin by informing you that I have succeeded in securing a splendid *Pterodactylus*. I do not know a more perfect or more instructive specimen and I have already been able to correct several current statements concerning the whole family which are not accurate. What gives special value to this specimen is the circumstance that the two sides are preserved upon corresponding plates, separated from one another as the rock split open and exposed the body of the animal; so that what is not plainly visible upon one plate, may be seen upon the other and the whole skeleton thus studied in all its parts. You know that two restorations of the animal have been attempted, one by Wagler in his "Naturliches System der Amphibien," the other by Goldfuss in his paper upon *Pterodactylus crassirostris* in Acta nova Nat. curios. My specimen shows plainly that both these restorations are imperfect, that of Wagler in the bend of the articulations of the forearm and the omission of the metacarpal joint, that of Goldfuss in the suppression of an entire joint of the hand. The metacarpal part of the whole hand having been overlooked unless it differed completely from the type of *Pterodactylus longirostris*. As I advance in my examination, I shall no doubt obtain additional information upon other points. I am sure, for instance, that the number of fingers is incorrectly stated; there are only three short fingers in the hand, and four perfect ones in the foot. So at least in the type of *P. longirostris*.[x]

Very truly yours

L AGASSIZ

[x] It is very desirable that Prof. Marsh should make us acquainted with the character of the web said to be preserved in his specimen.

AGASSIZ to BAIRD

CAMBRIDGE, MASS. *Oct. 15, 1873*

My dear Baird,

Everything I have done concerning the study of N. American animals since I have lived in the U. St. was done with a view to advancing science in my adopted country and not to promote my own interests. You are therefore welcome to all the drawings I had made of our fishes, for your publications. There is a large pile of them and of very unequal value. Some are mere colored sketches, others are finished drawings, some are in natural size, others much reduced. Moreover they are at this moment somewhat scattered among my papers, as they have been used at different times by Dr. Steindachner, Mr. Bliss and myself and never kept together as a whole. But it will not take long to find them all. There is only one restriction I would put upon the use of this material. I have always considered Gill's work in Ichthyology as a curse upon Nomenclature, and I do not want that my labors should go in any way to help his course and if he is to work up the fishes and connect his atrocious principles of nomenclature with good illustrations, it may contribute to fix his name among those who are unable to go to the bottom of things. To this I am not willing to lend my hand even in the remotest manner.

Yours very truly
L AGASSIZ

BAIRD to AGASSIZ

WASHINGTON, *Oct. 15, 1873*

My dear Professor,

Yours of the 10th with its memoranda about the Pterodactyl has been received, & I am much obliged to you for it. I have already made up a little article which will go into Harper's Weekly, as soon as room can be found for it. Do not forget that I shall always be happy to have from you any notes of this kind and also in regard to the general collections of your staff & the special labors and doings of your collectors.

The Konopicky pictures have not reached me, but will doubtless come to hand in due season, when I shall acknowledge them & turn them over to the Secretary of War for his action.

Very truly yours,
SPENCER F. BAIRD

BAIRD to AGASSIZ

WASHINGTON, *October 17, 1873*

My dear Professor,

I am very much obliged to you for your very generous offer to give me the use of any and all your drawings of our American fishes; but fear that possibly, the conditions you attach may render it impossible for me to claim them.

In regard to my proposed work of the fishes of the United States, first I must necessarily obtain Mr. Gill's assistance, as his knowledge of the species is much more thorough than my own, & he has more time to attend to the technical portion. My work has always intended to be truly scientific in habits. Special features will be in biographical materials which I have engaged in collecting for a long time, much of it is entirely original and unpublished. Published as a Congressional document in large numbers & distributed to Sportsmen & amateurs generally, the interest of the work would be especially in its biography & illustrations, to the general reader the question whether a fish bore one particular name or another not entering into the account. I have brought together an immense mass of facts already, & many of the species I have monographed. It is not my intention, by any means, to resign to Mr. Gill the reputation of this work; neither do I propose to have it appear under our joint name, but to state the specific portion for which each person is to be credited, if indeed I give Mr. Gill's name at all on the title page.

Again in regard to Mr. Gill, he has really become, within the last few years, extremely conservative, so much so, that he is now inclined to unite many species into one, which he formerly considered distinct. A similar change of view has also occurred in regard to his ideas as to genera and species, & the simple list of the fishes of the United States, as prepared by him to be published shortly in my report, will, I think, satisfactorily substantiate what I say.

If therefore, you are satisfied to let me have the pictures, and will send them to me, I will at once go over them carefully, & after selecting such as I can make use of, will immediately return the rest to you, & commence the transfer to wood for the purpose of engraving at once.

You have doubtless heard from Mr. Milner before this, in reference to the Sandusky fishes. He will be very happy to do all you desire in this connection, in accordance with my instructions. He writes me he was obliged to return the check from inability to have it cashed, & he asked me to have it exchanged for a postal order, which can be more readily managed. I have mentioned the firm of Logan and Company the probability of your wanting more of the 75 percent alcohol that they have been in the habit of distilling for the Smithsonian. I found they had about concluded not to prepare any more of this spirit; but they say that if the two establishments desire it they will make it for our special benefit.

Have you heard of the wonderful discoveries of fossil vertebrates by Hayden's party, from an entirely new locality, that no one knows of? Cope has been exploring it & has already obtained over 100 new species of great interest. The formation occupies an intermediate position between the beds that have furnished so rich results heretofore to Hayden & Marsh.

Very truly yours,
S. F. BAIRD

BAIRD to AGASSIZ

Nov. 25, 1873

My dear Professor,

I instructed Mr. Charles G. Atkins, in charge of the salmon hatching establishment at Bucksport, to send me any salmon that might die during the operations of taking these eggs & he has forwarded to me a greater number than I care to keep. I have therefore had five of the best, packed in ice & sawdust & sent to you by express, as I feel quite confident you will be glad of the opportunity of obtaining male and female salmon in their spawning condition, which is quite different — as you know, from that of the rest of the year. Please let me know if they reach you in good condition.

I was glad to find from Mr. Milner that he was able to send you a good many fishes this fall, but not so many as he hopes to procure on a future occasion.

Very truly yours,
S. F. BAIRD

INDEX

"Contributions" from, 86; Baird
sends boxes to, 202
Gibbs, Charles D., 213
Gibbs, Richard W., 62, 65
Girard, Charles, 12, 27, 30; Baird offers
specimens to, 30, 39; his monograph
of *Cottus*, 40, 41; description of fishes
by, 53; Agassiz critical of, 54, 55;
Baird defends, 57; authenticated
specimens of, 64; bibliography by, 93,
94
Glyptemys, 105, 106, 119
Gobio, 28
Goldfuss, George A., 225
Goode, G. Brown, 7
Gopher, 137
Gould, A. A., 210
Grant, Ulysses S., 198
Graptemys, 104
Gray, Asa, 7, 13; professor of botany
at Harvard, 26; aids in translating
Iconographic Cyclopedia, 32
Gray, John Edward, description of
snakes by, 58; turtle descriptions by,
91, 106, 107; Agassiz's criticism of,
137; A. sends echinoderms to, 166;
letter from, 167, 170; characterization
of Tubularidae, 173
Great Lakes, 217
Greenland, 192
Grystes, 47, 73, 217–219
Guadalupe, 127, 128
Guiana, 185
Gulf of Mexico, 83
Guyot, Arnold, 35, 36, 42
Gymnopus, 107, 123
Gypochelys, 103

Haiti, 96
Haldeman, Samuel S., 11, 28, 36, 40, 104
Hall, Charles F., 198, 200, 202
Hall, James, mentioned by Baird, 32,
48; Agassiz examines crinoids with,
71
Hannover, Germany, 50
Harris, T. W., 110
Hartung, Mr., 204
Harvard University, 14, 23; Agassiz and
Gray both teachers at, 26; A. and
Girard associated with, 27; Putnam

an assistant to A. at, 95; library, 114;
Shaler a professor at, 208
Hassler, voyage of, 207, 210, 211
Havana, Cuba, Poey sends fishes from,
79; Poey sends turtles from, 124;
Baird sells Agassiz's publications to,
143; sending of alcohol to, 154, 157
Hayden, Ferdinand V., 15; mentioned
by Baird, 132; discovery of fossil
vertebrates by, 227
Hayes, Isaac I., 157
Helminthopaga, 185
Henry, Joseph, 8, 10, 11, 13. (Many
other references to Henry through-
out the letters.)
Hessel, Rudolph, 216, 217, 224
Heterandria, 76
Heterodon, 56, 59
Holbrook, John Edward, turtle eggs
from, 90, 126; "Erpetology" by, 97,
98; descriptions by, 99, 106, 117, 137
Holder, J. B., 152, 153
Hollidaysburg, Pa., 64
Holothuria, 223
Hoy, Philo Romayne, 89, 113, 117, 130,
131
Hopkins, E. M., 171
Hudson River, 78
Hudson's Bay, 159
Hudson's Bay Co., 160, 171, 172
Humboldt, Alexander von, 126
Hyatt, Alpheus, 173, 204
Hydrapsis, 88, 90
Hydrargyras, 26, 46, 48, 87
Hydridae, 59
Hydromedusa, 90
Hydrophidae, 59
Hyla, 64, 66
Hyloids, 68
Hylodes, 68
Hyodon, 47
Hypsolepis, 31, 73, 74, 75
Hystrix, 39

Illinois, home state of Robert Kennicott,
69; fishes from, 73
Indiana, 105
International Exchanges, Smithsonian,
21
Iowa, fishes from, 73; turtles from, 105,